The Life and Death of Stars

S381
The
Energetic
Universe

2

Sean Ryan

S381 COURSE TEAM

Course Team Chair	Dr Andrew Norton
Authors	Dr Carole Haswell, Dr Ulrich Kolb, Dr Sean Ryan
Reader	Dr Mark Jones
Course Manager	Gillian Knight
Editor	Dr Rebecca Graham
Course Secretaries	Valerie Cliff, Tracey Moore
Software Designer	Dr Will Rawes
Multimedia Producer	Dr Kate Bradshaw
Graphic Designer	Debbie Crouch
Graphic Artist	Pam Owen
Picture Researcher	Deana Plummer
Consultants	Dr Katherine Blundell, Oxford University
	Dr Atsunori Yonehara, Tsukuba University
Block Readers	Dr Christopher Tout, Cambridge University
	Professor Andrew King, Leicester University
	Dr Christine Done, Durham University
Course Assessor	Professor Michael Merrifield, Nottingham University

This publication forms part of an Open University course S381 *The Energetic Universe*. The complete list of texts which make up this course can be found on the back cover. Details of this and other Open University courses can be obtained from the Call Centre, PO Box 724, The Open University, Milton Keynes MK7 6ZS, United Kingdom: tel. +44 (0)1908 653231, e-mail ces-gen@open.ac.uk

Alternatively, you may visit the Open University website at http://www.open.ac.uk where you can learn more about the wide range of courses and packs offered at all levels by the Open University.

To purchase this publication or other components of Open University courses, contact Open University Worldwide Ltd, The Berrill Building, Walton Hall, Milton Keynes MK7 6AA, United Kingdom: tel. +44 (0)1908 858785; fax +44 (0)1908 858787; e-mail ouwenq@open.ac.uk; website http://www.ouw.co.uk

The Open University
Walton Hall, Milton Keynes
MK7 6AA

First published 2002

Edited, designed and typeset by The Open University.

Printed and bound in the United Kingdom by Bath Press, Bath.

ISBN 0 7492 9764 6

1.1

CONTENTS

AIM

The aim of Block 2 is to study how stars form, how they sustain their light output for long periods of time, what happens to them as they age, their impact on the production of the elements, and what becomes of them when they exhaust their fuel.

LEARNING OUTCOMES

This block provides opportunities for students to develop and demonstrate the following learning outcomes:

1 A familiarity with the terminology which is used to describe the properties and evolutionary behaviour of isolated stars.

2 The ability to manipulate numbers, algebraic symbols and mathematical functions in equations.

3 An appreciation of the techniques of differentiation and integration and the ability to manipulate differential equations which are of relevance to astrophysics.

4 The ability to derive and manipulate quantitative theoretical models of physical processes and to derive physical estimates.

5 The ability to organize and clearly present relevant information in response to defined tasks, including the expression of mathematical and scientific concepts using clear, concise and correct scientific prose.

6 The ability to learn from a variety of sources and media including textbooks and journal articles which are not specifically written for an undergraduate audience.

7 The ability to evaluate and synthesize information from a variety of sources and media.

8 The ability to search for and download relevant information from the World Wide Web.

9 The ability to use spreadsheets to model physical processes and present the results graphically.

10 An understanding of how stars form, what happens to them as they age, and what becomes of them when they die.

11 Knowledge of the main evolutionary stages in the lives of stars and an understanding of the physical processes that sustain their energy output during each stage, determine the duration of each stage and determine the progression from one stage to the next.

12 An understanding of the relationship between different stages of stellar evolution and the production of the chemical elements.

INTRODUCTION

In Block 2, *The Life and Death of Stars*, you will study the processes that lead to the formation of stars, the energy sources that fuel them, what they do during their lifetime, and what happens when their fuel runs out. From Block 1, you will have a general idea of some events in the life cycles of stars. Block 2 is intended to take you beyond a *description* of events to an understanding of the physical processes which bring them about. That is, the block will not only tell you *what* happens, but will provide you with the physical tools to understand *why*, and to carry the physics forward to work out what will happen as a star ages.

This block is divided into nine sections, with the expectation that you will study one section each week. It is designed around the textbook *The Physics of Stars* by A. C. Phillips, but does not follow the same layout. Remember, you will not be required to read the textbook from cover to cover. Rather, you will be directed to read particular sections, while commentaries, explanations, and questions are provided in this Study Guide. Like Block 1, this Study Guide provides a range of activities – readings from Phillips, pen and paper calculations, and using your computer to make computations with a spreadsheet or to access interactive multimedia tutorials and Internet databases. Additional comments on *some* of the activities are provided at the end of the Study Guide. To help you plan your study effectively, activities and questions which are likely to take more than 15 minutes are accompanied by an *estimate* of the time required to complete the task.

We use the word 'textbook' to refer to Phillips' book, 'Study Guide' to refer to the printed work you are reading now, and 'block' for the collection of materials (textbook, Study Guide, multimedia resources) that support your study of *The Life and Death of Stars*.

Remember, this is a course in astrophysics, not mathematics. Whenever you write down an equation or compute a result, ask yourself what the equation/computation is illustrating. If at the end of some calculation you aren't sure what it means, go over it again thinking about the *physics* of the problem. Mathematics is a valuable tool in your studies, but don't confuse the tool with the trade.

A special comment should be made about the questions in this Study Guide. You may be tempted to regard them as optional extras to help you revise. *Do not fall into this trap!* The questions are not part of the *revision*, they are part of the *learning*. Several of the important concepts are developed through the questions and nowhere else. Therefore, you should attempt every question. You will find solutions at the end of this Study Guide, but do try to solve the questions yourself first before looking at the answer. A table of physical constants is also given at the end of the Study Guide; use these values as appropriate in your calculations.

A few comments should also be made about spreadsheet exercises. One of the advantages of spreadsheets is that they allow you to compute results for complex equations. They also allow you to plot results easily, which can help you visualize the relationships between two or more variables. Try to develop the habit of using the spreadsheet application as an aid to your own learning. For example, if you are having difficulty visualizing what an equation represents, then make a quick spreadsheet graph of the equation with some reasonable choices for the variables, and see what it looks like. That is, don't wait to be *advised* to use a spreadsheet, make it work for you when you want it to. Hopefully you will develop spreadsheet skills which are also beneficial elsewhere. One final word of caution: don't be tempted to skip the spreadsheet exercises on the grounds that you won't be asked to repeat them in the exam. While it is true that you won't be doing spreadsheet calculations in the exam, you *will* be expected to understand the physics that the spreadsheet exercises in this block develop.

1 THE COLLAPSE OF SELF-GRAVITATING GAS

We begin this section by reviewing the Hertzsprung–Russell diagram – an important tool for understanding the properties and evolution of stars and so an appropriate starting point for this block. We then look at the physics that determines which gas clouds collapse to form stars and which do not – you will see that the energy balance and pressure balance within the cloud hold the key.

1.1 A road map for stellar evolution: the Hertzsprung–Russell diagram

When we observe stars, the two most obvious characteristics are their brightness and colour. Once allowance is made for differences in distance, distinct relationships are found between luminosity and colour as illustrated in the **Hertzsprung–Russell (H–R) diagram** (e.g. Figure 1). In such a diagram, the absolute brightness of stars is plotted against their colour, spectral type or temperature. Stars are not distributed randomly in this diagram. The location of a star in the H–R diagram reflects its mass, radius, age, evolutionary state and chemical composition. The most densely populated regions of the figure are where stars spend most of their lives, whereas the probability of finding a star in a short-lived phase is much lower, so fewer stars are seen in such states. Note that the H–R diagram is a snapshot – a view at a single instant – of the evolutionary states of *many* stars. It is not the evolutionary track that an *individual* star traces out over its lifetime.

Figure 1 A schematic Hertzsprung–Russell diagram. This provides a snapshot of the luminosity and surface temperature of many stars at different stages of their evolution. Note that the temperature increases from right to left. Most of the stars lie along a diagonal band, from upper-left (hot and luminous) to lower-right (cooler and fainter), called the main sequence. The second most populated region of the diagram, top-right, is called the giant branch. The stars toward the lower-left lie on the white dwarf sequence.

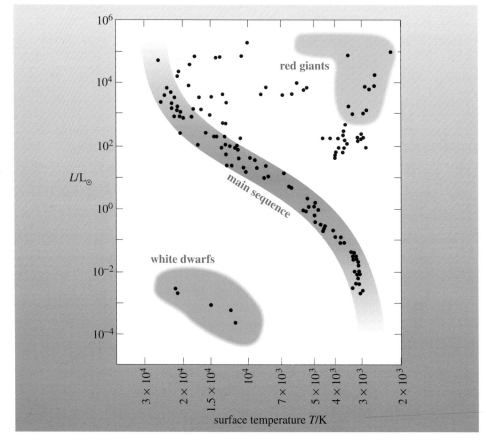

The H–R diagram can be presented in different ways. The original, observational diagram showed star brightness (measured as the **absolute visual magnitude**, M_V) on the vertical axis and stellar **spectral type** on the horizontal axis. Spectral type is very closely related to temperature and colour. Temperatures cannot be measured *directly* for many stars, but colours can be, so the *observational* H–R diagram is often a plot of M_V against **colour index** (such as $B - V$). The *theoretical* H–R diagram uses quantities more closely related to computations of stellar models, and plots luminosity, L, (energy radiated per unit time) against surface effective temperature, T_{eff}.

1.1.1 The effective temperature and the surface of a star

The **Stefan–Boltzmann law** states that the radiant flux F (radiant energy per square metre of surface area per second) from a **black body** of temperature T is given by $F = \sigma T^4$, where $\sigma = 5.671 \times 10^{-8}\,\mathrm{W\,m^{-2}\,K^{-4}}$ and is called the Stefan–Boltzmann constant.

The flux F passing through the surface of a spherical object of luminosity L and radius R (whose surface area is $4\pi R^2$) is simply

$$F = \frac{L}{4\pi R^2}$$

If the object is a black body, then its luminosity L, radius R and temperature T would be related by the equation

$$\frac{L}{4\pi R^2} = \sigma T^4$$

How does this equation for a black body relate to a star? Moreover, if the Sun is a ball of gas, what do we *mean* by its *surface*? Light is continually emitted and reabsorbed by the hot gas that is the Sun. Near its outer layers, the fog-like gas eventually becomes transparent enough that some of the light escapes without being reabsorbed. However, the transition from being opaque to becoming transparent happens over a large range of depths. This zone, which is almost 500 km thick, is called the **photosphere**, and is the closest we get to finding a surface for the Sun. The same is true in other stars, though the extent of the photosphere is even greater in giants.

Because a star does not have an opaque, solid surface, light reaching an observer comes from a *range* of depths in its gaseous outer layers, each layer having a different temperature. What temperature should be used to characterize the surface? A useful *convention* is to refer to the temperature which a black body of the same luminosity and radius would have. This is called the **effective temperature** T_{eff}, and is defined as $T_{eff}^4 = \frac{1}{\sigma}\frac{L}{4\pi R^2}$, or more commonly expressed as

$$L = 4\pi R^2 \sigma T_{eff}^4 \qquad (1)$$

From the definition, we see that the effective temperature is related to the flux through the surface of the star, but how does it compare to the temperatures of the gas in its outer layers? Fortunately, stars are very good approximations to black bodies, since they absorb any light falling on them. Consequently, *the effective temperature coincides with the temperature at an intermediate depth in the photosphere* of the star. Deeper layers have temperatures higher than T_{eff}, while shallower layers in the photosphere have temperatures lower than T_{eff}. We will use the effective temperature to characterize the outer layers or surface of the star, even though a star does not have a solid surface in the conventional sense.

Activity 1	30 minutes

The photosphere of the Sun

This activity is an interactive multimedia tutorial which will allow you to compare the temperatures in the outer layers of the Sun to its effective temperature, and to see the extent of the photosphere. From *The Energetic Universe* MM guide, start the package named 'The photosphere of the Sun', and follow the instructions on screen.

Keywords: **effective temperature**, **photosphere**, **Stefan–Boltzmann law**, **optical depth** ▪

▪ What do we mean by the surface of a star? What is the name given to this region? What are two ways of describing its temperature?

❑ The surface of a star is a zone, of order 500 km thick in the Sun, where its gas goes from being opaque to being transparent. This zone is called the photosphere. The temperature can be described for different depths throughout the photosphere, or more conveniently we can specify the temperature of a black body having the same flux – the effective temperature. ▪

1.1.2 Luminosity

The definition of **luminosity** as the energy radiated per unit time refers to the total energy, irrespective of which wavelengths are present. However, *measurements* of the energy received from a star are usually made over a finite range of wavelengths. For example, the absolute visual magnitude, M_V, is based only on part of the optical spectrum. Consequently, transformations must be made between the theoretical parameters, luminosity L and effective temperature T_{eff}, and their observational counterparts, the visual absolute magnitude M_V and colour index $(B - V)$ or spectral type. However, you will not need to do such transformations in this block.

The luminosities of stars are often quoted in units of the solar luminosity $L_\odot$ as an alternative to watts. This is because the Sun is the star with which we are most familiar, so is a useful reference in studies of others. Although SI units are used widely, in astrophysics non-SI units are also in widespread use, and it is necessary for you to develop a familiarity with both.

1.1.3 The radius of stars and the H–R diagram

Activity 2	45 minutes

The H–R diagram

Now read Section 1.7 of Phillips (pages 33–38). Aim to gain an overall impression of the physical factors that determine the location of a star in the H–R diagram and which affect its evolution. You may find it helpful to note the following:

• Phillips (Equation 1.40) considers the flux *f received* from a star. This is lower than the flux *F* through the *surface* of the star by a factor R^2/d^2, where R and d are its radius and distance.

- Phillips uses the symbol T_E for effective temperature, whereas we use the more usual T_{eff}.

Keywords: **apparent magnitude, absolute magnitude, bolometric correction, parsec, effective temperature, luminosity, Hertzsprung–Russell diagram, main sequence, red giant, white dwarf** ▧

The formula that relates T_{eff} to luminosity L and stellar surface radius R is given in Equation 1 (Phillips 1.43). Note that this expression involves three variables, L, R and T_{eff}, so if two are specified then the third can be calculated. Moreover, two of these are the axes of the theoretical H–R diagram, T_{eff} and L, so the third variable, R, can also be calculated for the H–R diagram.

◼ Equation 1 gives the relationship between the luminosity, effective temperature and radius of stars. How should it be changed for white dwarfs which are fading away, or young protostars that have yet to begin nuclear burning?

❑ Don't mess with that equation! It works just fine as it is, for any thermal source of energy. It therefore applies to *all* stages of stellar evolution. ◼

45 minutes

Stellar radii

In this activity you will draw curves on Figure 1 to show where stars of radii $10R_\odot$, $1R_\odot$ and $0.1R_\odot$ lie.

To do this, calculate the luminosities of stars having radii of $10R_\odot$, $1R_\odot$ and $0.1R_\odot$, for six values of effective temperature: 2000 K, 4000 K, 6000 K, 10 000 K, 20 000 K and 40 000 K. Use the values for the solar effective temperature, luminosity and radius, and the Stefan–Boltzmann constant σ given in Appendix A2 at the end of this Study Guide. You could use a calculator to do this, but it will be less tedious, and good practice, if you use a spreadsheet.

If you need help on using spreadsheets, consult the section 'Comments on activities' at the end of this Study Guide. When you have finished, or if you get seriously stuck, you may want to compare your work with Figure 2 (overleaf) or with a sample spreadsheet solution which is given in the Multimedia resources.

Keywords: none ▧

Do you understand the spacing and shape of the curves in Figure 2, which shows the result of Activity 3? The curves are straight lines, separated by equal amounts, and the middle one passes through the Sun. A key thing to note is that both Figure 1 and Figure 2 are plotted using log–log scales, rather than simple linear scales. The spacing and shapes of the curves can be understood by taking logarithms of the equation $L = 4\pi R^2 \sigma T_{eff}^4$, giving

$$\log_{10} L = \log_{10}(4\pi\sigma) + 2\log_{10} R + 4\log_{10} T_{eff}$$

(Recall that $\log_{10} AB = \log_{10} A + \log_{10} B$, and $\log_{10} x^a = a\log_{10} x$.)

If you compare the equation $\log_{10} L = \log_{10}(4\pi\sigma) + 2\log_{10} R + 4\log_{10} T_{eff}$ to the general equation for a straight line, $y = mx + c$, you can see that it is the equation for a straight line where $\log_{10} L$ is on the y-axis and $\log_{10} T_{eff}$ is on the x-axis. The coefficient of the x-axis term, i.e. the slope, is $m = 4$. The intercept, c, is

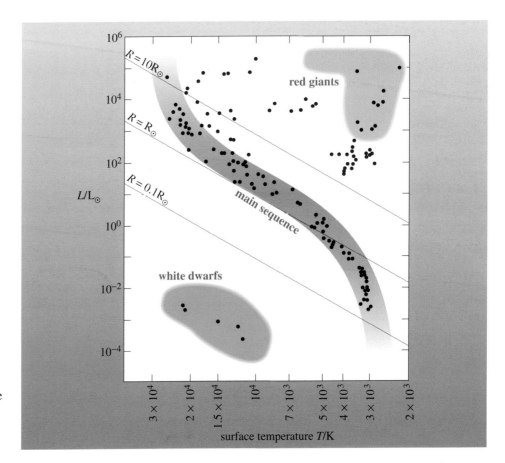

Figure 2 A schematic Hertzsprung–Russell diagram. The sloping lines indicate where stars would have radii $R = 0.1R_\odot$, $1R_\odot$ and $10R_\odot$.

$\log_{10}(4\pi\sigma) + 2\log_{10}R$ which clearly depends on the value of R. Increasing or decreasing R by a factor of 10 changes $2\log_{10}R$ (and hence $\log_{10}L$) by $+2$ or -2 respectively, thus offsetting the locus of the $0.1R_\odot$ and $10R_\odot$ stars by equal amounts but in opposite directions.

■   What fundamental properties of a star uniquely define its location in the H–R diagram, and how do these properties vary across the H–R diagram?

❏   The H–R diagram shows three fundamental properties: luminosity L which is plotted on the logarithmic vertical axis and increases upwards, effective temperature T_{eff} which is plotted on the logarithmic horizontal axis and increases to the *left*, and radius R, related to the other two by $L = 4\pi R^2 \sigma T_{eff}^4$, which is constant along diagonal lines of slope 4 from upper-left to lower-right, and increases towards the upper-right of the diagram. ■

1.2 A self-gravitating gas cloud

Figure 3 shows a known birthplace of stars. Stars form in cold, dark gas clouds if the gravity within the cloud is sufficient to make the cloud collapse. In this section we investigate the conditions under which a cloud can contract to form stars. In Section 2, we will begin following the evolution of these objects as they approach stardom.

Figure 3 Dense, cool clouds of hydrogen gas made opaque by dust grains, in M16 – the Eagle nebula. They are silhouetted against the emission nebula behind, which is excited by the UV flux from young, massive, hot stars off the top of the image. The UV radiation is also photo-evaporating the exposed ends of the dense gas clouds, giving rise to fine wisps of boiled-off gas. Within the dense, dark clouds new stars are forming.

1.2.1 Overview

The starting point for the formation of a star is a cloud of cold gas, composed primarily of hydrogen ($\approx 90\%$ by number of atoms; see Figure 4) and helium ($\approx 10\%$). The cloud collapses due to its own gravity, and as gravitational potential energy is released and converted into heat, the pressure, density and temperature of the material increase. This causes the cloud to begin glowing, initially at infrared and later at optical wavelengths. Ultimately, if the cloud core reaches sufficiently high temperatures – in excess of several million kelvin – nuclear reactions begin. These thermonuclear reactions provide a non-gravitational source of energy release, whose heating provides pressure to help support the gas against further collapse. This changes the behaviour of the object for which, previously, gravitation was the dominant factor, and marks the transition of the object to a star. By definition, a *star* is an object in which nuclear reactions *are* (or *have been*) sufficient to balance surface radiation losses. In contrast, a **brown dwarf** is a collapsing object whose mass is too small ($M \lesssim 0.08 M_{\odot}$) to achieve the temperatures required to initiate sufficient nuclear reactions to balance surface radiation. These low-mass, cool objects slowly convert gravitational potential energy into heat as they gradually collapse. (A typical dictionary definition of a brown dwarf is that it is a star that has not initiated nuclear reactions. As you will discover later in this block, nuclear reactions do not suddenly switch on when some temperature is reached. Rather, their rates increase as the temperature increases. For this reason, we give a more precise definition of a brown dwarf as an object in which nuclear reactions are insufficient to balance surface radiation losses.)

Figure 4 Hydrogen makes up $\approx 90\%$ of the *number* of atoms in a star, but only $\approx 70\%$ of the *mass*, because helium atoms, though less common, have four times the mass. The small contribution from heavier elements (about 2% by mass in the Sun) has been ignored.

element	fraction	
	by number	by mass
H	$9/10 = 90\%$	$9/13 \approx 70\%$
He	$1/10 = 10\%$	$4/13 \approx 30\%$

The preceding paragraph conveys little of the physics that determines which clouds become stars, how that transformation occurs, how long the process takes, or the characteristics of the resulting star. The aim of this section is to provide that understanding.

Most of what follows concentrates on the formation of a single star. We believe that the physics for most of this is reasonably well understood. However, star formation is still an active research field, for while the contraction of a single star can be described realistically, there are major uncertainties in the formation of groups of stars, and it is believed that stars generally form in clusters rather than alone. Star clusters may range in size from a few tens to almost a million stars. Even for different ages and chemical compositions, the range of masses of stars that form are very similar from one cluster to the next. That is, the distribution of star masses that arises from a collapsing cloud is far from random, and the same pattern, many low-mass stars and few high-mass stars, is found everywhere. However, our understanding of how this **initial mass function (IMF)** arises is far from complete. For simplicity, in this block we concentrate on the collapse of single stars.

Before studying the collapse of a gas cloud to form, for example, a star of the mass of the Sun, we need to learn about self-gravitating bodies generally. The gravitational collapse of a gas cloud to form a star begins with a system that is out of equilibrium – otherwise it would not collapse – and ends with an almost static system where an equilibrium exists between the tendency to collapse due to self-gravity, and the tendency to expand due to huge internal pressure. We will follow the change from a state of disequilibrium to one of equilibrium, but in order to do so, we need to understand the competing forces and know what determines whether or not equilibrium has been achieved. The next few subsections deal with those topics first.

1.2.2 Self-gravity versus internal pressure

The gravitational force which makes a gas cloud contract is the mutual gravity of all of its particles. It would be difficult to add up the forces exerted by all of the constituent particles for a randomly shaped gas cloud, but by assuming spherical symmetry, the problem is greatly simplified and becomes manageable. Although gas clouds are not spherical at the start of the collapse, they certainly are by the end, and it is a reasonable assumption to make throughout the process.

In Activity 4, you will see that Phillips uses the mathematical technique of integration to express the mass of a star as the sum of many small spherical shells. *You will not have to write or solve many integrals in this block*, but you will encounter them in the readings and it will make your study clearer if you spend a little time becoming familiar with them rather than skipping over them whenever they appear. The following box contains a summary on definite integrals of specific relevance to Activity 4.

DEFINITE INTEGRALS

A definite integral is a shorthand way of writing the sum of some quantity whose values may vary. For example, the definite integral on page 5 of Phillips

$$m(r) = \int_0^r \rho(r') 4\pi r'^2 \, dr'$$

seeks to compute the total amount of matter enclosed by a spherical shell of radius r. If the density were uniform throughout the body, then the mass would just be the volume, $(4/3)\pi r^3$, multiplied by the uniform density, ρ, giving $m(r) = (4/3)\pi r^3 \rho$. However, because the density for a spherical gas cloud *varies with radius*, it is necessary to compute the mass differently.

The problem is handled by considering n thin, concentric shells of radius r' and minuscule thickness $\delta r'$, each of which has a different density $\rho(r')$ (Figure 5). The thickness of each shell is chosen to be small enough, i.e. n large enough, that the variation in density across each shell, or equivalently in adjacent shells, is negligible. The mass δm of each thin shell is approximated by the thin-shell volume multiplied by the density at that radius, i.e.

$$\delta m \approx (\text{surface area} \times \text{thickness}) \times \text{density}$$

$$\approx 4\pi r'^2 \times \delta r' \times \rho(r')$$

It is conventional to write the minuscule increment, in this case $\delta r'$, at the end of the equation, giving

$$\delta m \approx 4\pi \rho(r') r'^2 \delta r'$$

The total mass *enclosed by* the shell at radius r is simply the sum of the mass in each of the n thin shells, so

$$m(r) = \sum_{i=1}^{n} \delta m \approx \sum_{i=1}^{n} 4\pi \rho(r') r'^2 \, \delta r'$$

In the limit where the thin-shell thickness becomes infinitesimal, the approximation becomes exact. In this case, we replace the symbol δ (signifying a minuscule but finite increment) with 'd' (signifying an infinitesimal increment), and replace the summation sign $\sum$ for discrete steps with the integration sign $\int$ for infinitesimal intervals. We write

$$m(r) = \int_{r'=0}^{r'=r} dm = \int_{r'=0}^{r'=r} 4\pi \rho(r') r'^2 \, dr'$$

where the sum is now written using the integral symbol. The limits of the sum are also modified, so that instead of describing the sum as being from the shell labelled $i = 1$ to the shell labelled $i = n$, we now write the radii of the shells over which we integrate, which in this case is from the shell at radius $r' = 0$ to the shell at radius $r' = r$.

If we are to make further progress and evaluate this enclosed mass, we have to know *how* the density varies with radius, i.e. we need an expression for $\rho(r')$. An advantage of writing this as a definite integral rather than a numeric sum is that the mathematical rules of integration often allow us to simplify the expression for $m(r)$ without having to do long, tedious, and at best approximate numerical calculations.

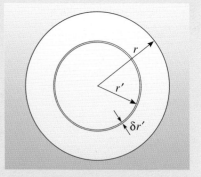

Figure 5 A sphere of radius r may be treated as the combination of many very thin shells. One such thin shell, having radius r', thickness $\delta r'$ and density $\rho(r')$ is shown. The mass of that shell of radius r' is $\delta m \approx 4\pi r'^2 \times \delta r' \times \rho(r')$.

Gravitational contraction

Read the first subsection of Section 1.2 of Phillips (pages 5 and 6).

Pay particular attention to Fig. 1.1 and the associated discussion, as this underlies all analysis of stellar collapse and equilibrium. Note that since dP/dr is the pressure gradient, dP/d$r \times \Delta r$ is the change in pressure ΔP over the radial interval Δr. Also, recall that pressure is force per unit area, and acceleration is force per unit mass and can be written d^2r/dt^2.

Keywords: **acceleration**, **acceleration due to gravity**, **pressure** ■

The following equation captures a crucial relationship for the formation and evolution of a star.

$$-\frac{d^2r}{dt^2} = g(r) + \frac{1}{\rho(r)}\frac{dP}{dr} \qquad \text{(Phillips 1.3)}$$

$$\text{where} \quad g(r) = \frac{Gm(r)}{r^2}$$

It shows that the net contraction or expansion of a star depends on competition between gravity, which acts to make the star collapse, and internal pressure, which tends to support it against gravity. (Often we refer to the internal pressure as the pressure support.)

■   How should this equation be modified for white dwarfs whose nuclear reactions have ceased?

❑   No change is required; the equation is general. Many of the equations for the structure and evolution of stars were worked out long before nuclear reactions and the proton-proton chain were known about. Nuclear reactions provide the energy that *prolongs* a star's life, but gravity *drives* their evolution. ■

Over the star's lifetime, the relative strengths of these forces change greatly: during star formation, gravity dominates; during its stable phase the forces are balanced; and at the end of its life the forces may differ throughout the star, causing the core to collapse while the outermost layers expand at thousands of kilometres per second. The sequence of events and their duration depends on *how* the pressure support is provided. As you study the *details* of stellar evolution in the remainder of this block, keep that *general* principle in mind.

> Competition between the opposing forces provided by gravity and pressure support are what determines the evolution and the ultimate fate of a star.

In the next readings (in Activities 5 and 6), Phillips considers two limiting cases of his Equation 1.3.

•   The first considers unimpeded collapse, where there is no pressure support. This is called **free fall**. It is found by setting the pressure gradient to zero: dP/d$r = 0$.

- The second case is where the pressure gradient just balances the gravitational acceleration, so there is no net acceleration. This is called **hydrostatic equilibrium**, and is found by setting the net acceleration to zero: $d^2r/dt^2 = 0$.

1.2.3 Free fall

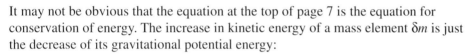

Free fall

Read the subsection 'Free fall' from Phillips (pages 6 and 7).

PHILLIPS

You will not be expected to reproduce the integration at the top of page 7, so do not dwell on this. Instead you should concentrate on the physics, that an unopposed gravitational collapse results in the conversion of gravitational potential energy into kinetic energy, and that the time taken for the collapse can be calculated using Equation 1.4 in Phillips.

It may not be obvious that the equation at the top of page 7 is the equation for conservation of energy. The increase in kinetic energy of a mass element δm is just the decrease of its gravitational potential energy:

$$\Delta E_{KE} = -\Delta E_{GR}$$

$$E_{KE}(r_{final}) - E_{KE}(r_0) = -\left(\frac{-Gm_0\delta m}{r_{final}} - \frac{-Gm_0\delta m}{r_0}\right)$$

$$\frac{1}{2}\delta m v_{final}^2 - \frac{1}{2}\delta m v_0^2 = \frac{Gm_0\delta m}{r_{final}} - \frac{Gm_0\delta m}{r_0}$$

but we can divide by δm and note that $v_0 = 0$

$$\frac{1}{2}v_{final}^2 = \frac{Gm_0}{r_{final}} - \frac{Gm_0}{r_0}$$

Of course, v can be written dr/dt.

Keywords: **free-fall time** ■

Question 1

Phillips shows (Equation 1.4) that the free-fall time for the unopposed gravitational collapse of a sphere of initial uniform density ρ is $\tau_{FF} = (3\pi/32G\rho)^{1/2}$. Compute the free-fall time for a sphere of uniform density gas having the same mass and radius as the Sun. (Use the values of physical constants given at the end of this Study Guide.) (*Note*: Phillips uses the symbol t_{FF} for the free-fall time, whereas we adopt the symbol τ_{FF}; τ is often used for timescales and avoids confusing the timescale with the variable t = time. Of course, it does not really matter what *symbol* you choose, so long as you know what its physical significance is and you are consistent in its use.) ■

■ What does your answer to Question 1 tell you about the gravitational force of the solar material?

❑ The result that the free-fall time of a uniform sphere having the mass and radius as the Sun is only about half an hour indicates that the gravitational force of the matter in the Sun is *not* unopposed! Otherwise the Sun would quickly collapse. ■

1.2.4 Hydrostatic equilibrium and the virial theorem

Activity 6

Hydrostatic equilibrium

Read the subsection 'Hydrostatic equilibrium' from Phillips, to the end of the last complete paragraph on page 8 (pages 7 and 8).

Phillips uses integration by parts on page 8. *You will not be expected to do this*, but if you *wish* to follow it, recall that

$$\int u \, dv = uv - \int v \, du,$$ and set $u = 4\pi r^3$ and $v = P$ (so $dv = dP$)

Keywords: virial theorem, ultra-relativistic particles, non-relativistic particles ◼

Gravity, which acts to make a body collapse, can be opposed by internal pressure if the pressure is greater in the centre, i.e. if a pressure gradient exists, with pressure decreasing outwards. Hydrostatic equilibrium exists when gravity is just balanced by the pressure gradient, so the body neither contracts nor expands. Clearly, the evolution of the system will be slow compared to the free-fall time, and the lifetime long, when this condition is met.

When hydrostatic equilibrium exists, there is no net acceleration of the gas, i.e. $d^2r/dt^2 = 0$, so the pressure gradient and gravity are in balance and related by

$$\frac{dP}{dr} = -\frac{Gm(r)\rho(r)}{r^2} \qquad \text{(Phillips 1.5)}$$

A second result in the reading you have just completed, the virial theorem, is obtained from the condition for hydrostatic equilibrium:

$$\langle P \rangle = -\frac{1}{3}\frac{E_{GR}}{V} \qquad \text{(Phillips 1.7)}$$

The virial theorem and hydrostatic equilibrium for self-gravitating bodies are key ingredients for understanding the formation and evolution of stars, as you will see in the next section.

◼ Describe the meaning of the virial theorem (Phillips Equation 1.7) in words.

❏ The volume-averaged pressure needed to support a self-gravitating body in hydrostatic equilibrium is one-third of the gravitational potential energy density (the gravitational potential energy per unit volume). The negative sign is required because the gravitational potential energy is defined as negative, while the pressure must be positive.

(*Note*: Many quantities can be expressed as densities, meaning they are expressed per unit volume. You have already met the mass density $\rho = M/V$ (mass per unit volume). The number density $n = N/V$ is the number of particles per unit volume, and the energy density is the amount of energy per unit volume.) ◼

1.2.5 Pressure and the kinetic energy density

The pressure of an ideal gas can be written in terms of the momentum p and velocity v of its constituent particles,[1]

$$P = \frac{1}{3}\frac{N}{V}pv \qquad (2)$$

The ratio N/V is just the number of particles per unit volume, i.e. number density n.

We can write two expressions for the momentum and velocity of the particles depending on whether the gas is classical (non-relativistic) or relativistic:

For *non-relativistic* particles, we write $p = mv$ and hence $pv = mv^2 = 2 \times \frac{1}{2}mv^2$. Then Equation 2 becomes

$$P = \frac{1}{3}\frac{N}{V} \times 2 \times \frac{1}{2}mv^2 = \frac{2}{3} \times \frac{1}{V} \times N\frac{1}{2}mv^2$$

where $\frac{1}{2}mv^2$ is the kinetic energy *per particle*, and $N\frac{1}{2}mv^2$ is the kinetic energy E_{KE} of the ensemble of N particles, i.e.

$$\text{for \underline{non-}relativistic particles } P_{NR} = \frac{2}{3}\frac{E_{KE}}{V} \qquad \text{(rewrite of Phillips 1.9)}$$

For *ultra-relativistic* particles, the velocity approaches the speed of light, so $pv = pc$. Then Equation 2 becomes $P = \frac{1}{3}\frac{N}{V}pc$. For ultra-relativistic particles, the kinetic energy *per particle* is pc, so Npc is the kinetic energy E_{KE} of the ensemble of N particles, i.e.

$$\text{for \underline{ultra-r}elativistic particles } P_{UR} = \frac{1}{3}\frac{E_{KE}}{V} \qquad \text{(rewrite of Phillips 1.10)}$$

The significance of these expressions once they are combined with the virial theorem will become clear in the next reading from Phillips (Activity 7).

■ Under what conditions might we need to consider ultra-relativistic particles rather than classical (non-relativistic) particles?

❑ Ultra-relativistic particles travel with $v \approx c$, so either they must be massless or very hot. Important examples of the former are photons and neutrinos, while very hot particles may be found in the collapsed cores of very massive stars. We will see later in the course that relativistic effects become important when photons or very hot particles are responsible for providing the pressure support of a star. ■

---

[1] Strictly we should use the average of the momentum–velocity vector dot product, but it makes no difference for our example.

1.3 Stability and the virial theorem

Having studied the competing forces of gravitation and pressure support in a gas cloud, we will soon investigate the conditions under which a cloud collapses to form a star. However, before doing that, we look more closely at the conditions for the stability of gas under two distinct conditions: a classical ideal gas, and a gas in which the particles providing the pressure support move with relativistic velocities, i.e. $v \approx c$. The former is important in star formation, and the latter is important for later stages of stellar evolution.

Activity 7   **15 minutes**

The virial theorem and total energy

Read subsections 'Equilibrium of a gas of non-relativistic particles' and 'Equilibrium of a gas of ultra-relativistic particles' in Phillips (pages 10 and 11). Phillips combines information on gas pressures to express the condition for hydrostatic equilibrium in terms of the kinetic energy, gravitational potential energy, and total energy of the particles, to derive new conditions.

Keywords: **radiation pressure** ■

Non-relativistic case

For non-relativistic particles, $P_{NR} = \dfrac{2}{3}\dfrac{E_{KE}}{V}$ (rewrite of Phillips 1.9)

Combined with the virial theorem, $\langle P \rangle = -\dfrac{1}{3}\dfrac{E_{GR}}{V}$ (Phillips 1.7) this implies that $-1/3E_{GR} = 2/3E_{KE}$, or

$$2E_{KE} + E_{GR} = 0 \qquad \qquad \text{(Phillips 1.11)}$$

Since the total energy is just $E_{TOT} = E_{KE} + E_{GR}$, it follows that

$$E_{TOT} = -E_{KE} \quad \text{and} \quad E_{TOT} = \tfrac{1}{2}E_{GR} \qquad \text{(Phillips 1.12)}$$

Several consequences of these relations can be stated. The binding energy ($-E_{TOT}$) of a system in hydrostatic equilibrium is the kinetic energy of translational motion, so a highly bound system is very hot, and a loosely bound system is cool. If a cloud collapses slowly enough to remain close to hydrostatic equilibrium, then as the gravitational energy E_{GR} and total energy E_{TOT} decrease, the kinetic energy E_{KE} must increase. That is, a self-gravitating system which collapses slowly enough to remain close to hydrostatic equilibrium heats up. Thus, contracting cloudlets become hotter and hotter as they collapse. If the temperature becomes high enough to initiate thermonuclear reactions at a rate sufficient to balance surface radiative losses, then a star is born. Otherwise, a brown dwarf results.

Ultra-relativistic case

For ultra-relativistic particles, $P_{UR} = \dfrac{1}{3}\dfrac{E_{KE}}{V}$ (rewrite of Phillips 1.10)

Combined with the virial theorem, $\langle P \rangle = -\dfrac{1}{3}\dfrac{E_{GR}}{V}$ (Phillips 1.7), this implies that $-1/3 E_{GR} = 1/3 E_{KE}$, or

$$E_{KE} + E_{GR} = 0 \qquad\qquad \text{(Phillips 1.13)}$$

Since the total energy is just $E_{TOT} = E_{KE} + E_{GR}$, it follows that $E_{TOT} = 0$!

That is, in the ultra-relativistic case, the system is at the boundary of being bound (i.e. $E_{TOT} < 0$) and unbound (i.e. $E_{TOT} > 0$). If a bound system approaches the ultra-relativistic limit, it moves closer towards becoming unbound. As photons are ultra-relativistic, stars in which a large fraction of the pressure support is provided by radiation can approach this unbound limit. This limit is in fact approached in massive stars, and may be a factor in setting the upper limit on the mass of stable main-sequence stars.

■ Why does $E_{TOT} < 0$ correspond to a bound system and $E_{TOT} > 0$ correspond to an unbound system?

❑ The total energy is the sum of the kinetic and gravitational potential energies. The gravitational potential energy is negative ($E_{GR} = -GMm/r$) and approaches zero as the masses M and m approach infinite separation. If their kinetic energy is positive when the potential energy has become zero (in which case $E_{TOT} > 0$), they are not bound to one another. If, on the other hand, the kinetic energy is less than the magnitude of the potential energy ($E_{KE} < |E_{GR}|$ and consequently $E_{TOT} < 0$), then as the objects move apart by converting kinetic energy into potential energy, the kinetic energy reduces to zero before the potential energy increases to zero; in this case the objects are confined to a negative potential and hence are bound to one another. ■

Images of collapsing clouds

We have established that stars form from collapsing gas clouds whose total energy is less than zero. Use the Image Archive to examine a sample of images of star-forming regions, like that shown in Figure 3, to become familiar with the appearance of stellar nurseries. You may also wish to view a few emission nebulae for comparison, though you should note that the two are often found in close proximity.

From your selection of images, note in particular the contrast between the dark, obscuring, dense cold clouds within which new stars are forming, and the hot, glowing clouds excited by the most massive stars that have already come to life. The presence of dark, obscuring clouds is a common feature of star-forming regions. These indicate that the clouds from which stars form are *cold*. We can tell they are cold because:

• hot clouds emit light, and are seen as glowing HII regions or emission nebulae.

• clouds owe their darkness to the presence of cosmic dust which absorbs any light very well. Dust survives only in cold environments.

Keywords: **HII region, molecular cloud, cosmic dust** ■

■ From an energetics point of view, why do stars (which are *hot*) form preferentially in *cold*, dark clouds?

❑ Cold clouds have less kinetic energy than hot clouds, so they are more likely to have a negative total energy and hence be gravitationally bound. ■

1.4 The gravitational potential energy of a uniform sphere

We have seen that the stability of a cloud depends on its gravitational potential energy. You should see once in your studies how that energy is calculated; we do so here.

A cloud can collapse if its total energy, given by the sum of the gravitational potential energy and kinetic energy of its constituent particles, is less than zero: $E_{TOT} = E_{GR} + E_{KE} < 0$.

The gravitational potential energy of a system of *two* particles of mass M and m is $E_{GR} = -GMm/r$, but what is the potential of a *sphere* of particles? Example 1 evaluates this. The result is useful because a sphere of particles is a good approximation to a star, and an adequate approximation to a collapsing cloud. The worked example will develop your ability to:

- express physical ideas in a mathematical form, and
- understand what equations containing integrals mean.

Although you will not be required to solve or write many integrals in this block, it will help you greatly to gain familiarity with them, i.e. to understand what they mean when you see them, so follow the worked example below.

Example 1

What is the gravitational potential energy of a sphere of mass M, radius R and uniform density ρ?

Solution

Step 1: *Describe the physical ideas using mathematics*

The gravitational potential energy of any collection of particles is given by the sum of the potential energies of each of the constituent particles. Recall (see Figure 6a) that for two point masses m_1 and m_2 separated by a distance r, the gravitational potential energy is $E_{GR} = -Gm_1m_2/r$. For our example, we need to consider not just point masses, but the mass distributed in a sphere of uniform density. In a spherically symmetric mass distribution, a particle at a radius r from the centre feels the gravitational force of all particles *closer* to the centre as if they were all concentrated *at* the centre, but the forces exerted by particles *further* out are *perfectly balanced* by particles on the opposite side of the sphere. (These are very convenient properties of spherical mass distributions.) Consequently, material located beyond radius r can be neglected for *this* particle.

Consider (Figure 6b) the gravitational potential energy of a small piece of the mass, δm, lying at some distance r from the centre. We will use the *new* variable $m(r)$ to describe the mass of the part of the sphere interior to δm, which is at radius r. In the centre of the sphere where $r = 0$, $m(r) = 0$, and at the outer edge where $r = R$, $m(r) = M$. Since the force exerted by spherically distributed matter *exterior* to δm is zero and can be ignored, the gravitational potential energy of the mass δm due to the sphere of mass M is

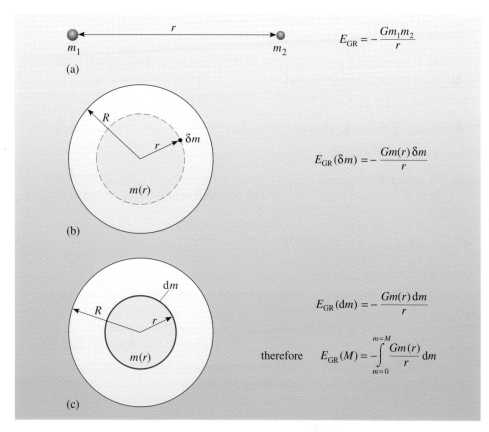

Figure 6 Diagrams related to the integral equation in Example 1. (a) Gravitational potential of two point masses. (b) Gravitational potential of a tiny mass δm a distance r from the centre of a sphere of mass M, where mass $m(r)$ is inside radius r. (c) Gravitational potential of a thin shell of mass $\mathrm{d}m$ a distance r from the centre of a sphere of mass M, where mass $m(r)$ is inside the shell at radius r.

$$E_{\mathrm{GR}}(\delta m) = -\frac{Gm(r)\,\delta m}{r} \quad \text{for the mass element } \delta m$$

The *total* gravitational potential energy of the *entire* sphere is merely the sum of the $E_{\mathrm{GR}}(\delta m)$ values for all pieces of the total sphere. The mathematics of integration helps us account for all of the δm pieces. First of all, note that any other same-sized pieces of mass at the same radius r as δm have the same gravitational potential energy. Consequently, we can write for an entire thin shell of mass $\mathrm{d}m$, rather than just a single piece δm (see Figure 6c), that

$$E_{\mathrm{GR}}(\mathrm{d}m) = -\frac{Gm(r)\,\mathrm{d}m}{r} \quad \text{for the mass shell } \mathrm{d}m \text{ at radius } r$$

This equation follows trivally from the one above, but it is conventional to write infinitesimal quantities, such as $\mathrm{d}m$ in this equation, on their own at the end of the expression, rather than as part of the numerator (top line). For this reason we rewrite the last equation as

$$E_{\mathrm{GR}}(\mathrm{d}m) = -\frac{Gm(r)}{r}\,\mathrm{d}m$$

The two forms are identical mathematically.

To find the gravitational potential energy of the entire sphere, we add up the potential energy of each of the thin shells. We must sum over the full mass of the sphere from the centre (where the enclosed mass $m = 0$) to the outside edge (where the enclosed mass $m = M$). Using the notation of integration, the gravitational potential energy is given by

$$E_{\mathrm{GR}} = -\int_{m=0}^{m=M} \frac{Gm(r)}{r}\,\mathrm{d}m \quad \text{for the entire sphere (e.g. Phillips 1.6)}$$

23

Step 2: *Use the available information*

At the moment, the integration involves *two* variables that change as you go from the centre to the edge of the shell, r and m. Somehow we need to eliminate one of these variables from the equation, but we have not yet discovered *how* $m(r)$ depends on r. We will do that now. We are told that the density (ρ) is uniform, i.e. it does not depend on r, so we can write an expression for r in terms of m, and will then be able to eliminate the variable r entirely from the integral. Since the density of material interior to some radius r can be written $\rho = \text{mass/volume} = m(r)\big/\frac{4}{3}\pi r^3$, we can write $r = \left(\dfrac{3}{4\pi\rho}m\right)^{1/3}$. The integral can then be rewritten

$$E_{\text{GR}} = -\int_{m=0}^{m=M} Gm\left(\frac{4\pi\rho}{3m}\right)^{1/3} dm$$

Step 3: *Tidy up and complete the integration*

There are a lot of constants, which can be taken out of the integrand to simplify it to

$$E_{\text{GR}} = -G\left(\frac{4\pi\rho}{3}\right)^{1/3}\int_{m=0}^{m=M} m^{2/3}\, dm$$

The rest is straightforward; the integrand is a simple polynomial, and since

$$\int x^n\, dx = \frac{1}{n+1}x^{n+1} + C \quad \text{for } n \neq -1$$

(where C is an unknown constant of integration that will in any event cancel out in our definite integral), we have

$$E_{\text{GR}} = -G\left(\frac{4\pi\rho}{3}\right)^{1/3}\left[\frac{3}{5}m^{5/3} + C\right]_{m=0}^{m=M}$$

Recall that the definite integral in square brackets must be evaluated at the two boundaries, the result for the lower boundary then being subtracted from the result for the upper.

$$E_{\text{GR}} = -G\left(\frac{4\pi\rho}{3}\right)^{1/3}\left[\left(\frac{3}{5}M^{5/3} + C\right) - \left(\frac{3}{5}0^{5/3} + C\right)\right]$$

$$= -G\left(\frac{4\pi\rho}{3}\right)^{1/3}\left[\frac{3}{5}M^{5/3}\right]$$

Since $\rho = \text{mass/volume} = M\big/\frac{4}{3}\pi R^3$, we can write

$$E_{\text{GR}} = -\frac{3}{5}G\left(\frac{4\pi}{3}\frac{M}{\frac{4}{3}\pi R^3}\right)^{1/3} M^{5/3}$$

$$= -\frac{3}{5}G\left(\frac{1}{R^3}\right)^{1/3} M^{6/3} = -\frac{3}{5}\frac{GM^2}{R}$$

That is, the gravitational potential energy of a spherical cloud of gas of mass M, radius R and uniform density is just

$$E_{\text{GR}} = -\frac{3}{5}\frac{GM^2}{R}$$

■ The gravitational potential energy for a *uniform*-density sphere is
$E_{GR} = -\dfrac{3}{5}\dfrac{GM^2}{R}$. A star is more centrally concentrated than a uniform sphere, i.e. its density increases towards the centre. Will its potential energy be more negative than $E_{GR} = -\dfrac{3}{5}\dfrac{GM^2}{R}$ or closer to zero?

❏ Think of starting with a *uniform*-density star of radius R_A (see Figure 7). Normally if it collapsed further to radius R_B, its gravitational potential energy would decrease, i.e. become more negative. Begin again with a uniform-density star of radius R_A, but now keep the outer radius constant while allowing *some* of the gas to collapse further, so that the density increases towards the centre. As *some* material will have sunk deeper into its gravitational potential well, the gravitational potential energy again will have decreased, i.e. become more negative, even though its outer radius is still R_A. That is, the star will no longer lie on the uniform-density curve, but you can tell that it must be *below* rather than *above* that curve, perhaps near A′. Therefore a centrally concentrated star has a gravitational potential energy which is more negative than the value derived for a uniform density sphere. (Provided you knew the real density distribution, you could still calculate the gravitational potential energy, but it would be a more involved calculation than in Example 1.) ■

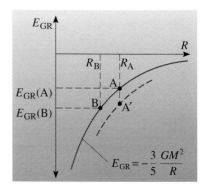

Figure 7 Schematic of the gravitational potential energy of a uniform density sphere, as a function of its radius R.

Activity 9   **30 minutes**

The mass of a sphere (optional)

Often the main difficulties students have with integration is expressing a physics problem mathematically. Key to this is simplifying a complex system into one composed of many small parts whose properties can be estimated more easily, and adding up these estimates to give a result for the whole system. For instance, in Example 1 the biggest challenge was not having to integrate $m^{2/3}$, but working out that this was what was required.

This is a short (optional) activity on calculating the mass of a sphere. It *doesn't* teach you how to do integrations, but it *does* show you how a sphere can be subdivided into separate shells whose mass can be estimated, and that those mass estimates can be combined to approximate the whole sphere. If you have difficulty seeing how to subdivide a system to calculate its integrated properties, this activity might help. From *The Energetic Universe* MM guide, start the activity 'The mass of a sphere'. Select **Task 1** to begin.

Keywords: none ■

1.5 The Jeans criterion for gravitational collapse

The Jeans criterion for collapse simply restates that a gas cloud whose total energy is negative is bound and collapses, whereas a cloud whose total energy is positive does not. This simple criterion can be developed into limiting values for the mass and density of potential star-forming regions. The following reading explores these limits.

Conditions for gravitational collapse

Read Phillips Section 1.3 to the end of the subsection 'Conditions for gravitational collapse' (pages 13–15).

You will see the integral from Example 1 (Phillips 1.6) is used to evaluate the gravitational potential energy (Phillips 1.16).

Keywords: **Jeans mass**, **Jeans density** ■

The Jeans criterion for collapse is simply that the cloud must be bound, i.e. $E_{TOT} < 0$.

Since $E_{TOT} = E_{KE} + E_{GR}$, this condition is equivalent to saying $E_{KE} + E_{GR} < 0$, or $E_{KE} < -E_{GR}$. Since the gravitational potential energy is negative by definition, we can rewrite this as $E_{KE} < |E_{GR}|$ (Phillips 1.18).

■   If the kinetic energy of the gas must be less than some critical value if it is to collapse, what does this suggest about the temperature of star-forming clouds?

❑   The kinetic energy limit requires that clouds be relatively cold if they are to be able to form stars. Hot clouds have too much kinetic energy and will not collapse to form stars unless they cool. ■

The Jeans condition can also be expressed in terms of limits on the mass and density of clouds that are to form stars. If the mass of a cloud exceeds some value for its temperature and radius, called the Jeans mass,

$$M > \frac{3kT}{2G\overline{m}} R \equiv M_J \qquad \text{(Phillips page 14)}$$

or equivalently if its average density exceeds some value for its temperature and mass, called the Jeans density,

$$\rho > \frac{3}{4\pi M^2} \left(\frac{3kT}{2G\overline{m}} \right)^3 \equiv \rho_J \qquad \text{(Phillips 1.19)}$$

then the cloud is bound and collapses due to self-gravity.

Question 2

What would be the radius (in parsecs, astronomical units and solar radii) of a spherical cloud of molecular hydrogen (H_2) at a temperature of 20 K, with a Jeans mass equal to the mass of the Sun?

(*Hint*: Assume that the mass of a hydrogen molecule, H_2, is 2 atomic mass units (amu) – see box). ■

Question 3

Calculate the free-fall time for a sphere of uniform-density molecular hydrogen gas having the mass of the Sun, starting at a temperature of 20 K and the Jeans density. ■

ATOMIC MASS UNIT

The atomic mass unit (amu) is defined as 1/12 of the mass of a ^{12}C atom (including its electrons). This is *approximately* the mass of a proton; it is about 0.7% less than m_p, because some of the mass of the 12 nucleons is carried away by small particles or radiated away as energy when they bind into a nucleus. Sometimes this constant is given the symbol u, where u = 1 amu = 1.661×10^{-27} kg.

Question 4

Compute the Jeans mass (in units of the solar mass) for two cases:

(a) Neutral atomic hydrogen gas typical of the cool interstellar medium ($T = 100$ K, and 10^6 atoms per cubic metre).

(b) Molecular hydrogen gas typical of cold, dense molecular clouds ($T = 10$ K, and 10^9 particles per cubic metre).

(*Hint*: The mass per unit volume ρ is just the number of particles per unit volume n multiplied by the mass of each particle $\overline{m}$, $\rho = n\overline{m}$.) ∎

The results from Question 4 show that the different environments lead to very different structures; the warmer, diffuse interstellar medium will only form very massive clusters of stars, whereas much smaller clusters can form from cold, dense molecular clouds.

1.6 Summary of Section 1

1 The Hertzsprung–Russell diagram is of fundamental importance for describing the properties of stars and for tracking their evolution.

2 The H–R diagram has two forms. The observational H–R diagram plots absolute visual magnitude M_V versus colour index (often $B - V$) or spectral type. The theoretical H–R diagram plots luminosity L versus effective temperature T_{eff} on a log–log scale.

3 Three main regions of the H–R diagram are: the main sequence, the red giant branch and the white dwarf sequence.

4 $L = 4\pi R^2 \sigma T_{eff}^4$ relates stellar radius, luminosity and effective temperature. Loci of constant radius in the H–R diagram are diagonal lines from upper-left to lower-right.

5 Hydrostatic equilibrium exists when the outward force due to the pressure gradient balances the inward gravitational force in every point through the star. This is expressed mathematically as $\frac{dP}{dr} = -\frac{Gm(r)\rho(r)}{r^2}$. The dynamical evolution of the system will be slow when this condition is approached.

6 The virial theorem, which is derived from the condition for hydrostatic equilibrium, concludes that the average pressure needed to support a self-gravitating system is minus one-third of the gravitational potential energy density $\langle P \rangle = (-1/3)E_{GR}/V$.

7 For non-relativistic particles, the pressure P_{NR}, volume V and kinetic energy E_{KE} are related via $P_{NR} = (2/3)E_{KE}/V$. Combining this with the virial theorem gives $E_{TOT} = -E_{KE} = (1/2)E_{GR}$. Since E_{KE} is positive, the total energy of a system in hydrostatic equilibrium is negative, and hence the object is bound. The equivalent expressions for ultra-relativistic particles are $P_{UR} = (1/3)E_{KE}/V$ and $E_{TOT} = 0$. This indicates that an object whose pressure support comes from ultra-relativistic particles is unstable, because $E_{TOT} = 0$ puts the system at the boundary between bound and unbound configurations.

8 Stars in which much of the pressure support comes from radiation pressure rather than gas pressure rely more on ultra-relativistic particles (photons) than on non-relativistic particles (atoms) for pressure support. As noted above, the virial theorem indicates that such objects are unstable. This may help set the upper limit on the mass of main-sequence stars, because such high-mass stars have appreciable radiation pressure.

9 The Jeans criterion for collapse, $E_{TOT} < 0$, can be re-expressed in several ways: a cloud of radius R collapses if its mass M exceeds the Jeans mass

$$M > \frac{3kT}{2G\overline{m}}R \equiv M_J$$

a cloud of mass M condenses if its average density exceeds the Jeans density

$$\rho > \frac{3}{4\pi M^2}\left(\frac{3kT}{2G\overline{m}}\right)^3 \equiv \rho_J$$

10 The free-fall time depends on the initial density of the cloud, and is given by

$$\tau_{ff} = \left(\frac{3\pi}{32G\rho}\right)^{1/2}$$

2 THE ROAD TO STARDOM

In Section 1 we saw that a cloud can collapse if its total energy is negative, and we developed the Jeans criterion for the mass or density of such clouds. In this section we follow that collapse, see what objects we observe that correspond to this phase of evolution, and track the final approach of pre-main-sequence stars to stardom.

2.1 Collapse and cooling in the temperature–density diagram

The H–R diagram provides a vital framework in which to follow the evolution of stars. In studying the collapse of self-gravitating gas, a different diagram – the temperature versus density diagram – turns out to be equally helpful in tracing the evolution of contracting gas.

2.1.1 The temperature–density diagram

From Question 4, the Jeans mass, rewritten in terms of the temperature and density of a gas cloud, is

$$M_J = \sqrt{\frac{3}{4\pi\rho}\left(\frac{3kT}{2G\overline{m}}\right)^3} \qquad (3)$$

■ For a *given* Jeans mass, what is the proportionality between the temperature and density of gas?

❑ Since we are considering a *given* mass, we treat M_J as a *constant*, so the quantity within the square-root of Equation 3 must also be constant. In that case,

$$\frac{3}{4\pi\rho}\left(\frac{3kT}{2G\overline{m}}\right)^3 = \text{constant}, \text{ so } \rho = \frac{3}{4\pi \times \text{constant}}\left(\frac{3kT}{2G\overline{m}}\right)^3, \text{ i.e. } \rho \propto T^3 \blacksquare$$

Remember that the Jeans mass describes objects at the transition between bound and unbound states; more massive objects collapse, whereas less massive objects expand. The quantities T and ρ along this boundary are related by $T \propto \rho^{1/3}$.

Just as we used the relation between luminosity, effective temperature and radius to draw lines of fixed radius in the Hertzsprung–Russell diagram in Activity 3, we can draw lines of fixed critical mass in the temperature versus density plane.

Question 5

(a) Rearrange the expression for the Jeans mass, written in terms of the temperature and density (Equation 3), to give the temperature as a function of the mass and density of the gas of a cloud satisfying the Jeans condition.

(b) Take logarithms of both sides of the resulting equation, write an expression for $\log_{10} T$ in terms of one constant term and two variable terms. Describe the shape of the curve for a *given* Jeans mass in a diagram of log temperature versus log density.

(*Hint*: Recall that $\log_{10} AB = \log_{10} A + \log_{10} B$, and $\log_{10} A^k = k\log_{10} A$.) ■

The temperature–density plane

This activity is to help you understand the temperature–density plane. You will calculate three curves in the plane and plot them using a spreadsheet. The curves will then be discussed in the text following the activity.

Use the results of Question 5, either part (a) or (b), to compute the curves, for neutral hydrogen gas, for three protostellar masses $1M_\odot$, $10M_\odot$ and $100M_\odot$ in the temperature–density plane. Use the graphics capability of the spreadsheet to draw these in a log–log plot.

Hint 1: Choose perhaps three density values in the range $-22 \le \log_{10}(\rho/\mathrm{kg\ m}^{-3}) \le -16$, and compute the critical temperature for each mass and density combination.

Hint 2: For the mass of neutral hydrogen, use the sum of the mass of one proton and one electron, whose values are given in Appendix A2.

If you get stuck, don't forget to look in the section 'Comments on activities' at the end of this Study Guide.

Keywords: none ▪

■ Refer now to the temperature–density plane you have just computed. What does it mean if a $100M_\odot$ cloud lies above the line for a Jeans mass of $100M_\odot$?

❏ A cloud lying above the Jeans line for its mass has a temperature higher than required for collapse, and hence its total energy E_{TOT} is positive. Internal pressure overcomes self-gravity and the cloud expands unless it cools. ■

Conversely to the case considered in the question, clouds which are cooler than the Jeans line for their mass tend to collapse. The Jeans line for a given mass can therefore be regarded as a critical boundary. Objects above the line for their mass do not collapse, but objects below do. The Jeans line marks the boundary in the temperature–density plane between collapsing and expanding objects.

The boundary between collapse and expansion may also be thought of in terms of timescales. We have already met the free-fall time, which Phillips shows (Equation 1.4) is $\tau_{\mathrm{FF}} = (3\pi/32G\rho)^{1/2}$. At the other extreme, when internal pressure forces greatly exceed the gravitational force, the cloud expands essentially at the speed of a pressure wave, i.e. at the velocity of sound c_{s}, and an expansion time τ_{e} may be defined as the time taken for sound to travel the radius R of the cloud, $\tau_{\mathrm{e}} = R/c_{\mathrm{s}}$. The critical boundary between collapse and expansion therefore corresponds to the case where the expansion and free-fall times are equal, i.e. the opposing processes balance one another.

■ In Activity 11, it was found that the Jeans line for a $100M_\odot$ cloud lies above the line for a $10M_\odot$ cloud (at a given density). Using words, explain why.

❏ The Jeans line marks the boundary between clouds with total energy $E_{\mathrm{TOT}} > 0$ and $E_{\mathrm{TOT}} < 0$, where the total energy is the sum of the gravitational potential energy and the kinetic energy. The gravitational potential energy depends on the *square* of the mass, whereas the kinetic energy is proportional to the number of particles and hence is only *linearly* proportional to the mass. In a more massive cloud, the impact of the gravitational potential energy is greater than the kinetic energy, and so the cloud sits in a deeper (more negative) gravitational potential energy. It can therefore sustain higher temperatures before the total energy becomes positive, so the Jeans line moves to higher temperature at higher mass. ∎

For a cloud below the Jeans line for its mass, there is therefore a tendency to collapse. However, cooling of the cloud plays a major role in determining what actually happens. We will consider two cases below: first, the evolution of a gas cloud when there are no exchanges of **heat** (thermal energy) with its surroundings, and secondly the more usual case where the cloud radiates into its environment.

2.1.2 Adiabatic collapse

An **adiabatic process** is one in which there is no heat flow by any means (e.g. radiation, conduction) between a system and its environment. In such a system, the pressure P, volume V, and density ρ of an ideal gas obey the relations

$$PV^{\gamma} = \text{constant} \tag{4}$$

and

$$P \propto \rho^{\gamma} \tag{5}$$

where γ is the adiabatic index. The adiabatic index γ takes a value between 1 and 5/3 depending on the number of **degrees of freedom** s (see box overleaf) of the particles making up the gas, with

$$\gamma = \frac{1 + (s/2)}{(s/2)}$$

Question 6 **15 minutes**

(a) Show that for an adiabatic process affecting an ideal gas, temperature $T \propto \rho^{\gamma-1}$.

Hint: An ideal gas conforms to the relation $PV = NkT$, where N is the total number of particles in the gas, k is the Boltzmann constant, and P, V and T are the pressure, volume and temperature. Note that N/V is the number density of gas particles, n, and multiplying this by the mean mass of a molecule $\overline{m}$ gives the mass density of particles, $\rho = n\overline{m} = N\overline{m}/V$. Thus $P = \rho kT/\overline{m}$.

(b) Comment on the shape of the curve $T \propto \rho^{\gamma-1}$ – called an adiabat – in the log temperature versus log density diagram.

(c) Calculate the value of the slope of the adiabat in the log temperature versus log density diagram for an ideal gas with three degrees of freedom.

(d) Compute the range of all possible slopes for adiabats in this diagram.

(e) Calculate the slope for the case $\gamma = 4/3$. ∎

DEGREES OF FREEDOM

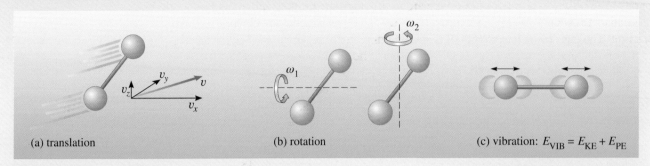

Figure 8 Three forms of energy of a diatomic molecule.

The total energy of a gas particle is said to arise from s degrees of freedom when there are s independent terms in the expression for that energy, each term arising from the square of a displacement or velocity. An ideal, monatomic gas has just three degrees of freedom, corresponding to independent velocities in each of the x-, y- and z-directions. However, molecular ideal gases have a few additional degrees of freedom associated with molecular rotation and vibration, and non-ideal gases have even more associated with ionization. Figure 8 shows that a diatomic molecule has three forms of energy: translational, rotational and vibrational. These give rise, respectively, to three degrees of freedom due to velocities in three independent directions, two degrees of freedom due to there being two independent axes about which the molecule can rotate (a rolling motion about the axis joining the atoms is not counted), and two degrees of freedom due to the kinetic and potential energies of vibration, giving a total of seven degrees of freedom.

The concept of degrees of freedom is very valuable because each degree of freedom contributes $kT/2$ to the average energy of each gas particle. Thus the average energy of each gas particle in a monatomic ideal gas is $3kT/2$. The discussion above indicates that a diatomic ideal gas can have average energies up to $7kT/2$ per gas particle (molecule), but at low temperature ($T \lesssim 100$ K) the rotational and vibrational degrees of

freedom appear to freeze out, leaving just the same number as for a monatomic gas (see Figure 9). Consequently, in cold gas clouds, the energy of molecular hydrogen gas (H_2) may be calculated as if each particle contributes just $(3/2)kT$ to the average energy.

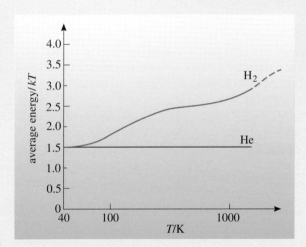

Figure 9 Average energy per gas particle (in units of kT) for helium (monatomic) and molecular hydrogen (H_2) gas. As molecular hydrogen is cooled, the vibrational and later the rotational degrees of freedom freeze out, so that cold molecular hydrogen has the same three degrees of freedom as an ideal monatomic gas.

There are several important results in Question 6. Question 6(b) shows that the adiabat of an ideal gas has a slope $\gamma - 1$ in the logarithmic temperature–density plane. Question 6(e) evaluated this for the particularly significant case with $\gamma = 4/3$. The adiabats for such a gas have a slope $\gamma - 1 = 1/3$, and they will lie *parallel to* the Jeans line. The gas still expands or contracts depending on whether it is hot and tenuous or cold and dense respectively, i.e. whether it lies above or below the Jeans line in the temperature–density diagram. However, because the adiabats run parallel to the Jeans line, they do not intersect it, and hence no stable equilibrium state will be reached. (Recall that the critical Jeans line is where the total energy $E_{TOT} = 0$, or alternatively where the free-fall time equals the expansion time, $\tau_{ff} = \tau_e$.)

We now add the adiabats to the logarithmic temperature–density diagram constructed in Activity 11. The key thing to note is that adiabats for an ideal gas with three degrees of freedom have a different slope (2/3) to the Jeans line (1/3), and therefore must cross it at some point. This is shown in Figure 10.

Consider a Jeans line first. Clouds lying below (which is the same as to the right of) the Jeans line *for their mass* are too cool and dense to be stable, and collapse. Conversely, clouds lying above (= to the left of) the Jeans line for their mass are too hot and tenuous to be stable, and expand. The next question is, how will that collapse or expansion proceed? Systems that are collapsing adiabatically (e.g. point A in the figure) move to higher density, which is towards the right. As the adiabat slope $\gamma - 1$ for an ideal gas is positive, the temperature also increases. The adiabat eventually crosses the Jeans line at point E. Therefore, the position of the object in the temperature–density diagram moves from point A towards point E, in the direction indicated by the arrow. Now consider an object lying above the Jeans line, where the tendency is to expand. Such an object, e.g. at point B, expands to lower density, thus moving to the left in the figure, and since the adiabats have positive slope, it also moves to lower temperature. Hence it moves from point B towards point E. In both cases, once the objects obtain temperatures and densities lying on the Jeans line, any tendency to move off the line is met by expansion or contraction to move it back onto the line. That is, the Jeans line indicates a stable equilibrium configuration for *adiabatic* processes, and objects reaching this position cease to collapse (nor will they expand) under adiabatic conditions.

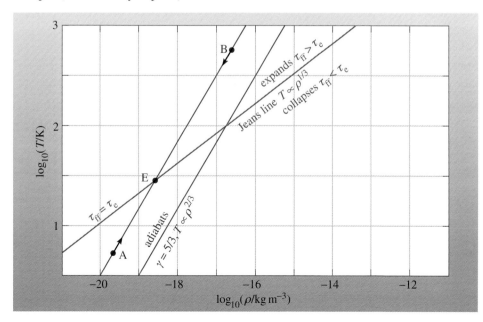

Figure 10 Schematic of logarithmic temperature–density diagram, showing the Jeans line (for $100M_\odot$) with $T \propto \rho^{1/3}$, and two adiabats for $\gamma = 5/3$, giving $T \propto \rho^{\gamma-1} = \rho^{2/3}$.

■ The Jeans line is stable under *adiabatic* processes, but stars exist. What does this tell us about the collapse of gas clouds to form stars?

❑ The fact that stars do collapse from gas clouds indicates that they must do so *non*-adiabatically. That is, they must radiate energy into their environment (or in rare cases heat up) while they collapse. ■

As foreshadowed above, the contractions of gas clouds are not adiabatic, and for this reason we must consider cooling processes as well.

YOU MAY WISH TO NOTE ...

(This material is not examinable, and is included for interest only.)

The condition for hydrostatic equilibrium can be rewritten in terms of the adiabatic index, giving

$$E_{\mathrm{TOT}} = -(3\gamma - 4)E_{\mathrm{IN}} \qquad \text{(Phillips 1.15)}$$

where E_{IN} is the internal energy. A consequence of this is that material whose adiabatic index is $\gamma = 4/3$ has a total energy of zero, so is unbound.

2.1.3 Non-adiabatic collapse and the importance of cooling

In reality, gas clouds are subjected to a variety of heating and cooling mechanisms. Heating occurs by **cosmic rays** (mostly completely ionized atoms) and incoming photons. Cooling is achieved via escaping photons, emitted either when atoms and molecules de-excite or as thermal infrared radiation from dust. The latter tends to be more important, because dense, collapsing clouds become opaque to their own radiation except in the infrared. (Infrared astronomy is currently undergoing rapid technological advancement which is enabling many new observations of previously hidden astrophysical sites.)

The temperature–density diagram can be divided into upper and lower regions, where cooling and heating dominate respectively; see Figure 11. Just as the Jeans line could be viewed as the state at which *dynamical* timescales for expansion and collapse, τ_e and τ_{ff}, balanced, so the division between net heating and net cooling can be viewed as the balance between *thermal* timescales for heating and cooling, τ_h and τ_c. Note that this balance occurs at $T \approx 20\,\mathrm{K}$.

The importance of cooling comes about as follows. For clouds in the upper left portion of the temperature–density diagram, we know already that $\tau_c < \tau_h$ and $\tau_e < \tau_{ff}$. In addition, *the cooling time is substantially shorter even than the expansion time*, $\tau_c < \tau_e$, so the net trajectory of the cloud in this part of the figure is almost vertically downwards, not along the slope 2/3 adiabats (see Figure 12). Conversely, for very cold clouds (below the Jeans line and the thermal line), the heating timescale is shorter than the collapse timescale, $\tau_h < \tau_{ff}$, so the clouds move almost vertically upwards in the diagram. Cooling (or heating) comes to a halt once the protostellar cloud reaches the curve where heating and cooling timescales are equal.

Clouds having a density *lower* than the intersection of the Jeans line and the curve for balanced thermal timescales, point I in Figure 11 and Figure 12, reach the curve where heating and cooling timescales are equal when they are *above* the Jeans line, so end up in a state of continual expansion. These clouds are not about to form stars.

At densities *higher* than the intersection, I, clouds reach the curve for balanced thermal timescales below the Jeans line. They then collapse, move to the right towards higher density, at essentially constant temperature (i.e. *isothermally*) until the gas becomes opaque to its own radiation, i.e. **optically thick**. This inhibits further energy release from the system, and thereafter the process begins to resemble an adiabatic one. Evolution in the temperature–density diagram then follows the adiabats mapped out in the previous subsection.

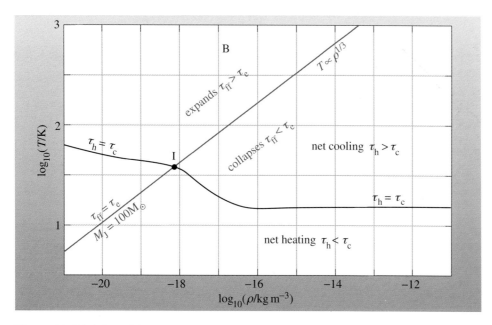

Figure 11 Division of the temperature–density diagram into regions in which net cooling (upper zone) and net heating (lower zone) occur. The Jeans line for a $100M_\odot$ cloud is shown for reference.

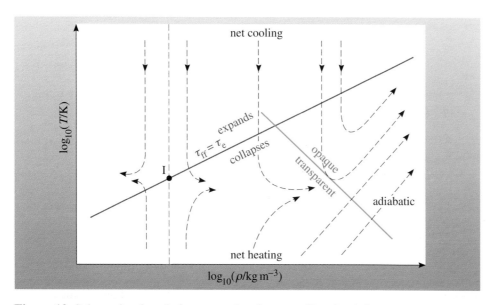

Figure 12 Schematic of evolutionary tracks of protostellar clouds in temperature–density diagram. The line at lower-right indicates where the matter becomes opaque to its own radiation.

The evolution of the protostellar clouds can therefore be summarized as follows. Initially, all objects are dominated by thermal timescales rather than dynamical ones, and move vertically in the temperature–density diagram without significant expansion or contraction. Once dynamical timescales become comparable to the thermal ones, the evolution changes. Objects of lowest initial density remain too hot to collapse, and ultimately expand. On the other hand, warm objects of higher initial density cool, then collapse at almost constant temperature until they become opaque to their own radiation, after which they collapse adiabatically as they approach stardom. We study the contraction stage in more detail in Section 2.2.

2.1.4 Fragmentation

As a protostellar cloud cools (moves vertically downwards in the temperature–density diagram), it crosses Jeans lines for successively lower masses. (See, for example, the Jeans lines you plotted for three different masses in Activity 11.) This means that smaller subregions of the cloud become able to collapse, independently of what the cloud as a whole is doing. This continues even when the object ceases to cool and collapses at uniform temperature – moves to the right in the diagram. More and more subregions become able to collapse in their own right. This process is called **fragmentation**, and describes the pattern whereby a large cloud collapses as a whole initially, but subsequently smaller subregions independently satisfy the Jeans criterion for collapse, and collapse independently of one another, on progressively smaller scales. Fragmentation also marks the transition of the object from being a protostellar cloud to a **protostar**.

Fragmentation can occur throughout the cooling and optically thin contraction phase. It is not until the adiabatic phase of evolution begins, once the cloud has become opaque to its own radiation, that the star ceases crossing lower-mass Jeans lines. Theoretical studies show that fragmentation seems possible down to masses as small as $\sim 0.01 M_\odot$, which is below the minimum mass of stars ($\approx 0.08 M_\odot$) but is higher than typical planetary masses, suggesting that planets form from the coalescence of smaller bodies (beginning with mere dust grains) rather than from the fragmentation of larger systems.

2.1.5 The non-adiabatic free-fall collapse

Once a protostellar cloud has cooled to ~ 20 K, whereupon the heating and cooling timescales are similar, and fragmented, contraction of the protostar follows (assuming the object is below the Jean's line for its mass in the temperature–density diagram). The next reading from Phillips follows this contraction phase, but first review the material on the electronvolt, and attempt Question 7.

THE ELECTRONVOLT

Atomic and molecular energies are often expressed using a non-SI unit, the electronvolt (eV). For example, the ionization energy of a hydrogen atom is 13.6 eV. One electronvolt is the energy required to move a charge equivalent to one electron through an electric potential difference of one volt, or $1\,\text{eV} = 1.602 \times 10^{-19}$ J. By dimensional analysis, since volts are joules per coulomb, and the charge on the electron is measured in coulombs, the product of these two must have units of joules, which confirms that the electronvolt is a measure of energy.

Question 7

An ideal gas at some temperature T contains particles with a range of energies. One energy, which is a valuable characteristic of the distribution, is the value kT. You will find that the product kT arises in many expressions involving thermal energy. For example, recall that each particle of an ideal gas has an average energy of $kT/2$ for each degree of freedom. Compute the characteristic temperature corresponding to the ionization energy of neutral hydrogen, $I = 13.6\,\mathrm{eV}$. ■

Although the correct result of Question 7 is that the energy 13.6 eV corresponds to $T \approx 158\,000\,\mathrm{K}$, this should *not* be interpreted as *the ionization temperature* of hydrogen. The reason why not is that ionization depends not *only* on the temperature but *also* on the free-electron density in the environment under consideration. The electron density dependence *reduces* the ionization temperature to a value *below* the kT-equivalent. In stellar photospheres, for example, hydrogen is mostly ionized around 10 000 K. Nevertheless, even the ionization calculation contains a term $\exp(I/kT)$, which illustrates the usefulness of the kT-equivalent.

Once the Jeans criterion is satisfied and the non-adiabatic collapse begins, gravitational potential energy is liberated. However, the temperature of the object does not rise freely. Instead, the liberated gravitational potential energy causes the dissociation of molecular hydrogen and after that the ionization of the atomic hydrogen. Until ionization is essentially complete, the temperature does not rise above that required for ionization. The total energy required to dissociate and then ionize the hydrogen is calculated from the dissociation and ionization energies and the number of molecules $M/2m_\mathrm{H}$ and (later) atoms M/m_H present in the cloud. These processes are detailed in the next reading (Activity 12).

Activity 12   15 minutes

Contraction of a protostar

Read the subsection 'Contraction of a protostar' from Phillips (pages 15–17).

Keywords: **dissociation, ionization** ▦

■ Phillips began the reading by stating that a solar-mass fragment of a protostellar cloud at 20 K that becomes capable of contracting has a radius ~10^{15} m. Did you stop and wonder where this number came from? Where *does* it come from?

❑ The fragment clearly satisfies the Jeans criterion under these conditions. The equation for the Jeans mass, $M_\mathrm{J} = \dfrac{3kT}{2G\overline{m}} R$ is easily rearranged to give an expression for the radius in terms of the mass, temperature, and mean particle mass. The expression obtained, $R_\mathrm{J} = \dfrac{2G\overline{m}}{3kT} M_\mathrm{J}$, is called the **Jeans length**. It is the radius that encloses the Jeans mass. ■

Question 8

Evaluate the Jeans length for a solar-mass protostar of molecular hydrogen at 20 K.

(*Hint*: Assume that the mass of a hydrogen molecule is $2u$.) ■

Once hydrogen is completely ionized, the gas has become a plasma of protons and (more importantly) electrons, and hence increasingly opaque to its own radiation.[2] Further liberation of gravitational potential energy, which is not required for ionizing the atoms and which can no longer readily escape, results in the heating of the protostar. As the radiation cannot escape easily, the collapse becomes more like an adiabatic one. This increases the temperature and pressure, and hence the star begins its approach to hydrostatic equilibrium. Note also that once the hydrogen is ionized, the adiabatic index achieves the value $\gamma = 5/3$, whereas in the molecular state lower values are obtained. With the material being more opaque, it also comes into **thermodynamic equilibrium**, which is to say that the temperature characterizing the *radiation* is simply the *kinetic* temperature of the gas.

In the case of a one-solar mass protostar, this process takes some 10^5 years, which is the free-fall time from an initial density $\rho = 10^{-16}\,\mathrm{kg\,m^{-3}}$. Over that time, the radius decreases from $\sim 10^{15}\,\mathrm{m}$ ($\sim$7000 AU) to $\sim 10^{11}\,\mathrm{m}$ ($\sim$0.7 AU $\approx 150 R_\odot$). The average internal temperature reaches $\sim$30000 K by the time the protostar attains hydrostatic equilibrium (see Phillips page 16).

The attainment of hydrostatic equilibrium slows the contraction of the protostar, but does not halt it, as energy is being radiated. The phase of evolution where the optically thick protostar is powered by the liberation of gravitational potential energy, is called the Kelvin–Helmholtz contraction. It involves two stages, the Hayashi contraction followed by Henyey contraction, which we study in the next section.

2.2 Kelvin–Helmholtz contraction of the protostar

In the previous subsections we studied a gravitationally collapsing gas cloud and its fragmentation into protostars. In this next subsection, we follow protostars as their contraction proceeds, and study the stages they pass through as they approach stardom.

2.2.1 The Hayashi birth-line

Work by C. Hayashi in the 1960s showed that a star cannot achieve hydrostatic equilibrium if its outer layers are too cool. Two important concepts in understanding Hayashi's work are **opacity** and **convection**. We will study these concepts before continuing with Hayashi's findings; read the two boxes on the next three pages and then attempt the following questions.

■ Consider what you have learnt about opacity. If the absorbing particles in Figure 13 exhibit a Kramers opacity, and their temperature is doubled, what happens to the opacity and their absorption cross-sections? If the particles are electrons, so the opacity is electron scattering, what happens to the opacity if the temperature is doubled?

❑ The opacity of particles exhibiting a Kramers opacity decreases if the temperature is increased. The overall opacity would decrease by a factor $2^{3.5} \approx 11$, to $\approx 10^{-4}\,\mathrm{m^2\,kg^{-1}}$. Since there are still 11 particles, we infer that their individual

---

[2] If you have read about the origin of the cosmic microwave background radiation, it may help you to consider this increase of opacity in a protostar as the reverse of what happened on a cosmological scale 3×10^5 yr after the Big Bang. Then, the expanding Universe had cooled enough to allow electrons and protons to combine to form neutral hydrogen atoms. This elimination of free electrons, and hence reduction in electron scattering, allowed the radiation of that era to travel through space unimpeded henceforth. That same radiation is still observed today, albeit redshifted by a factor of $\approx$1000, as the cosmological microwave background radiation (CMBR)!

absorption cross-sections must also decrease by a factor of ≈ 11, to $\approx 9 \times 10^{-5}\,\text{m}^2$. Electron scattering, on the other hand, depends only on the *number* of free electrons, *not* their *temperature*, so in the second case the opacity would be unchanged. ∎

■ Table 1.2 of Phillips (page 19) gives the central temperature and central density of the Sun. Use these values to mark a cross on Figure 14 indicating the conditions in the solar centre. Based on where it lies, do you expect the opacity of the material in the core of the Sun to be dominated by a Kramers opacity or by electron scattering?

❑ The point for the solar centre lies just above the curve for $\rho = 10^5\,\text{kg m}^{-3}$, at $\log_{10}(T/\text{K}) = 7.19$, where the opacity is seen to be $\approx 2 \times 10^{-1}\,\text{m}^2\,\text{kg}^{-1}$. This is still on the sloping part of the opacity–temperature curves, indicating that Kramers opacity still dominates over electron scattering. ∎

OPACITY

The opacity, κ, of some material is its ability to block radiation. It is expressed as an absorption cross-section per unit mass, $\text{m}^2\,\text{kg}^{-1}$, or $\text{cm}^2\,\text{g}^{-1}$ in cgs units. Perfectly transparent matter would have an opacity of zero (see Figure 13). (The definition of opacity given in Collins is different from the one used here, which is more common in considering stellar structure.)

κ is the Greek lower case letter kappa.

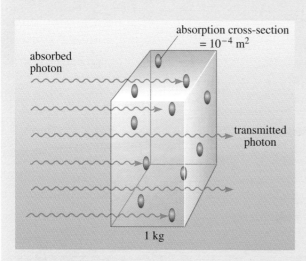

Figure 13 Schematic of opacity: If 1 kg of material contains 11 particles, each presenting an absorption cross-section of $10^{-4}\,\text{m}^2$, the opacity of the material is $11 \times 10^{-4}\,\text{m}^2\,\text{kg}^{-1}$. In practice, the number of particles will be much larger than 11, and the absorption cross-section of each will be much smaller than $10^{-4}\,\text{m}^2$.

The opacity of material is caused by several physical processes, the four most common being: **bound-bound** atomic transitions, **bound-free** transitions (i.e. ionization), **free-free** (thermal **bremsstrahlung**) interactions, and **electron scattering** (especially in fully ionized [hot and/or low-density] material where there are a lot of free electrons). To calculate the opacity of some material, the contribution of each process must be computed, and all contributions added. Fortunately, this has been done for us, and two useful generalizations can be made:

1   For solar-composition material at temperatures $T \gtrsim 30\,000\,\text{K}$, the opacity κ is dominated by free-free and bound-free absorption, for which $\kappa \propto \rho T^{-3.5}$ (see Figure 14). Any opacity of this form, $\kappa = \kappa_0 \rho T^{-3.5}$, is called a **Kramers opacity**, after the person who first found this form.

2   In low-density environments and at very high temperature, scattering by free electrons dominates. In electron scattering, the absorption per free electron is independent of temperature or density, so this opacity source has an almost constant absorption per electron, and therefore per unit mass (kg) of ionized material. It is responsible for the flat tail at high temperature in Figure 14, which sets a lower limit on the opacity at high temperature and low density. (The small decrease in the electron scattering opacity at $T \gtrsim 10^7$ K is due to **special relativity**; note that at $T = 2 \times 10^7$ K, electrons move at $0.1c$!)

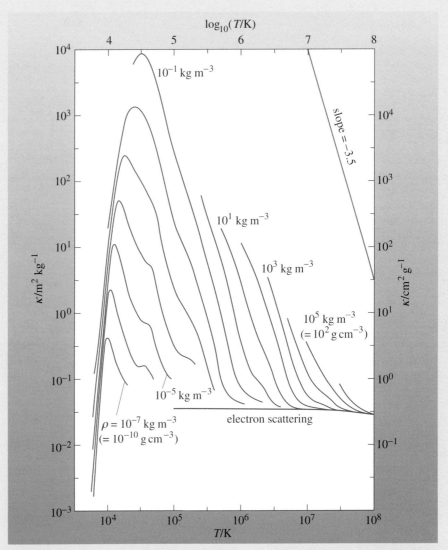

Figure 14 Opacity for solar-composition material, as a function of temperature (on the horizontal axis) and density, in a log–log plane. Each curve is labelled by the value of the density ρ in $m^2\,kg^{-1}$. In the regime $T \gtrsim 30\,000$ K, i.e. $T \gtrsim 10^{4.5}$ K, the curves (in the log–log plane) are roughly linear with slope -3.5, and more or less uniformly spaced for equal increments of log density, confirming that $\log_{10} \kappa = \text{const} + \log_{10} \rho - 3.5 \log_{10} T$, or equivalently $\kappa \propto \rho T^{-3.5}$. Electron scattering has an almost constant cross-section per unit mass, and is the dominant opacity at high temperatures and low densities, where it sets a lower bound on the opacity values.

CONVECTION

Convection is motion within a fluid in a gravitational field, driven by differences in density from place to place. Less-dense material rises, whereas more-dense material falls. Often density differences are the result of temperature differences, and in this case fluid motion also transfers heat from one place to another.

Convection can be a very important mechanism of transporting energy (heat) throughout the star, especially when the opacity of stellar material is high since that prevents radiation from transporting energy. High opacity means that radiation does not travel easily through the stellar material, and a steep radiative temperature gradient is set up. The reason is straightforward: if a hotter layer is prevented by high opacity from shining on a cooler layer further out, then radiation is prevented from heating up the cooler layer.

Steep radiative temperature gradients are notorious for making stars unstable to convection. Figure 15 helps illustrate this by comparing two cases for (A) low-opacity material and (B) high-opacity material. Consider a small cell of hot gas that is briefly displaced upward in the star. The displaced cell expands and cools slightly because the pressure is lower further out in the star. (Recall from hydrostatic equilibrium that pressure decreases outwards.) In the case with low opacity, case A, photons from deep in the star have warmed the layers higher up, so the displaced cell is no hotter than the material surrounding it. However, in case B having high opacity, the photons from deep in the star cannot reach material higher up, so that material is much cooler compared to case A. That is, a steeper temperature gradient exists in case B. Since the displaced cell is *warmer* than its new (relatively cool) surroundings, it follows the old adage that hot air rises, and *continues* to rise. Consequently, large scale motions of material result. This motion is convection.

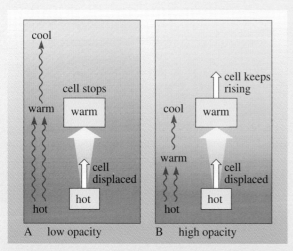

Figure 15 Convective instability. A cell of material is displaced upwards in a star, and expands because of the decreasing pressure. If the opacity is low (case A), its new environment is at a similar temperature because it has been warmed by the photons, but if the opacity is high, the new environment is cooler and the displaced cell keeps rising. In case B, convection sets in.

Hayashi showed that there is a boundary on the right-hand side of the H–R diagram cooler than which hydrostatic equilibrium, and hence stable stars, cannot exist. It lies at an effective temperature of around $T_{eff} \approx 3000$ to 5000 K (depending on the star's mass, chemical composition and luminosity). Objects to the right of that boundary are out of hydrostatic equilibrium, and collapse rapidly until the surface temperature reaches the value corresponding to stability. In consequence, collapsing protostars enter the H–R diagram near that boundary.

Stars at the Hayashi boundary are fully convective. The reason, given what you know about opacity and convection, is easy to understand. First, since the opacity of protostellar matter decreases with temperature, approximately as $\kappa \propto \rho T^{-3.5}$, *cool objects have high opacity*. Second, high opacity leads to steep radiative temperature gradients, and third, steep temperature gradients lead to convective instability. Putting these three things together, the coolest stars are more likely to be convectively unstable.

A new protostar continues to contract, remaining at the Hayashi convective boundary. As that boundary is almost vertical in the H–R diagram, stars up to a few times the mass of the Sun ($M \lesssim 3M_\odot$) collapse with almost constant surface temperature. Recall from Section 1 that the luminosity, temperature and radius of a star are related by $L = 4\pi R^2 \sigma T_{eff}^4$ (Equation 1). Since the star's temperature changes very little during this stage, the equation tells us that the luminosity is proportional to the square of the radius. As its radius R is still decreasing due to contraction, the luminosity decreases significantly. It is therefore expected that protostars enter the H–R diagram around $T_{eff} \approx 4000$ K at high luminosity, and fade as they contract. The paths protostars take in the H–R diagram during this evolutionary stage are called **Hayashi tracks** (Figure 16a).

As the protostar continues to contract, its *core* gets hotter and its opacity *decreases*, because for Kramer's opacity, $\kappa \propto \rho T^{-3.5}$. As a result of the decreasing opacity, the radiative temperature gradient becomes shallower and the condition for convection eases. Eventually the core becomes non-convective (radiative).

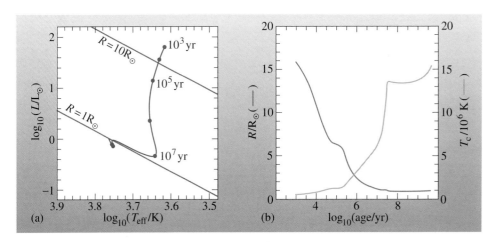

Figure 16 (a) H–R diagram with pre-main-sequence (Hayashi) track for the Sun. The red dots indicate elapsed times of 10^3, 10^4, 10^5, 10^6, 10^7, 10^8 and 10^9 yr. (b) Evolution of radius and central temperature with time.
[Data kindly provided by D. A. VandenBerg]

2.2.2 The Henyey contraction to the main sequence

Stars of mass $M \lesssim 0.5M_\odot$ reach the main sequence at the bottom of their Hayashi tracks. Higher mass pre-main-sequence stars evolve to higher effective temperatures (i.e. from right to left across the H–R diagram) before initiating thermonuclear reactions to supply the energy radiated from the surface. As the star evolves from the base of its nearly vertical Hayashi track (where stars are fully convective) to the main sequence, it is in hydrostatic equilibrium, and its luminosity is fuelled by the slow gravitational collapse. This is called the **Henyey** phase. We now examine that evolution, and seek to calculate the path taken by pre-main-sequence stars in the H–R diagram. In fact, you are about to do your first stellar evolution calculations in this course, and derive the path that a star takes in the H–R diagram!

■ Given that a pre-main-sequence star is still contracting during the Henyey phase, is it safe to say that it is in hydrostatic *equilibrium*?

❑ Yes, it is safe to say this. Although the star must continue to contract to release gravitational potential energy to make up for surface loses due to radiation, the contraction time is much longer than the free-fall time, and therefore the star is in hydrostatic equilibrium during this phase. (We calculate the contraction time explicitly later in this section.) ■

To produce an evolutionary track for a pre-main-sequence star, we need to calculate how its luminosity and surface temperature change. It is important to remember that the temperature, pressure, and density change with radius r inside a star. To illustrate this, Figure 17 shows the internal structure of the Sun, from the centre ($r/R_\odot = 0$) to the edge ($r/R_\odot = 1$). To derive an evolutionary track, we begin by making an assumption, called the **homology** assumption, which says that as the star gets smaller, its structure changes by *the same factor at all radii*. That is, if the radius contracts by some factor A, causing the central temperature to increase by a factor B, then the temperature *everywhere* in the star increases by a factor B. The density and pressure profiles also scale in this fashion, though by *different* factors C and D. What we would like to know are the relationships between the scaling factors A for radius, B for temperature, C for density, etc. We will derive them in Example 2 below.

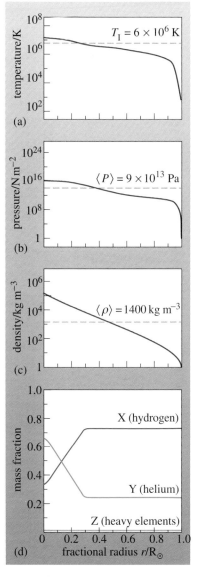

Figure 17 Variation, with radius r, of (a) temperature $T(r)$, (b) pressure $P(r)$, (c) density $\rho(r)$ and (d) composition in the solar interior. Note that the vertical axis is logarithmic in (a)–(c). Dotted horizontal lines in (a)–(c) give the average values.

How do the luminosity and surface temperature of a pre-main-sequence star change as it contracts?

(The answer to this will tell us how the star moves in the H–R diagram!)

Solution

Step 1: *What parameters do we need?*

We begin by identifying what stellar parameters we need to know if we are to track a star's evolution, find how those stellar parameters scale with the overall radius of the star, R, and then combine these scaling relations to find the variation of luminosity and surface temperature which trace the star's path in the H–R diagram. The expression from Equation 1

$$L = 4\pi R^2 \sigma T_{\text{eff}}^4$$

gives us one equation with three variables, and hence two unknowns. We need another equation relating L to R, or T_{eff} to R, in order to specify R in terms of L or T_{eff} and eliminate it from the equation, leaving a relation between L and T_{eff}.

We turn to one of the results from the area of **radiative transport** for a second relationship between the luminosity, temperature, and radius. Radiative transport is the topic explaining how energy conveyed by photons propagates through a star. Both sources and sinks (opacity) of radiation must be considered. It isn't a difficult topic, but would take more time and space than is necessary in the middle of a discussion of star formation. For this reason, we simply state the equation that we will use: where energy transport is dominated by **radiative diffusion**, the luminosity at some radius r within in the star depends on the temperature $T(r)$, temperature gradient dT/dr, density $\rho(r)$ and opacity $\kappa(r)$ at that radius according to the equation

$$L(r) = -4\pi r^2 \frac{4ac}{3} \frac{T^3(r)}{\rho(r)\kappa(r)} \frac{dT}{dr} \qquad \text{(e.g. Phillips 3.27) (6)}$$

where $a = 4\sigma/c$, known as the radiation (or radiation density) constant.

ENERGY TRANSPORT

There are three forms of energy transport generally: conduction, convection and radiation. Conduction is unimportant in most stars except dense, compact stellar remnants. The relative importance of radiative diffusion and convection differs throughout a star and changes over its lifetime. Stages where convection becomes particularly important are discussed later in the block

Step 2: *Re-scale the parameters by the contracting radius R of the star*

Scaling the density

The mean density of a star whose radius is R and of mass M is given by $\rho = M/\frac{4}{3}\pi R^3$. Under the assumption of homology, if the *mean* density scales with the contracting radius as R^{-3}, then so does the density at *any* radial distance r. Hence we can write

$$\rho(r) \propto R^{-3} \qquad (7)$$

Scaling the pressure

In hydrostatic equilibrium

$$\frac{dP}{dr} = -\frac{Gm(r)\rho(r)}{r^2} \qquad \text{(Phillips 1.5) (8)}$$

By the assumption of homology

- a pressure interval dP scales in the same way as the central pressure P_c,
- a radial interval scales in the same way as the radius R, and
- the density scales in the same way as the mean density ρ,

so the hydrostatic equilibrium condition becomes

$$\frac{P_c}{R} \propto \frac{\rho}{R^2} \propto \frac{R^{-3}}{R^2} = R^{-5}$$

so $P_c \propto R^{-4}$, or more generally

$$P(r) \propto R^{-4} \qquad (9)$$

Scaling the temperature

From the ideal gas law (e.g. Phillips 2.19), $P = nkT = (\rho/\overline{m})kT$, so
$T(r) \propto P(r)/\rho(r)$, where the '(r)' symbols remind us that this relation holds at any
radius r within the star. Using the scaling relations for density $\rho(r) \propto R^{-3}$ (Equation
7) and pressure $P(r) \propto R^{-4}$ (Equation 9), we can write the scaling relation for
temperature as $T(r) \propto R^{-4}/R^{-3}$,

i.e. $T(r) \propto R^{-1}$ (10)

Scaling the opacity

Assuming the opacity is a Kramers opacity, $\kappa(r) \propto \rho(r)T(r)^{-3.5}$, and using Equations
7 and 10, we find $\kappa(r) \propto R^{-3}(R^{-1})^{-3.5}$,

i.e. $\kappa(r) \propto R^{0.5}$ (11)

Scaling the temperature gradient

A temperature increment dT scales with the contraction in the same way as T, which
is proportional to $1/R$. Similarly, a radial increment dr scales in the same way as R.
Therefore the temperature gradient dT/dr responds as $(1/R)/R = 1/R^2$,

i.e. $dT/dr \propto R^{-2}$ (12)

Scaling the luminosity

We can now use the scaling relations (Equations 7, 10, 11 and 12)

$$\rho(r) \propto R^{-3}$$

$$T(r) \propto R^{-1}$$

$$\kappa(r) \propto R^{0.5}$$

$$dT/dr \propto R^{-2}$$

to rewrite Equation 6,

$$L(r) = -4\pi r^2 \frac{4ac}{3} \frac{T^3(r)}{\rho(r)\kappa(r)} \frac{dT}{dr}$$

and find the dependence of $L(r)$ on rescaling of R. Writing Equation 6 as a
proportionality we have

$$L(r) \propto r^2 \frac{T(r)^3}{\rho(r)\kappa(r)} \frac{dT}{dr}$$ (13)

Putting Equations 10, 7, 11 and 12 into this, we have

$$L(r) \propto R^2 \frac{(R^{-1})^3}{R^{-3}R^{0.5}} \frac{1}{R^2} \propto \frac{1}{R^{0.5}}$$ (14)

i.e. $L(r) \propto R^{-0.5}$

By the homology assumption, if the luminosity at any radius r scales as $R^{-0.5}$, then
so does the surface luminosity

i.e. $L \propto R^{-0.5}$ (15a)

That is, luminosity increases as the reciprocal square root of the contracting radius. Equivalently,

$$R \propto L^{-2} \tag{15b}$$

Step 3: *Clarify the Henyey path in the H–R diagram*

Finally, we know from Equation 1 that $L = 4\pi R^2 \sigma T_{\text{eff}}^4$. Writing this as proportionalities, we have $L \propto R^2 T_{\text{eff}}^4$.

We can use Equation 15b to eliminate R, and then write the relation between L and T_{eff} for any radius of the contracting star, giving

$$L \propto (L^{-2})^2 T_{\text{eff}}^4 \propto L^{-4} T_{\text{eff}}^4$$

or $\qquad L^5 \propto T_{\text{eff}}^4$

That is to say, during the Henyey contraction, the luminosity varies as the (4/5)-power of effective temperature:

$$L \propto T_{\text{eff}}^{4/5} \blacksquare$$

Figure 18 shows a line of slope 4/5 (= 0.8) in the log–log version of the H–R diagram. By comparing this with the evolutionary tracks based on more detailed models shown in the figure, you can confirm that the homologous collapse approximation leads us to a good representation of the collapse process. That is, you have been able to show how a pre-main-sequence star evolves in the H–R diagram. Not bad for only your second week on this block!

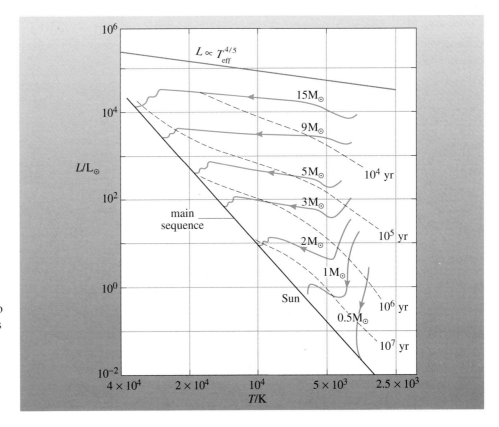

Figure 18 H–R diagram showing the final collapse to the main sequence – the Kelvin–Helmholtz phase – for a range of masses. Also shown is a blue line of slope 4/5 as derived under the homologous collapse assumption, which is found to be a reasonable representation of the true collapse for $M \gtrsim M_\odot$.

■ Look more closely at the pre-main-sequence tracks shown in Figure 18. We predicted evolutionary tracks of slope 4/5. Do both high-mass and low-mass stars actually follow such a slope, or are there differences? If there are differences, why might this be?

❑ Figure 18 shows that the high-mass stars do evolve at close to the expected slope, while low-mass stars, e.g. the Sun, evolve slightly more steeply. This tells us that one of the assumptions in our argument that holds for high-mass stars does *not* hold so well in lower-mass stars. Either something about their structure or the way they collapse differs. The assumption that fails is that energy transport is dominated by radiative diffusion rather than convection. The envelopes of lower-mass stars experience more convection, and hence they deviate more from the expected slope of 4/5. ■

2.3 Observations of young pre-main-sequence objects

Having studied the *theory* of the collapse of gas clouds and the contraction of protostars towards the main sequence, it is time to turn to the *observable* Universe and see what evidence we find of **young stellar objects (YSOs)**.

Once protostellar objects become opaque and start to heat up, we might expect them to become visible. However, for some of the high-luminosity phase of their pre-main-sequence life, stars may not be visible at optical wavelengths due to their being cloaked in dust remaining from the dense molecular cloud in which their collapse began. However, the dust may be heated by the star and radiate strongly at infrared wavelengths. Developments in **infrared astronomy** and **submillimetre astronomy** are making it possible to study young stellar objects that are still enshrouded by dust and gas from the clouds out of which they formed (e.g. see Figure 19). These make it possible to observe objects which are not yet visible at optical wavelengths. X-rays coming from the hot **coronae** of young **active stars** are also increasingly being used to probe these obscured systems.

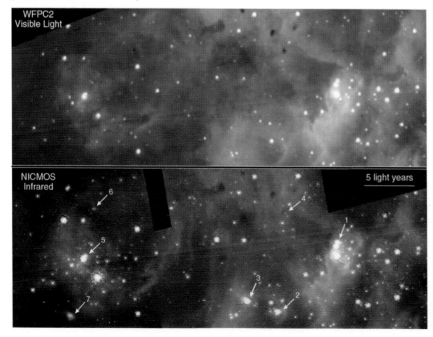

Figure 19 A comparison of visible light and infrared images of a star-forming region (30 Dor). Many sources that are not seen at visible wavelengths are revealed in the infrared to be very bright. This is due to longer wavelengths being less scattered by dust that is ubiquitous in star-forming regions.

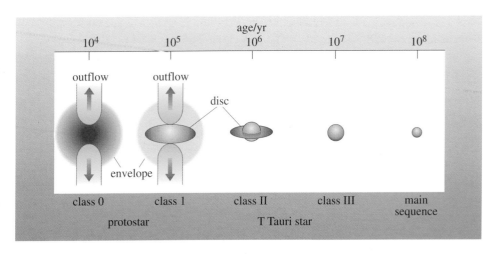

Figure 20 A schematic diagram of the evolution of a pre-main-sequence star from the protostar stage, where bipolar outflows can be measured, through the T Tauri stage where outflows are disappearing but the protostellar (and possibly protoplanetary) disc still remains, to the stage where the star becomes a genuine main-sequence object.

The range of pre-main-sequence objects observed has led to an evolutionary sequence being envisaged, shown schematically in Figure 20. Radio data complement the infrared and submillimetre observations, and show many protostars to have **bipolar outflows** – gas flowing away from a central object along an axis, presumably its rotation axis, at velocities of several tens of $km\,s^{-1}$. The reason that the outflowing material streams along an axis, rather than in all directions, is believed to be due to the influence of a disc or torus (doughnut) of material which remains for a time around the protostar. In our earlier descriptions of protostellar collapse, we ignored material which, though unstable to gravitational collapse, would possess too much angular momentum (rotation) to let it collapse down to a small sphere. The expected fate of such material is that it would collapse only partially before colliding with other high angular momentum material and forming a rotating disc or torus about the star. This belt of dense material would prevent outflowing gas from escaping in the orbital plane, but would allow escape in the directions towards the poles. Magnetic fields, which are complex and poorly understood, and were also ignored in our description of collapse, may also play a role in collimating the polar outflows. These outflows can now also be observed at optical wavelengths (see Figure 21).

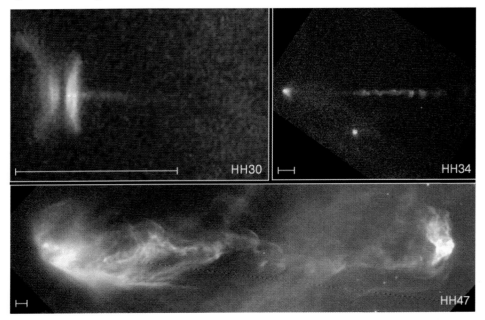

Figure 21 Jets of outflowing material associated with young stars. In HH30, the obscuring protostellar disc is seen almost edge-on. The scale bar in each image is 1 AU.

Stars of the **T Tauri** type are believed to be very young pre-main-sequence objects in the mass range 0.2–2.0$M_\odot$ that are making their first appearance. They are found in regions of space where considerable dense gas and infrared-emitting dust remains (left over from recent star formation). They show other indications of youth such as **mass loss**, especially via bipolar outflows, rapid rotation, and high abundances of the fragile element lithium which many stars destroy during their life. The temperatures and luminosities of T Tauri stars, i.e. their positions in the H–R diagram, are close to the Hayashi boundary at which protostars first appear (see Figure 22), consistent with the locations of the theoretical Hayashi tracks.

In some high-mass objects, which are hotter than T Tauri stars and hence have even stronger radiation pressure, the outflow velocities reach into the hundreds of km s^{-1}.

Some signs of youth remain visible even after stars reach the main sequence. One such class of objects is the **Vega-excess stars**, named after the first star in the class. These are very close to or even on the main sequence, but show unusually large excesses of infrared radiation (compared to a bare photosphere). The radiation is thought to come from a dust shell or disc surrounding the star, which has been heated by the starlight to $T \approx 100$ K and which therefore emits thermal radiation at

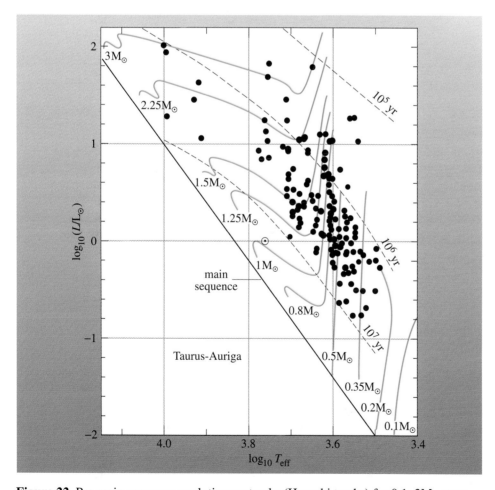

Figure 22 Pre-main-sequence evolutionary tracks (Hayashi tracks) for 0.1–3$M_\odot$ stars, and locations of known T Tauri stars. Evolutionary times are also shown. The locations of the T Tauri stars are consistent with ages of ~10^6 years.

infrared wavelengths. Such circumstellar discs are believed to be the structures from which planets may form around their young host stars. A particularly well studied example is **Beta Pictoris** (β Pic), where the disc is seen almost edge-on. This enables its profile to be studied in some detail (Figure 23). Circumstellar discs around young stars are regarded as likely places for the formation of planets, and are also called protoplanetary discs or **proplyds**. Such discs, while primarily gaseous, contain enough dust to scatter the light and make the discs opaque. Several examples have been seen silhouetted against the bright background of the Orion nebula (Figure 24).

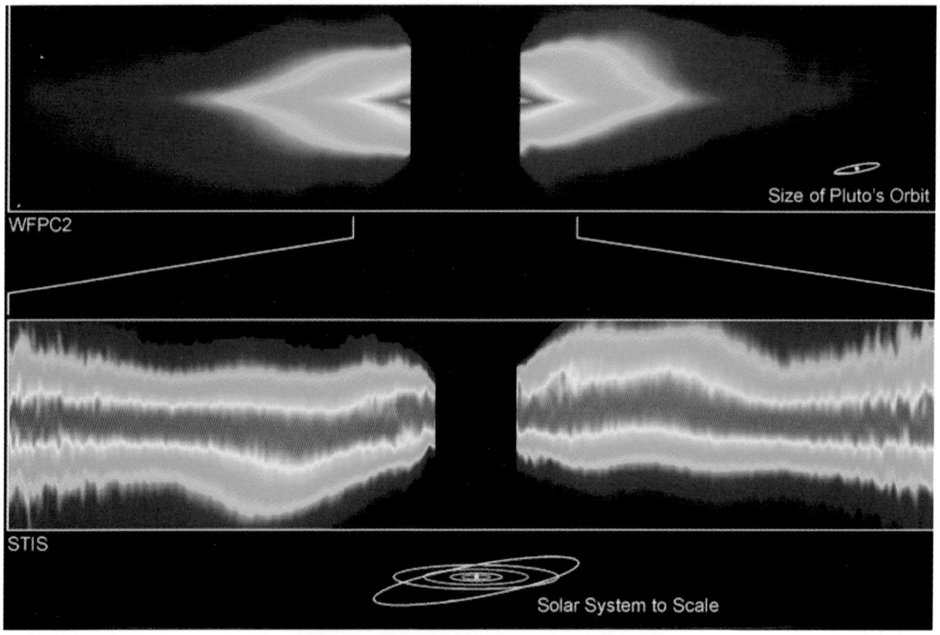

Figure 23 The circumstellar/protoplanetary disc around β Pic, with the central star masked to shield the telescope from its intense light. The disc is visible because it scatters light from the central star. The asymmetries in the disc are evidence that it has been influenced by the gravity of other unseen stars or giant planets. The lower image traces the disc to 15 AU from the star.

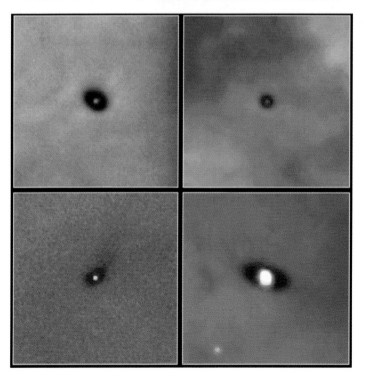

Figure 24 Protoplanetary discs (proplyds) and their host stars, roughly only 10^6 years old, seen silhouetted against the bright background of the Orion nebula. The discs range in size from 2–8 times the diameter of the Solar System.

Young stellar objects

Use the Image Archive to locate images of a selection of young objects associated with star formation. You may find it helpful to search using the keywords highlighted above. Attempt to describe what you are seeing in each image *before* you read its caption, and then read it to clarify what stage of protostellar or pre-main-sequence evolution you are viewing.

Keywords: none ■

■ Some of the young objects appear dark against a bright background, such as the proplyd discs in Orion, some are seen faintly in the company of another object, such as the disc around β Pic, and others are brighter than anything else in the image, such as the young stars in the Doradus image. What is the *common* feature, and what is responsible for their *diverse* appearances?

❑ The common feature is dust. The proplyds in Orion are seen against a bright background in visible light because the dust in the disks makes them opaque to visible light. Hence they appear dark at visible wavelengths. However, dust scatters infrared wavelengths much less than optical wavelengths, so many young objects can be seen directly at infrared wavelengths, such as in the Doradus image. (Young cool objects also emit much more of their energy at infrared than optical wavelengths.) Finally, the β Pic disc is visible because the dust in that object scatters starlight from the star β Pic, which makes it visible at optical wavelengths, but only if the light from the star is blocked from the telescope. ■

2.4 The Kelvin–Helmholtz contraction timescale

So far we have considered the appearance of protostars as they evolve towards the main sequence, but we have not yet considered how long the process takes. We have already met the free-fall time, but once a protostar becomes opaque to its own radiation, fragmentation and free-fall come to an end, and the star enters the Kelvin–Helmholtz phase. The evolutionary rate is much slower than during the free-fall collapse, as now the opacity of the material determines the rate at which the liberated gravitational energy can be radiated from the surface of the protostar. We will determine the lifetime of the object during the Kelvin–Helmholtz phase in this subsection.

You know from the virial theorem that for an object in hydrostatic equilibrium, one half of the liberated gravitational potential energy is stored as kinetic energy (heat), the other half having been radiated away. We can therefore ask the following: if the Sun had been radiating at its current luminosity fuelled solely by gravitational collapse, how long would it have taken to collapse to its current size? The gravitational potential energy liberated, treating it as a *uniform* density sphere (see Example 1), is

$$E_{\text{lib}} = -\Delta E_{\text{GR}} = \frac{3}{5}\frac{GM_\odot^2}{R_\odot} - \frac{3}{5}\frac{GM_\odot^2}{R_{\text{initial}}} = \frac{3}{5}GM_\odot^2\left(\frac{1}{R_\odot} - \frac{1}{R_{\text{initial}}}\right)$$

Since $R_{\text{initial}} \gg R_\odot$, $1/R_{\text{initial}} \ll 1/R_\odot$, so $E_{\text{lib}} \approx (3/5)GM_\odot^2/R_\odot$. The time taken to radiate half of this, at the Sun's current luminosity of $L_\odot$, is

$$\tau = \frac{0.5 E_{\text{lib}}}{L_\odot} = \frac{3}{10}\frac{GM_\odot^2}{R_\odot L_\odot}$$

Recall, however, that the constant in this expression, 3/10, comes from the assumption of a *uniform* density sphere, which causes the gravitational potential energy of the sphere, the liberated energy, and the timescale all to be underestimated. Acknowledging this uncertainty, the portion *excluding* the uncertain constant is called the **Kelvin–Helmholtz contraction time**[3] *of the Sun*, given by

$$\tau_{\text{KH},\odot} = \frac{GM_\odot^2}{R_\odot L_\odot} \tag{16}$$

Question 9

Evaluate the Kelvin–Helmholtz time for the Sun, in (a) seconds and (b) years. ■

Note in your answer to Question 9 that the Kelvin–Helmholtz contraction time for the Sun is much longer than the free-fall collapse time of the initial cloud, which was $\tau_{\text{ff}} \sim 10^5$ yr.

- ■ You have now shown (Question 9) that the Kelvin–Helmholtz contraction time for the Sun is $\approx 3 \times 10^7$ yr. What does this indicate about the possible lifetime of the Sun?

- ❏ Even without considering nuclear energy sources, we can derive a possible lifetime for the Sun of ~30 million years. In fact, astronomers believed for a time that the Sun was powered by slow gravitational collapse, and that it would last for about this length of time. However, that belief pre-dated the discovery, from radioactive-decay dating, that some rocks on the Earth were orders of magnitude older. This forced astronomers to acknowledge that some other energy source was delaying the gravitational collapse of the Sun. That energy source was later revealed with the discovery of thermonuclear fusion (which you will study in the next section of this block). ■

The Kelvin–Helmholtz time can be generalized to stars of other mass by maintaining the same parameter dependence, and normalizing to our result for the Sun, i.e. multiplying by 1 and then rearranging

$$\tau_{\text{KH}} = \frac{GM^2}{RL} = \frac{GM^2}{RL} \times \frac{\left(\frac{GM_\odot^2}{R_\odot L_\odot}\right)}{\left(\frac{GM_\odot^2}{R_\odot L_\odot}\right)} = \left(\frac{GM_\odot^2}{R_\odot L_\odot}\right) \times \frac{\left(\frac{GM^2}{RL}\right)}{\left(\frac{GM_\odot^2}{R_\odot L_\odot}\right)}$$

$$\approx 3\times 10^7 \text{yr} \times \left(\frac{M}{M_\odot}\right)^2 \frac{1}{R/R_\odot}\frac{1}{L/L_\odot}$$

[3]The definition of the Kelvin–Helmholtz timescale given in Collins does not adequately distinguish between this timescale and the free-fall timescale. Note that the Kelvin–Helmholtz timescale includes consideration of the rate at which the liberated gravitational potential energy is radiated, whereas the free-fall timescale is for an unopposed collapse.

This can be reduced further to just an explicit dependence on mass by making some approximations.

First, from Figure 1 (Phillips Fig. 1.6), it can be seen that the plot of $\log_{10} L$ versus $\log_{10} T_{\mathrm{eff}}$ has a main sequence slope for stars near $1 M_{\odot}$ of ≈ 8, from which we infer that for solar-type stars on the main sequence

$$L \propto T_{\mathrm{eff}}^8 \tag{17}$$

Next, you know that $L = 4\pi R^2 \sigma T_{\mathrm{eff}}^4 \propto R^2 T_{\mathrm{eff}}^4$, so we can substitute for T_{eff} using Equation 17, $T_{\mathrm{eff}} \propto L^{1/8}$, and write $L \propto R^2 L^{4/8}$, i.e. $R^2 \propto L^{1-4/8} = L^{1/2}$, or $R \propto L^{1/4}$.

Our expression for the Kelvin–Helmholtz time then becomes

$$\tau_{\mathrm{KH}} \approx 3 \times 10^7 \text{ yr } \times \left(\frac{M}{M_{\odot}}\right)^2 \left(\frac{1}{L/L_{\odot}}\right)^{1/4} \frac{1}{L/L_{\odot}}$$

$$= 3 \times 10^7 \text{ yr } \times \left(\frac{M}{M_{\odot}}\right)^2 \left(\frac{L}{L_{\odot}}\right)^{-5/4}$$

We now use a relationship between mass and luminosity to write this solely in terms of the mass. Phillips Fig. 1.4 reveals the **mass–luminosity relation** for main-sequence stars. At low mass, the main trend is steeper than the illustrated slope $L \propto M^3$, but it is shallower at higher mass. That is, the exponent changes slowly with mass. For solar-mass stars, the relation $L \propto M^{3.5}$ is usually adopted. (You could draw a line of slope 3.5 through the solar point ($1 M_{\odot}$, $1 L_{\odot}$) to convince yourself of this.) Substituting for the luminosity then approximates the Kelvin–Helmholtz time for solar-type stars as

$$\tau_{\mathrm{KH}} \approx 3 \times 10^7 \text{ yr } \times \left(\frac{M}{M_{\odot}}\right)^2 \left[(M/M_{\odot})^{7/2}\right]^{-5/4}$$

$$= 3 \times 10^7 \text{ yr } \times \left(\frac{M}{M_{\odot}}\right)^{2 - \left(\frac{7}{2} \times \frac{5}{4}\right)}$$

$$\approx 3 \times 10^7 \text{ yr } \times (M/M_{\odot})^{-2.4}$$

(Remember that this is only an approximation, as both the main-sequence slope $\log_{10} L$ versus $\log_{10} T_{\mathrm{eff}}$ and the mass–luminosity relation vary slowly with mass.) This emphasizes that the contraction times of low-mass stars are much longer than the contraction time of the Sun, and conversely high-mass stars contract faster.

A fit to *numerical* models of the time to contract (τ_{cont}) to the main sequence (ms) give results slightly longer than the Kelvin–Helmholtz time, by a factor of a few:

$$\tau_{\mathrm{cont}} \approx 8 \times 10^7 (M/M_{\odot})(L_{\odot}/L_{\mathrm{ms}}) \text{ yr}$$

You may be surprised that the exponents in this equation do not appear to resemble those derived above. This is because the mass M and main-sequence luminosity L_{ms} are closely correlated, so one compensates for differences in the other. We can see that the dependence on mass derived from the numerical models is in fact remarkably similar, even though the coefficient is larger. Using the same approximate mass–luminosity relation for main-sequence stars as above, $L_{\mathrm{ms}}/L_{\odot} = (M/M_{\odot})^{3.5}$, we can rewrite the numerical result as $\tau_{\mathrm{cont}} \approx 8 \times 10^7 (M/M_{\odot})^{-2.5}$ yr which has essentially the same mass-dependence as we derived above.

2.5 A star is born

We finish this section by looking at the conditions found in a protostar which successfully ignites hydrogen on the main sequence.

A new stage of evolution — stardom on the main sequence — is reached if the temperature in the core of the protostar becomes sufficiently high to initiate nuclear reactions that release energy. If this can occur, then nuclear energy replaces gravitational energy as the means of replenishing energy that is lost through radiation from the surface of the star. The nuclear energy release also maintains the core temperature and hence the pressure that supports the star against further collapse. The timescale of evolution changes dramatically if this state can be achieved.

By far the major constituent of stars is hydrogen, which accounts for typically 90% (by number) of the nuclei. The most important nuclear reactions are, consequently, those which involve the fusion of hydrogen nuclei (protons) into heavier nuclei – **hydrogen burning**. Hydrogen has the lowest ignition temperature of common nuclear species, between ~2×10^6 to 1×10^7 K (depending on which book you read, since the onset is gradual as the temperature increases), compared to $\geq 10^8$ K for heavier species. (See Phillips, Table 1.3 (page 26).) So, hydrogen burning is the first substantial thermonuclear process that is ignited in the core of a contracting, heating-up protostar. (Actually, reactions between a proton and a deuteron – the nucleus of the heavier isotope of hydrogen – can be initiated at even lower temperatures, ~2×10^5 K, about 10^5 years after the collapse begins, but there are so few deuterons they are destroyed quickly, and the net effect is merely to slow the evolution of the protostar briefly. We will not discuss this energy source further.)

Activity 14	15 minutes

Thermonuclear fusion in the Sun

Read the subsection 'Thermonuclear fusion in the sun', in Phillips (pages 23–25). The proton-proton chain described in this reading is not the only hydrogen-burning reaction in stars (there is another called the CNO cycle, which we will discuss in Section 4.5), but it is the main one for stars whose mass is similar to or less than the Sun. This reading is only introductory; we will study the nuclear burning processes in greater detail later in this block. However, you should pay particular attention to the discussion of the thermonuclear thermostat on the second half of page 24. This concept proves to be very important in understanding how stars evolve.

Keywords: **thermonuclear reaction, nuclear fusion, proton-proton chain, deuterium, deuteron, coulomb barrier, weak nuclear interaction, electromagnetic interaction, strong nuclear interaction, neutrino** ■

The final comment to make on evolution towards the main sequence concerns the small drop in luminosity which occurs just as the star reaches the main sequence. This marks the stage at which thermonuclear energy generation becomes the dominant fuel source, replacing gravitational collapse which has fuelled the star, via the virial theorem, until this point. It is perhaps surprising that the onset of this most powerful energy source brings about the *lowest* luminosity in the object's history so far! This remarkable result is because the luminosity of the star is *not* determined by its energy generation *mechanism*, but by the rate at which energy is transported from the inside of the star to the outside. *The energy-transport rate determines the burning rate, and not vice versa as you may have expected!* This comes about because of the thermostat mechanism described by Phillips on page 24. The energy generation mechanism determines *how long* it can shine at that luminosity, but not what the luminosity is.

2.6 Summary of Section 2

1   The adiabatic index is $\gamma = \dfrac{1 + (s/2)}{(s/2)}$, where s is the number of degrees of freedom of the particles. For an ideal monatomic gas, or cold diatomic gas, $s = 3$ so $\gamma = 5/3$, whereas a gas with more internal degrees of freedom has $s > 3$ and $1 < \gamma < 5/3$.

2   The temperature–density (log–log) diagram can be used to track the changing parameters of collapsing gas clouds. The Jeans criterion indicates that the critical boundary for collapse has the form $\log_{10} T = (1/3)\log_{10} \rho + \text{constant}$. Adiabatic collapse would have a slope 2/3, and would terminate at the Jeans line, thus *failing* to form stars. Rather, collapse is initially *non*-adiabatic. Initially clouds cool, until heating and cooling timescales become comparable. High-density clouds then collapse almost isothermally until they become optically thick, after which they contract almost adiabatically.

3   The Jeans equations show that if the cloud collapses (R decreases and ρ increases) without heating up, then progressively smaller submasses satisfy the Jeans criterion. This leads to fragmentation of the collapsing cloud.

4   A $1 M_\odot$ molecular cloud fragment that has just become unstable to collapse at a temperature of 20 K would have a Jean's density

$$\rho_J = \frac{3}{4\pi M^2}\left(\frac{3kT}{2G\overline{m}}\right)^3 = 4 \times 10^{-16}\,\text{kg}\,\text{m}^{-3}$$

and hence a radius R given by $\rho_J = M/(4/3)\pi R^3$, i.e. $R = 1.1 \times 10^{15}\,\text{m}$ $= 1.5 \times 10^6\,R_\odot$.

5   A cloud collapses almost isothermally and in free-fall ($\tau_{ff} \approx (3\pi/32G\rho)^{1/2}$ $\approx 10^5$ yr) until the liberated gravitational energy has completely dissociated molecular hydrogen (H_2) and then ionized atomic hydrogen. For $1 M_\odot$ of hydrogen, this amount of energy is liberated when the protostar collapses to $R \approx 130 R_\odot$ ($E_{lib} \approx -E_{GR,final} \approx GM^2/R_{final}$).

6   Ionization of hydrogen increases the free-electron density and hence also increases its opacity. The protostar becomes opaque to its own radiation and heats up, and the pressure slows the collapse. The protostar approaches hydrostatic equilibrium. By the time hydrostatic equilibrium has been established, the internal temperature has risen to ~30 000 K.

7   The Hayashi convective boundary exists because:

   •   cooler stellar material has higher opacity; Kramers opacity $\kappa \propto \rho T^{-3.5}$;

   •   high opacity impedes the radiative heating of layers further out and hence leads to a steep radiative temperature gradient;

   •   a steep radiative temperature gradient promotes convection.

   The boundary is at $T_{eff} \approx 3000$–5000 K (depending on mass, composition and luminosity), and protostars descend along the boundary from high luminosity to low luminosity at roughly constant surface temperature.

8   With hydrostatic equilibrium established, the star enters the long Kelvin–Helmholtz phase in which it *slowly* collapses, remaining in hydrostatic equilibrium, at a rate sufficient to replenish the energy radiated from the surface. The core heats up as it contracts, and as the opacity decreases, it becomes less convective. During the subsequent Henyey contraction, the luminosity evolves as $L \propto \sim T_{\mathrm{eff}}^{4/5}$. The timescale for the Kelvin–Helmholtz phase is given by

$$\tau_{\mathrm{KH}} = GM_{\odot}^2/R_{\odot}L_{\odot} \approx 3 \times 10^7 \, \mathrm{yr}$$

for the Sun, or $\tau_{\mathrm{KH}} \approx 3 \times 10^7 \, \mathrm{yr} \times (M/M_{\odot})^{-2.4}$ for solar-type stars. Numerical models suggest slightly longer contraction times $t_{\mathrm{cont}} \approx 8 \times 10^7 (M/M_{\odot})^{-2.5} \, \mathrm{yr}$.

9   If the stellar core reaches $T_{\mathrm{c}} \approx 2 \times 10^6 \, \mathrm{K}$, hydrogen ignites and thermonuclear burning provides a new energy source to replenish the losses at the stellar surface.

10 The luminosity of the star is *not* determined by its energy generation *mechanism*, but by the rate at which energy is transported from the inside of the star to the outside. The energy-transport rate determines the burning rate, and not vice versa. The mechanism of energy production does, however, determine the *length of time* over which the luminosity can be sustained.

12 Protostars are generally still cloaked in dust, but can be observed in radio, infrared, and X-ray wavelengths. Bipolar outflows (along the rotation axis) are often seen, along with evidence for circumstellar discs. As the dust is blown away from the luminous protostar, a T Tauri pre-main-sequence star appears in the H–R diagram near the fully convective (Hayashi) boundary.

3 NUCLEAR FUSION

We have now seen how cold gas clouds collapse to form stars, where by definition a star is an object which ignites hydrogen burning sufficiently to balance energy losses by radiation from its surface. In this section we take a detailed look at the process of nuclear fusion. We examine the quantum properties essential for it to occur, and then study the rates at which the reactions proceed.

3.1 Quantum mechanical properties of particles

Quantum physics is vital to understanding fusion, because of the very small sizes of nuclei. We begin this subsection by considering just how small a ucleus is, and then investigate the consequences.

3.1.1 Nuclear dimensions

The radius R of a nucleus containing A **nucleons**, i.e. having an atomic mass number A, is $R \approx r_0 A^{1/3}$, where $r_0 = 1.2 \times 10^{-15}$ m. Since volume V varies as R^3, this relation tells you immediately that $V \propto A$. That is, doubling the number of nucleons in a nucleus doubles the volume occupied. In this sense, *nuclei are incompressible*, whereas *atoms* can be packed together with greatly *varying density*.

■ Consider for a moment just how compact the nucleus is compared with the size of an atom. A convenient unit for measuring the radius of an atom is the Bohr radius, approximately 0.5×10^{-10} m. Atomic radii are typically a few to a few tens of Bohr radii, or of order 10^{-10} m. Nuclei are therefore of order 10^5 times smaller in radius. Think of some examples of things that differ in size by that factor, to get an impression of how compact the nucleus is compared to the atom within which it resides.

❏ Here are some examples.

- An atom with a radius the same as the Earth's orbit (1 AU) would have a nucleus much smaller than the Sun! Since 1 AU $\approx 1.5 \times 10^{11}$ m, the scaled nucleus would have a radius 1.5×10^6 m, about the same as the Moon!

- The continent of Australia is roughly 4000 km across. An atom this size would have a nucleus only 40 m across, about the size of Sydney Opera House.

- The M25 ring road around London has a diameter of order 40 km. If an atom had a radius this size, the nucleus would still be only 0.4 m across, or the size of a rubbish bin in central London.

- An athletics stadium is typically about 100 m across, so an atom on this scale would have a nucleus the size of a pinhead.

- As a final example, an atom the size of a house 10 m across would have a nucleus only 0.1 mm in diameter, smaller than the full-stop at the end of this sentence.■

3.1.2 Wave functions and Schrödinger's equation

Before going on with this section, briefly review the following material on vector differentiation, as this tool will soon be used to study the quantum mechanical properties of nuclear particles.

DIFFERENTIATION AND VECTOR OPERATORS

Recall that the derivative df/dx of one variable or function f with respect to another variable x is a measure of how much f changes due to changes in x. If f depends not only on x but also other variables as well, such as y and z, then the derivative of f with respect to x *while y and z are held constant* is called the **partial derivative** of f with respect to x, and is written $\partial f/\partial x$. (Note the use of curly ∂ rather than straight d symbols.)

The symbol ∇, called grad, combines the shorthand notation of vectors with differentiation. The grad symbol ∇ is a vector symbol, having the three components $(\partial/\partial x, \partial/\partial y, \partial/\partial z)$. Each of these is a partial derivative – differentiation with respect to one variable whilst holding all others constant. It is used in conjunction with a dependent variable or function, for example f, so that $\nabla f = (\partial f/\partial x, \partial f/\partial y, \partial f/\partial z)$. Where vector problems are simplified to one dimension, ∇ becomes $\partial/\partial x$.

Notice a subtle difference between the type of vector used for position, $\boldsymbol{r}$, and that used for grad. Whereas the vector components of $\boldsymbol{r}$, e.g. (r_x, r_y, r_z), indicate the *values* of the variable, the vector components of ∇ are *operators* which tell you what to *do* to some other variable – in this case calculate its partial derivatives. For this reason, ∇ is described as a vector operator, while $\boldsymbol{r}$ is a vector variable.

As an example of how the grad operator works, imagine that you have measured the temperature at many places in a room, and have found that you can describe it by some equation depending on x, y and z. For instance, the temperature may be higher on one side of the room near a heat source, and cooler on the opposite side near a poorly insulated window. The temperature T is a scalar variable and has no direction associated with it. Now consider the quantity ∇T: it is a vector variable because grad is a vector operator, and ∇T has components $(\partial T/\partial x, \partial T/\partial y, \partial T/\partial z)$. These components tell how the temperature changes in the x-, y- and z-directions respectively, so ∇T is a vector variable giving the magnitude and direction of the temperature gradient. That is, ∇ gives the gradient of the function it operates on, which is why ∇ is called the grad operator.

Recall that when you have differentiated a function f with respect to x to obtain its derivative df/dx, you can differentiate that derivative to obtain the second derivative of f with respect to x, d^2f/dx^2. As an extension of the ∇ symbol, the ∇^2 symbol indicates that partial *second* derivatives are to be summed

i.e. $$\nabla^2 \equiv \nabla \bullet \nabla = \frac{\partial^2}{\partial x^2} + \frac{\partial^2}{\partial y^2} + \frac{\partial^2}{\partial z^2}$$

Example 3

We use Figure 25 to examine the use of the grad operator. The problem is: Calculate the temperature gradient in the room.

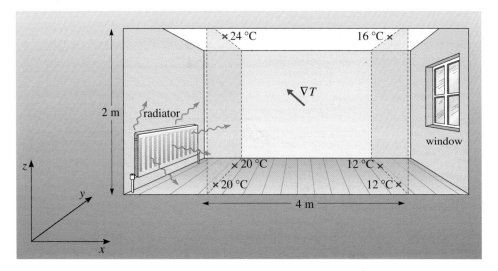

Figure 25 A sealed room has a radiator (heater) at one end, and a poorly insulated window at the other end. Six identical thermometers measure temperatures as indicated.

Solution

The temperature gradient ∇T is a vector whose components are $(\partial T/\partial x, \partial T/\partial y, \partial T/\partial z)$. We calculate each of these components one at a time from the figure. (If we had been given an equation describing the variation of temperature in the room, we could have differentiated that directly.) The x-axis runs from left to right along the room, the y-axis runs from front to back across the room, and the z-axis increases from the floor to the ceiling.

- $\partial T/\partial x$: The two pairs of thermometers at ground level indicate a temperature gradient of $-8\,°\mathrm{C}/4\,\mathrm{m} = -2\,°\mathrm{C}\,\mathrm{m}^{-1}$ along the room (the x-axis), assuming the gradient is linear;

- $\partial T/\partial y$: There appears to be no temperature gradient across the room ($0\,°\mathrm{C}\,\mathrm{m}^{-1}$ along the y-axis);

- $\partial T/\partial z$, There is a gradient of $+4\,°\mathrm{C}/2\,\mathrm{m} = +2\,°\mathrm{C}\,\mathrm{m}^{-1}$ vertically (the z-axis).

Hence $\nabla T = (-2, 0, +2)\,°\mathrm{C}\,\mathrm{m}^{-1}$

Even though *temperature* is a scalar, that is, a temperature measurement *has no direction* associated with it, we *can* assign a direction to the *temperature gradient*. The signs of the x-, y- and z-components of the vector representing the temperature gradient ∇T show that it is directed to the left and upwards at an angle of 45°, and has a magnitude

$$|\nabla T| = [(-2\,°\mathrm{C}\,\mathrm{m}^{-1})^2 + (0\,°\mathrm{C}\,\mathrm{m}^{-1})^2 + (2\,°\mathrm{C}\,\mathrm{m}^{-1})^2]^{1/2} \approx 2.8\,°\mathrm{C}\,\mathrm{m}^{-1}$$

Note also that besides the temperature varying from place to place, the gradient *also* may vary from place to place. (There are too few thermometers in this example to know.) ∎

■ If $\partial T/\partial x$ tells us how much the *temperature* changes in the x-direction, i.e. the temperature gradient, what does $\partial^2 T/\partial x^2$ tell us?

❑ $\partial^2 T/\partial x^2$ tells us how much the *temperature gradient* changes in the x-direction, i.e. the *gradient of the temperature gradient*. ■

Because nuclear particles have such small separations when they interact, comparable to their radius $r_0 \approx 10^{-15}$ m, it is important to consider the quantum mechanical (wave) properties of the particles as well as their classical behaviour. In fact, if nuclear particles did not have wave properties, then fusion reactions would be exceedingly rare and we would not be here to discuss them. This is because it is the wave properties of particles that allow them to sneak through the repulsive Coulomb barrier that otherwise would hold them apart. You will study the process of barrier penetration in the following subsection, but first we should consider how the wave properties of particles are described.

In **quantum mechanics** a particle, whose wave properties are fundamental to its behaviour, can be described by a mathematical device called a **wave function**. A wave function varies with position – x in one dimension, or r in three dimensions – and time t, and is written $\psi(x, t)$. It is called a wave function because it obeys a differential equation called **Schrödinger's equation**, the solutions of which have wave-like properties.

You don't need to know the origin of Schrödinger's equation, but we will see how it can be used. For many applications, the time-dependent part $\psi(t)$ of the wave function can be calculated separately from the spatial part $\psi(r)$, and a simplified time-independent form of Schrödinger's equation can be used. We will deal with that simplified form, and consider only the spatial (time-independent) part of the wave function. For two particles A and B with **reduced mass** (see box opposite) m_r, separation r, energy of approach E, and interacting with a potential energy $V(r)$, Schrödinger's equation (in its time-independent form – TISE) is

$$\left[-\frac{\hbar^2 \nabla^2}{2m_r} + V(r) \right] \psi(r) = E\psi(r) \quad \text{(e.g. Phillips 4.3)}$$

Note the occurrence of the grad operator. Note also that $\hbar \equiv h/2\pi$.

You may be wondering to what physical quantity the wave function ψ corresponds. Here you meet one of the conceptual hurdles in quantum mechanics, for although ψ can be calculated as a mathematical solution to the above equation, and graphs of a wave function can be plotted, a wave function *cannot be measured*! However, the *squared amplitude* of the wave function, $|\psi|^2$, corresponds to the **position probability density**, and that *can* be measured. Considering a one-dimensional (rather than three-dimensional) case, $|\psi|^2 \, dx$ is the probability that the particle described by the wave function ψ is located between x and $x + dx$. If the squared amplitude of a wave function is zero at some point A, then you can be sure that the particle will not be found at that point, whereas if the squared amplitude is greater than zero at some point B, then you know there is some probability that the particle will be found at point B. The higher the squared amplitude (= the position probability density), the more likely it is that the particle will be found there.

The preceding discussion of the *probability* that a particle will be found at some location emphasizes that on the small scales where wave properties become fundamental characteristics of objects, the word 'position' no longer has the same

REDUCED MASS

When a body A is accelerated by a force F exerted by another body, B, the acceleration a_A is given by the force divided by its mass m_A:

$$a_A = F/m_A$$

However, an equal and opposite force $-F$ is exerted on B by A, causing B to accelerate as well:

$$a_B = -F/m_B$$

The acceleration a_{AB} of A *relative* to B, since *both* are being accelerated, is slightly more complicated than the case where one particle remains at rest:

$$a_{AB} = a_A - a_B = \frac{F}{m_A} - \frac{-F}{m_B} = F\left(\frac{1}{m_A} + \frac{1}{m_B}\right) = F\left(\frac{m_B + m_A}{m_A m_B}\right)$$

Fortunately, this analysis shows that the acceleration is still of the form

$$\text{acceleration} = \text{force/mass}$$

provided the mass of the particles is replaced by the quantity

$$m_r = m_A m_B/(m_A + m_B)$$

which is called the *reduced mass*.

This quantity has units of mass, and if $m_B \gg m_A$ then $m_r \approx m_A m_B/m_B = m_A$, leading to the familiar result for when one particle (B) is very massive,
$a_{AB} = F/m_A$.

reliable meaning that we are accustomed to in the macroscopic (non-quantum) world. Think of any sort of wave that you are familiar with, e.g. water waves, sound waves, radio waves. A wave does not exist only at one point, but propagates in certain directions with certain amplitudes. So it is with particles on small scales when their wave properties become significant. They no longer exist just at one point, but have a presence in different places simultaneously. We can at best assign a probability to where the particle is if we try to detect its presence. The wave properties of particles have been verified experimentally through the electron-diffraction experiment and similar studies of other particles.

An important application of wave functions is to use them to calculate the position probability density of an incoming particle encountering the potential barrier around a nucleus. We will do this in the next subsection, but first let us consider the wave function for a simpler system: a particle in a very deep potential well. (The well could be the boundaries of a nucleus within which nuclear particles are confined, the boundaries of an atom within which electrons are confined, or some other.)

Figure 26a (top diagram) overleaf shows schematically a potential well of width L. The well is so deep that an infinite energy would be required for a particle to escape from it. We place a particle in the well, and then ask what its wave properties are. The wave properties are given by the solution to Schrödinger's equation, and associated with each permitted wave function is a permitted particle energy. Fortunately for us, the wave functions are plotted in Figure 26a (bottom diagram) below the schematic of the well. These are examined in Example 4 and the question below.

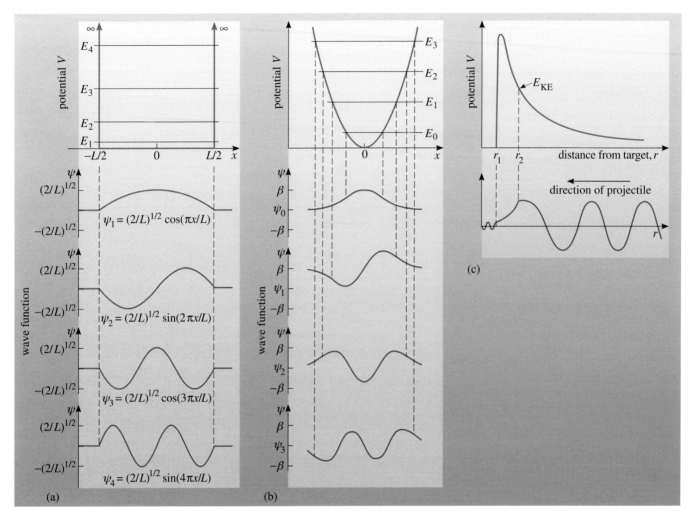

Figure 26 (a) (top) Graph of potential energy V against position x, for a potential well with infinite potential boundaries. (bottom) The wave functions associated with a particle in an infinitely deep potential well go to zero at the boundaries, so there is zero probability of finding the particle outside the well, i.e. beyond the potential boundary. (b) For a *non-infinite* potential, the wave functions are attenuated but non-zero even beyond the boundaries, in the region of high potential. (c) If a potential barrier is of a finite height and thickness, there is a non-zero probability of finding the particle beyond the barrier.

Example 4

Show that the wave function $\psi_1(x) = (2/L)^{1/2} \cos(\pi x/L)$ is a solution to Schrödinger's equation in *one dimension* for a flat potential well of potential V with infinitely high boundaries. Find the particle energy E associated with that wave function. Since the potential becomes infinite at the boundaries, confine your analysis to the range $-L/2 < x < L/2$.

(*Hint*: Recall that $\mathrm{d}\sin x/\mathrm{d}x = \cos x$, and $\mathrm{d}\cos x/\mathrm{d}x = -\sin x$.)

Solution

Since we are dealing with only one spatial dimension x instead of three dimensions $\mathbf{r} = (x, y, z)$, we begin by rewriting the time-independent form of Schrödinger's equation

$$\left[-\frac{\hbar^2 \nabla^2}{2m_{\mathrm{r}}} + V(\mathbf{r}) \right] \psi(\mathbf{r}) = E\psi(\mathbf{r})$$

in one dimension only. In three dimensions, $\nabla^2 = \partial^2/\partial x^2 + \partial^2/\partial y^2 + \partial^2/\partial z^2$.

The one-dimensional form of Schrödinger's equation is therefore

$$\left[-\frac{\hbar^2}{2m_r} \frac{\partial^2}{\partial x^2} + V \right] \psi(x) = E\psi(x)$$

which can also be written

$$\frac{\partial^2}{\partial x^2} \psi(x) = \frac{2m_r}{\hbar^2}(V - E)\psi(x)$$

To test whether the wave function $\psi_1(x) = (2/L)^{1/2} \cos(\pi x/L)$ is a solution to Schrödinger's equation, we substitute it into the left-hand side of the equation and see whether we get the right-hand side as a result:

$$\frac{\partial^2}{\partial x^2} \psi(x) = \frac{\partial^2}{\partial x^2} \left[\left(\frac{2}{L}\right)^{1/2} \cos\frac{\pi x}{L} \right]$$

Taking the constant outside, and expanding the differentiation gives

$$\frac{\partial^2}{\partial x^2} \psi(x) = \left(\frac{2}{L}\right)^{1/2} \frac{\partial}{\partial x} \left[\frac{\partial}{\partial x} \left(\cos\frac{\pi x}{L} \right) \right]$$

Now take the first derivative

$$\frac{\partial^2}{\partial x^2} \psi(x) = \left(\frac{2}{L}\right)^{1/2} \frac{\partial}{\partial x} \left(-\frac{\pi}{L} \sin\frac{\pi x}{L} \right)$$

take the constants outside the brackets

$$\frac{\partial^2}{\partial x^2} \psi(x) = -\left(\frac{2}{L}\right)^{1/2} \frac{\pi}{L} \frac{\partial}{\partial x} \left(\sin\frac{\pi x}{L} \right)$$

take the next derivative

$$\frac{\partial^2}{\partial x^2} \psi(x) = -\left(\frac{2}{L}\right)^{1/2} \frac{\pi}{L} \left(\frac{\pi}{L} \cos\frac{\pi x}{L} \right)$$

and take the constants outside

$$\frac{\partial^2}{\partial x^2} \psi(x) = -\left(\frac{\pi}{L}\right)^2 \left(\frac{2}{L}\right)^{1/2} \cos\frac{\pi x}{L} = -\left(\frac{\pi}{L}\right)^2 \psi(x)$$

This indeed matches the right-hand side of the rearranged Schrödinger's equation, $\frac{2m_r}{\hbar^2}(V(x) - E)\psi(x)$, provided we can identify the term $-(\pi/L)^2$ with $\frac{2m_r}{\hbar^2}(V - E)$, which is to say that

$$-\left(\frac{\pi}{L}\right)^2 = \frac{2m_r}{\hbar^2}(V - E)$$

so

$$-\frac{\hbar^2}{2m_r} \left(\frac{\pi}{L}\right)^2 = V - E$$

and therefore

$$E = V + \frac{\hbar^2}{2m_r} \left(\frac{\pi}{L}\right)^2$$

This shows that the stated wave function $\psi_1(x) = (2/L)^{1/2} \cos(\pi x/L)$ is indeed a solution to Schrödinger's equation, and furthermore we have shown that the energy associated with this wave function is $\pi^2 \hbar^2 / 2m_r L^2$ above the bottom of the well. ■

Question 10

Consider in turn each of the remaining wave functions in Figure 26a:

(a) $\psi_2(x) = (2/L)^{1/2} \sin(2\pi x/L)$,

(b) $\psi_3(x) = (2/L)^{1/2} \cos(3\pi x/L)$, and

(c) $\psi_4(x) = (2/L)^{1/2} \sin(4\pi x/L)$.

Show that each of these wave functions is a solution to the Schrödinger's equation in one dimension for a flat potential well V with infinitely high potential boundaries, and find the particle energy E associated with each wave function.

Hint 1: Since the potential becomes infinite at the boundaries, confine your analysis to the range $-L/2 < x < L/2$.

Hint 2: Recall that $d \sin x / dx = \cos x$, and $d \cos x / dx = -\sin x$. ■

Once you have derived all of the particle energies (that is, the energy associated with the wave functions describing the particles), answer the following question:

■ Consider the energy associated with the wave functions shown in Figure 26a and analysed in Example 4 and Question 10. Note that the energy of the particle is quantized. What happens to the energy of the particle if the distance across the potential well increases? Does this make sense?

❑ The particle energies are proportional to $1/L^2$, so as the physical size of the potential well increases, the energies decrease, and hence the spacings between the energy levels decrease. It therefore becomes harder to tell that the energies are in fact quantized. That is, larger physical sizes resemble the classical case where particle energies have a continuous permitted range, rather than discrete quantized values. ■

Activity 15   30 minutes

Solutions to Schrödinger's equation

This activity follows on from Example 4 and Question 10. Using a spreadsheet, plot each of the four wave functions ($\psi_1(x)$ to $\psi_4(x)$) for x values in the range $-L/2 < x < L/2$. In addition, calculate and plot the position probability density for each one.

Hints:

Choose $L = 1$ in some arbitrary unit of length, and make a column of x/L from -0.5 to $+0.5$ in some small step interval Δx. If you chose Δx intervals that are too large, your graphs will look rather coarse, but there is no need to sample too finely either, as the computational time will increase unnecessarily. Appropriate values of Δx are around 0.01 to 0.025, but you are free to experiment.

Don't type all of the values of x/L yourself! Instead type the first number (e.g. -0.5 in cell A7) and on the next row (cell A8) type a formula such as =A7+$B$4 where cell B4 contains your choice of Δx. Copy and paste this formula down the column until you have enough entries to span the range $x/L = -0.5$ to $+0.5$.

Make the next column your calculation of $\psi_1(x)$. In the first cell (e.g. cell B7) enter a formula such as =SQRT(2/$B$3)*COS(PI()*$A7) where cell B3 contains your value for L (= 1). Copy and paste this down the column.

The adjacent column could be used for the position probability density, $|\psi_1|^2$. In the first cell, e.g. C7, enter the formula =B7^2, and copy this down the columns.

Repeat this procedure in adjacent columns, varying the formula slightly, to calculate columns of ψ_2, $|\psi_2|^2$, ψ_3, $|\psi_3|^2$, ψ_4, $|\psi_4|^2$.

Then use the Insert/Chart option (twice) to make two plots, one plotting the four wave functions and one plotting the four position probability densities, as a function of x. Recall that to highlight multiple columns of a table that are *not* adjacent to one another, click and drag on the first to highlight that one, then release the mouse button, move the cursor to the next desired column, and then hold down the Control key while you click and drag on the second column.

When you have finished, see the section 'Comments on activities' at the end of this Study Guide.

Keywords: none ■

■ Look at the position probability densities you have plotted in Activity 15, corresponding to the four wave functions
$\psi_1(x) = (2/L)^{1/2}\cos(\pi x/L)$, $\psi_2(x) = (2/L)^{1/2}\sin(2\pi x/L)$, $\psi_3(x) = (2/L)^{1/2}\cos(3\pi x/L)$, and $\psi_4(x) = (2/L)^{1/2}\sin(4\pi x/L)$. Where in the well is the particle described by wave function ψ_1 *most* likely to be? What is the probability of finding the particle described by wave function ψ_2 in this location?

❑ The position probability density of wave function ψ_1 has a single peak in the centre of the well, so the particle has maximum probability of being found there, in the centre. However, wave function ψ_2 goes through zero at this location, so its position probability density is also zero at this point. The particle described by ψ_2 may be found on either side of the centre, but never right in the centre of the well. Its position probability density shows that it is most likely to be found half way between the centre and the edge, on either side. ■

3.1.3 Barrier penetration/quantum tunnelling

The existence of **quantum tunnelling**, otherwise known as **barrier penetration**, is key to the occurrence of fusion reactions. According to classical mechanics, a particle whose total energy is less than the potential energy of some barrier cannot pass that barrier. A simple example is a ball being thrown over a wall; unless the ball has sufficient kinetic energy to attain a height greater than the wall itself, there is no way it can reach the other side. That is, its kinetic energy must be enough that, once transformed to gravitational potential energy, it exceeds the gravitational potential energy at the top of the wall. In quantum mechanics, however, this restriction no longer holds. In quantum mechanics, the wave properties of the particle must also be considered, and although the wave function associated with a particle is attenuated by a potential barrier, the amplitude of its wave function goes to zero only for an *infinitely* high barrier (e.g. see Figure 26a). Where *finite* potential barriers exist in reality, the wave function *inside and beyond the barrier is non-zero* (Figure 26b), and hence the position probability density $|\psi_2|^2$ is also *non-zero*. In this case, there is a small but non-zero probability that a particle will make its way through a barrier that appears impenetrable or insurmountable from a classical viewpoint. If a ball and wall were small enough for quantum properties to dominate over classical ones, it would be possible for a ball thrown against the wall to leak through to the other side. Importantly, this would happen not because of any miniature holes or because the ball might punch a hole of its own, but merely because it could! As bizarre as this might seem, we shall soon see that this is precisely what happens during collisions of nuclei!

Very close to a nucleus (at distances of order 10^{-15} m), a force between nucleons called the **strong nuclear force** dominates over the Coulomb force and binds a nucleus together. Whereas the electrostatic Coulomb force repels protons and varies with distance as $1/r^2$, the strong nuclear force can both attract and repel. As the distance between nucleons increases beyond 10^{-15} m, the strong force rapidly becomes negligible. Consequently, the nucleus sits in a potential well – as it must to be stable – surrounded by a Coulomb potential barrier of finite height and width as shown schematically in Figure 26c. Due to barrier penetration in quantum mechanics, there is a non-zero probability of a particle whose energy is less than that of the barrier nevertheless making its way from outside the barrier to inside, and hence reaching the nucleus.

Activity 16   **30 minutes**

Thermonuclear fusion and barrier penetration

Read the beginning of 'Thermonuclear fusion in stars', Chapter 4 of Phillips, up to the end of the subsection on 'Barrier penetration' (pages 107–111). We discuss the details of this below, but while you read, note the following:

• Phillips analyses the three-dimensional case. Several simpler one-dimensional equivalents are given in this Study Guide following the activity.

• We have learnt already that the position probability density $|\psi|^2\,dx$ is the probability (in one dimension) that a particle will be found between locations x and $x + dx$. In three dimensions, the probability density has a $4\pi r^2$ term that reflects the spherical geometry, giving rise to $|\psi(r)|^2 4\pi r^2\,dr$ (given in the paragraph following Phillips Equation 4.3) – the probability that the particles will be found separated by a distance between r and $r + dr$.

• Phillips makes use of this in Equation 4.7 to express the probability of barrier penetration as the ratio of the fraction of particles reaching a separation r_N (the nuclear radius), to the fraction reaching the classical radius of the Coulomb barrier r_C:

$$P_{\text{pen}} = \frac{\text{fraction of particles reaching } r_N}{\text{fraction of particles reaching } r_C}$$

$$\text{i.e. } P_{\text{pen}} \approx \frac{|\psi(r_N)|^2 4\pi r_N^2\,dr}{|\psi(r_C)|^2 4\pi r_C^2\,dr} = \frac{|\exp(\chi r_N)|^2 4\pi r_N^2\,dr/r_N^2}{|\exp(\chi r_C)|^2 4\pi r_C^2\,dr/r_C^2} = \left\{\exp[-\chi(r_C - r_N)]\right\}^2$$

• Phillips Equation 4.8 is simply Equation 4.5 with the exact form of the Coulomb potential specified.

χ is the Greek letter chi, pronounced like the first two letters in 'kite'.

• You will not be required to reproduce the integration that leads from Equations 4.9 to 4.12, but the *results* Equations 4.10, 4.11 and 4.12 in Phillips are important and you should recognize these and understand what they mean.

Keywords: **Coulomb potential, Gamow energy** ■

It may not be obvious without knowing more advanced mathematics that the wave function in *three dimensions* given in Phillips Equation 4.6 is a solution to the Schrödinger equation. However, it is easy to show a similar result for the simplified *one-dimensional* case, where the time-independent Schrödinger equation may be written

$$\left[-\frac{\hbar^2}{2m_r}\frac{\partial^2}{\partial x^2} + V(x) \right]\psi(x) = E\psi(x)$$

It is easy to show that the wave function $\psi(x) = \exp(\chi x)$ is a solution of this equation if $V(x)$ is constant, and therefore that the wave function $\psi(x)$ decays exponentially while tunnelling through the barrier towards smaller x. In this case, $\chi^2 = (2m_r/\hbar^2)(V - E)$ as in Phillips 4.5 (except that Phillips uses a potential of constant height E_C – see Phillips Fig. 4.3 – whereas we retain the symbol V).

Question 11

Verify that the wave function $\psi(x) = \exp(\chi x)$ is a solution of the Schrödinger equation in one dimension when the barrier potential is constant.

Hint: $\dfrac{d}{dx}\exp(ax) = a\exp(ax)$ where a is a constant. ■

The probability of a particle successfully tunnelling through to the nucleus can be found by comparing the probability of finding a particle at the inner edge of the Coulomb barrier ($r = r_N$) with the probability of finding it at the outer edge of the Coulomb barrier ($r = r_C$, being much larger than r_N). For the one-dimensional case, the probability of finding a particle in an interval from x to $x + dx$ is $|\psi(x)|^2 dx$. Therefore the penetration probability is

$$P_{pen} \approx \frac{|\psi(r_N)|^2}{|\psi(r_C)|^2} = \left\{\exp[-\chi(r_C - r_N)]\right\}^2$$

which actually matches the result for the three-dimensional case (Phillips 4.7).

■ With reference to a square potential barrier, as in Phillips Fig. 4.2, consider qualitatively how the penetration probability depends on (a) the height of the barrier? (b) the width of the barrier?

❑ (a) The height of the barrier is given by E_C; increasing this increases χ, and hence reduces $P_{pen} \approx \left\{\exp[-\chi(r_C - r_N)]\right\}^2$. A higher barrier reduces the penetration probability, as expected.

(b) A wider barrier increases the distance between r_N and r_C, so reduces $P_{pen} \approx \left\{\exp[-\chi(r_C - r_N)]\right\}^2$. A wider barrier reduces the penetration probability, as expected. ■

So far we have considered rectangular potential barriers whose height is uniform over a range of separations, but more realistically, barrier potentials do vary with separation. For the Coulomb barrier, Phillips expresses the penetration probability in terms of the particle energy E, and the Gamow energy E_G which depends on the atomic number (and therefore charge) of the interacting nuclei, and hence the size of the Coulomb barrier:

$$P_{pen} \approx \exp\left[-\left(\frac{E_G}{E}\right)^{1/2}\right]$$

(Phillips 4.12)

$$\text{with} \quad E_G = 2m_r c^2 (pa Z_A Z_B)^2$$

(Phillips 4.10)

where α is the fine structure constant $\approx 1/137.0$.

■ Does a higher Gamow energy increase or decrease the probability of penetration?

❑ A higher E_G reduces the probability that the barrier will be penetrated. The Gamow energy measures the strength of the Coulomb repulsion, which determines the height of the Coulomb barrier. ■

Question 12

Calculate the Gamow energy (in both SI units and electronvolts) for the following reactions:

(a) the collision of two protons;

(b) the collision of a proton and a deuteron. (A deuteron, d, is a nucleus composed of one proton and one neutron; make the simplifying assumption $m_d = 2m_p$.)

(c) the collision of two ^{3}He nuclei. (^{3}He is the light isotope of helium, comprising two protons and one neutron. For simplicity, assume its mass, given by m_3, is $3m_p$.) ■

Note from Question 12 that the one *additional charge* on each ^{3}He nucleus compared with each ^{1}H nucleus increases the Gamow energy by a factor of 16(!) compared to the proton-proton collision. The *higher masses* increase this by a further factor of 3. You can see, therefore, that the Coulomb barrier is very high for interactions involving all but the lightest nuclei.

Question 13

In Question 7, you calculated the equivalence between temperatures and thermal energies. The centre of the Sun has a temperature of 15.6×10^6 K.

(a) Compute the kT energy equivalent of this temperature in SI units (joules, J) and in electronvolts (eV).

(b) Comparing this with the Gamow energies computed in Question 12, calculate the penetration probabilities for the same three interactions. ■

From the penetration probabilities calculated in Question 13, $\sim 10^{-10}$–10^{-60}, you can see that even with quantum tunnelling, the probability that any single nucleus will react is extremely small.

3.2 Fusion interactions

We now study fusion reactions generally, before calculating their rates in the next subsection.

3.2.1 Cross-sections

A widely used concept in physics where a collision or close interaction between two bodies occurs is the cross-section, usually given the symbol σ. The geometric cross-section for the collision between a small projectile and a large target is simply the cross-sectional area of the target. If some reaction may occur when they collide, the reaction cross-section is the geometric cross-section multiplied by the reaction probability. In the next reading (Activity 17), Phillips gives the analogy of a hard ball colliding with a 1 m^2 window and having a 10% probability of breaking it. In this case, the reaction cross-section is 10% of the geometric cross-section, or 0.1 m^2. If the same window were hit by a ball made of soft foam plastic, the probability of it breaking may be only 0.1%, and the reaction cross-section would be only 0.001 m^2. Note that the window is still the same physical size, 1 m^2, and the ball is the same size, but the reaction cross-sections are very different depending on the nature of the projectile and the strength of the interaction. Therefore, although the reaction cross-section of a target can be considered as an effective area, and has units of area, it should not be confused with the actual physical size of the target.

As atomic nuclei are very small, with radii of order 10^{-15} m, the cross-sectional areas are of order 10^{-30} m^2 (since area is proportional to radius squared). Nuclear physicists have defined the area 10^{-28} m^2 to be 1 barn, so cross-sections are typically measured in units of millibarns or microbarns. (The name for this unit, the barn, comes about from jokes that someone who is a poor shot couldn't hit a target as big as a barn. We have already seen that nuclei are incredibly small targets for fusion reactions. The largest nuclear cross-sections are, relatively speaking, as big as a barn, whereas smaller targets have cross-sections measured only in millibarns or microbarns.)

Don't confuse this σ with the Stefan–Boltzmann constant, which is also given the symbol σ.

Activity 17   **15 minutes**

Fusion cross-sections

The question of whether or not two nuclei interact must be addressed in terms of probabilities. The subsection 'Fusion cross-sections' on pages 111–112 of Phillips describes the factors that determine this. Read that now, and then work through the more detailed discussion provided below.

Pay particular attention to the form of Equation 4.16, and its relationship with Equation 4.12.

Keywords: **fusion cross-section, millibarn, mean free path, nuclear resonance** ▪

Recall from your study of the Gamow energy E_G that the thermal energies obtained in the interior of the Sun are very much smaller than the Gamow energy, which is to say that the probability of barrier penetration is exceptionally low (Question 13). This presents a significant challenge to efforts to make laboratory measurements of fusion cross-sections at the energies of interest to stellar astrophysicists. In practice, nuclear astrophysicists are forced to measure fusion cross-sections at higher energies, and then extrapolate down to lower energies using the cross-section formula. The **S-factor**, $S(E)$, usually varies only slowly with energy E, but if the energy coincides with one of the possible excited states of the target nucleus then resonant behaviour – leading to a strong increase in $S(E)$ and hence the reaction cross-section – is found. The possibility that low energy resonances go undetected adds another element of uncertainty to the extrapolation.

3.2.2 Energy dependence of fusion cross-sections

The expression for the fusion cross-section has three key parts.

$$\sigma(E) = \frac{S(E)}{E} \exp\left[-\left(\frac{E_G}{E}\right)^{1/2}\right] \qquad \text{(Phillips 4.16)}$$

- Previously in this section you obtained an expression for the probability of barrier penetration, which is exponentially dependent on the relative energy of the colliding nuclei: $P_{\text{pen}} \approx \exp[-(E_G/E)^{1/2}]$. The fusion cross-section reflects that penetration probability, giving rise to an energy-dependence governed by that exponential.

- At *low* energies, the fusion cross-section may be proportional to the square of the de Broglie wavelength, since that reflects the geometrical cross-section (area) of the particle. Since $\lambda_{\text{dB}} \equiv h/p$, where p is the relative momentum of the nuclei, and the kinetic energy of the particle is $E_{\text{KE}} = (1/2)mv^2 = p^2/2m$, it follows that $\lambda_{\text{dB}}^2 = h^2/p^2 = h^2/2mE_{\text{KE}}$. This gives rise to a $1/E$ term in the fusion cross-section.

- The product of these two terms with a constant of proportionality $S(E)$ gives rise to the standard expression for the cross-section. The S-factor is not strictly constant but is generally only weakly dependent on energy. (At energies close to excited states of the target nucleus, nuclear resonances arise and $S(E)$ may be strongly peaked.) S has units of energy × cross-section, which in SI units would be $J\,m^2$ but more typically is given as keV barns.

These three factors give rise to the final equation for the fusion cross-section.

■ Explain in a few lines the meanings of each of the terms in Phillips (Equation 4.16): $S(E)$, $1/E$, and the exponential term.

❑ $S(E)$ is the nuclear S-factor. This term varies only slowly with energy (except near resonances), but its size differs greatly depending on whether the interaction involves the weak force, the electromagnetic force, or the strong nuclear force.

$1/E$ is a term reflecting the lower-energy proportionality between the cross-section and the square of the de Broglie wavelength.

The exponential term is the barrier-penetration probability, which depends on the ratio between the energy of approach and the Gamow energy. The latter reflects the height of the Coulomb barrier. ■

3.2.3 Probabilities of interaction

Phillips uses standard rules of probabilities in his discussion of reaction cross-sections. Quite generally, the probability that an event A and an event B *both* happen, when the probabilities are *independent*, is simply the product of their individual probabilities. This is written $P(A \text{ and } B) = P(A) \times P(B)$.

Phillips divides the distance x travelled by a particle into N intervals of size Δx. The probability of there being no reaction in the first such interval Δx_1 is $1 - \sigma n \Delta x_1$ where there are n targets per unit volume. The probability of there being no reaction over two such intervals is given by the probability of no reaction in the first multiplied by the probability of no reaction in the second, or $(1 - \sigma n \Delta x_1) \times (1 - \sigma n \Delta x_2)$. Since there is no distinction between the size of Δx_1 or Δx_2, we can drop the subscript and write

$$P(\text{no reaction over two intervals}) = (1 - \sigma n \Delta x)^2$$

Extending this reasoning from 2 to N intervals gives

$$P(\text{no reactions over } N \text{ intervals}) = (1 - \sigma n \Delta x)^N$$

Note that Phillips defined the interval Δx as an *infinitesimal* interval, such that Δx approaches zero as N approaches infinity, so we should write

$$P(\text{no reactions over } N \text{ intervals}) = \lim_{N \to \infty} (1 - \sigma n \Delta x)^N$$

We can also replace Δx by its definition, x/N, giving

$$P(\text{no reactions over } N \text{ intervals}) = \lim_{N \to \infty} (1 - \sigma n x / N)^N$$

Note that we may regard the probability of there being no reactions over a distance x as the survival probability of the particle.

Phillips makes use of another standard mathematical result, this time dealing with products, that

$$\lim_{N \to \infty} (1 - a/N)^N = \exp(-a)$$

where a is any expression not involving N. Recognizing that a can be $\sigma n x$, Phillips finds that the probability of their being no collision as the particle travels the distance x is given by $\exp(-\sigma n x)$.

- Consider the form of Phillips Equation 4.14. What range of values does the cross-section σ take? What range of values does the number density of target particles n take? What then is the dependence on distance of the survival probability $P(x)$ that there is no interaction over some distance x? Does this seem reasonable? Sketch the form of $P(x)$ against x.

- ❑ The cross-section σ and the number of particles n must both be non-negative numbers (zero or positive), so the form of $P(x)$ against x is an exponential decay curve, taking the value 1 at $x = 0$. This is reasonable, because the survival probability of the projectile particle is 1 (i.e. survival is guaranteed) if it does not have to pass through any target particles ($x = 0$), and steadily decreases as the path through target particles lengthens (x increases to a positive number). Figure 27 provides a sketch of the survival probability as a function of distance. ■

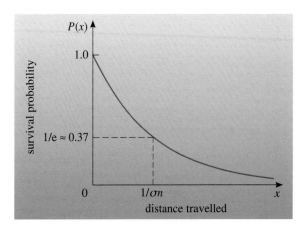

Figure 27 The survival probability $P(x)$ that *no* reaction occurs when the projectile travels a distance x in the target medium.

Consider the behaviour of the projectile particle's survival probability (Figure 27). As the path length increases, the survival probability P decreases, because there is more and more chance that the particle will hit one of the targets. However, the survival never quite reaches zero, because we can never be absolutely sure that it will hit a target, though the survival probability becomes incredibly small (i.e. survival is unlikely) if the path length x through the targets is very long.

■ Consider two environments, one with target density n_1 and one with a higher target density n_2. What does your understanding of the physics tell you should happen to the survival probability of the particle in medium n_2 compared to n_1? What does Phillips Equation 4.14 say? Do the two agree? Treat the sketch Figure 27 as being for n_1, and add a graph for medium n_2.

❑ A medium with more targets should reduce the survival probability, because the chance of a reaction will be greater. Phillips Equation 4.14 verifies this; $\sigma n x$ is always positive, so if n increases, then P decreases. The curve for medium n_2 has the same y-axis intercept but otherwise lies below the curve for n_1. Note, however, like the curve for n_1, it does not reach the value $P = 0$, even for large values of x (see Figure 28). ■

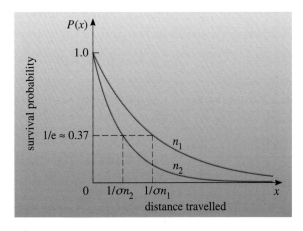

Figure 28 The survival probability $P(x)$ that *no* reaction occurs when the projectile travels a distance x in the target medium, for two target densities where $n_2 > n_1$.

3.2.4 Mean free path

Identical particles travelling through a medium of targets travel different distances before interacting. The average of the distances they travel prior to reaction is called the **mean free path**, and is a useful indicator of the condition of the target medium and the strength of the interaction.

Before calculating the mean free path for our particles, consider two different approaches to calculating the average of any group of numbers. Imagine we want the average (mean) of six distances (in arbitrary units): 2, 5, 2, 4, 3 and 2.

Approach 1

The first way of calculating the mean is to add up all of the numbers, and divide by the number of values:

$$\langle d \rangle = \frac{\sum_{i=1}^{6} d_i}{n} = (2 + 5 + 2 + 4 + 3 + 2)/6 = 18/6 = 3$$

Approach 2

A second way is to multiply each number by its frequency in the list, that is, the number of times it occurs, and divide by the sum of frequencies. For the example listed above, the numbers are $d_i = 2, 3, 4$ and 5, and their respective frequencies are $f_i = 3, 1, 1$ and 1. By this method, the average is

$$\langle d \rangle = \frac{\sum_{i=1}^{4} d_i f_i}{\sum_{i=1}^{4} f_i} = \frac{(2 \times 3 + 3 \times 1 + 4 \times 1 + 5 \times 1)}{(3 + 1 + 1 + 1)} = 18/6 = 3$$

These two methods are, of course, completely equivalent, but the second approach leads us to a method for calculating the mean of a *continuous* distribution of values. Two pieces of reasoning are required.

First, for some physics problems, we don't know how frequently particular values arise, but we do know their probabilities, which is equivalent to saying we know their frequencies for an (unachievable) infinite sample.

Second, although the above example involved discrete numbers (e.g. 1, 2, 3, etc.), we can generalize the problem for a continuous variable which is more likely to be useful in real physical problems. Following the second approach above for calculating the mean, if the probability distribution for some discrete variable x is $P(x)$, then the mean value is

$$\langle x \rangle = \frac{\sum_i x_i P(x_i)}{\sum_i P(x_i)} = \sum_i x_i P(x_i) \quad (\text{since} \sum_i P(x_i) = 1)$$

If the discrete steps in a sum are made smaller and smaller, the problem can be rewritten as an integral over a continuous dependent variable:

$$\langle x \rangle = \int_0^\infty x P(x) \, dx$$

where the discrete probability $P(x_i)$ above has now been replaced by the continuous probability density $P(x)\,dx$ which is the probability that x takes a value between x and $x + dx$.

If the probability that a particle travels a distance between x and $x + dx$ is $P(x)\,dx$, then the mean distance travelled by a group of these particles is found by multiplying each possible distance x by the probability $P(x)$ that that distance arises, summing this calculation for all possible distances, and dividing by the sum of the probabilities ($= 1$). Therefore the mean free path of the particle is $l = \int_0^\infty x P(x)\,dx$. The case given by Phillips is for the mean free path of a particle moving through a medium containing n target particles per unit volume. In this case, $P(x)\,dx$ is the probability of an interaction occurring over the interval from x to $x + dx$. This is the probability of there being *no* interaction over the distance 0 to x, *and* then an interaction occurring over the interval dx. The probability of two independent events A and B occurring is the product of their individual probabilities, so we can write this chain of logic as

$P(x)\,dx$ = the probability of an interaction occurring over the interval from x to $x+dx$

   = the probability of their being *no* interaction over the distance 0 to x, *and* there being an interaction over the interval dx

   = (the probability of their being *no* interaction over the distance 0 to x) $\times$ (the probability of an interaction occurring over the interval dx)

   = $\exp(-\sigma n x) \times \sigma n\,dx$

i.e. $P(x)\,dx = \exp(-\sigma n x) \times \sigma n\,dx$

and the mean free path is

$$l = \int_0^\infty x P(x)\,dx = \int_0^\infty x \exp(-\sigma n x)\sigma n\,dx$$

This expression is easily simplified. First, the σn term does not depend on the variable of integration x, so can be taken outside the integral, giving

$$l = \sigma n \int_0^\infty x \exp(-\sigma n x)\,dx$$

Second, it is a standard result that $\int_0^\infty x \exp(-ax)\,dx = 1/a^2$, where a does not depend on x, so we can complete the simplification

$$l = \sigma n \int_0^\infty x \exp(-\sigma n x)\,dx = \sigma n \times 1/(\sigma n)^2 = 1/(\sigma n) \qquad \text{(e.g. Phillips 4.15)}$$

To put this result into words, the mean distance — the mean free path — travelled by a class of projectiles before interacting with a target is given by 1 over the product of the target density and reaction cross-section. You will see later that the mean free path is closely related to the average time between collisions, and hence is a very useful quantity.

3.3 Thermonuclear fusion reaction rates

Fusion rates are crucial to our understanding of nuclear burning in stars. They are strongly dependent on temperature, and since the internal temperature of a star changes by several orders of magnitude as it evolves, different reactions occur at different stages of its life.

The main reading from Phillips for this topic is his subsection 'Thermonuclear reaction rates'. There are many concepts in this reading, so it has been split into two parts, the first of which is very short but lays some of the important foundations for what follows.

Activity 18

Thermonuclear reaction rates (I)

To begin your study of this topic, read the subsection 'Thermonuclear reaction rates' on pages 112–113 of Phillips, to the end of the paragraph containing Equation 4.19. Then return to this Study Guide which discusses some of the concepts in more detail.

Keywords: none ◾

■ Phillips shows in the first paragraph of the reading that if we neglect the motion of nuclei B and assume that all the A nuclei move with speed v, then the fusion rate is $R_{AB} = n_A n_B \sigma v$. However, there is no more reason to treat B as stationary and A moving than the reverse. Consider the situation in which nuclei A's motion is treated as negligible, and nuclei B move with speed v. First, think about the physics of the problem, not the equations, and write down how the fusion rate will change. Secondly, repeat Phillips' derivation, but for the new scenario, and see whether your expectations of the physics are borne out in the mathematics.

❑ The physics involves:

  (i)   the *relative* speed of the nuclei, which is independent of which nucleus is at rest,

  (ii) the energy barrier that must be penetrated, which governs the cross-section and does not depend on their motions, and

  (iii) the density of target and projectiles.

Therefore, it should make no difference to the rate equation which nucleus is at rest.

If you repeat Phillips' reasoning for the new situation, you should obtain exactly the same rate equation as appears in the text.

Nucleus B travels an average distance $d = 1/n_A \sigma$ before fusing with an A nucleus.

The average time before fusion is $\tau_B = d/v = 1/n_A \sigma v$.

Thus in unit volume of the gas, we have n_B nuclei of type B which fuse at a rate $R_{BA} = n_B \times 1/\tau_B = n_B n_A \sigma v$.

As, from Phillips page 113, $R_{AB} = n_B n_A \sigma v$, it is clear that $R_{BA} = R_{AB}$, as the physics arguments above indicate it must. ◾

3.3.1 The velocity-averaged cross-section

On page 113, Phillips calculates the mean of a continuously distributed variable, $\langle \sigma v_r \rangle$, as an integral of the quantity multiplied by its probability. This is analogous to our calculation of the mean distance $\langle x \rangle = \int_0^\infty x P(x)\,dx$, but with the independent variable changed from distance x to the speed–cross-section product σv_r, and the weighting function being the distribution of velocities rather than the distribution of penetration distances:

$$\langle \sigma v_r \rangle = \int_0^\infty \sigma v_r P(v_r)\,dv_r$$

The necessity of averaging over the velocity distribution alters the simplest expressions for the fusion rates slightly, to

$$R_{AB} = n_A n_B \langle \sigma v_r \rangle \quad \text{for dissimilar nuclei (Phillips 4.19)} \qquad (18a)$$

$$\text{and} \quad R_{AA} = (n^2/2)\langle \sigma v_r \rangle \quad \text{for fusion between identical nuclei} \qquad (18b)$$

The distinction between these two forms is explained in the next subsection.

3.3.2 The distinction between fusion involving dissimilar or identical nuclei

For identical particles, the product $n_A n_B$ in Phillips Equation 4.19 and others must be replaced by $n(n-1)/2$. For all practical cases $n \gg 1$, and we can simplify $n(n-1)/2$ as $n^2/2$ as in Equation 18b. The reason for the replacement is illustrated below. The key is to recall the significance of the product, not just its mathematical representation. The significance of the product is that it is the number of possible reactions between available particles.

If there are four particles of type A and four of type B, the possible combinations can be written as the following array, where a 'Y' has been used to signify possible reaction pairs.

	B1	B2	B3	B4
A1	Y	Y	Y	Y
A2	Y	Y	Y	Y
A3	Y	Y	Y	Y
A4	Y	Y	Y	Y

More generally, the number of possible combinations is $n_A n_B$.

Now consider reactions involving only one type of particle, which we label type A. Obviously a particle cannot react with itself, so we must exclude entries (A1, A1), (A2, A2), etc. The partially completed array, where 'N' signifies entries we may not count, is:

	A1	A2	A3	A4
A1	N			
A2		N		
A3			N	
A4				N

We also have to avoid double counting. If we fuse particle A1 with particle A2, we cannot also count a fusion of A2 with A1. That is, we can count entries either above or below the diagonal in the array, but not both. Doing the former, the array becomes:

	A1	A2	A3	A4
A1	N	Y	Y	Y
A2	N	N	Y	Y
A3	N	N	N	Y
A4	N	N	N	N

This gives six possible combinations, or more generally $(n^2 - n)/2$, which is equivalent to $n(n - 1)/2$, or $\approx n^2/2$.

3.3.3 Thermonuclear reaction rates

Activity 19   **30 minutes**

Thermonuclear reaction rates (II)

Read the remainder of the subsection 'Thermonuclear reaction rates' on pages 113–117 of Phillips, beginning with the sentence 'In most astrophysical situations … .'

- You will *not* be expected to remember the Maxwellian distribution (Equation 4.20) or to evaluate the integrals, but you should at least understand where the terms come from in the final expression for the fusion rate, and in particular how they relate to the cross-section.

- The Taylor expansion leading to Equation 4.24 is a lengthy piece of algebra that you will not be expected to have worked through.

- The Gamow energy on page 116, 35.5 MeV, should (in my view) read 32.8 MeV.

- A more complete derivation of the temperature-dependence of the fusion rate (Equation 4.29) is given below.

- Much of the discussion is about the temperature dependence of fusion rates, but note Phillips' final comment that the *S*-factor, which sets the overall scale of the rates, is determined by the nuclear physics and is usually smallest for reactions moderated by the nuclear weak force (involving the emission of a neutrino), larger for electromagnetic reactions (emitting photons), and larger still for nuclear strong force reactions.

Keywords: **Maxwell–Boltzmann distribution**, **Maxwellian distribution**, **Gamow window** ■

3.3.4 The Gamow window

Phillips (Equation 4.22) gives the reaction rate in terms of energy instead of relative speed:

$$R_{AB} = n_A n_B \left[\frac{8}{\pi m_r} \right]^{1/2} \left(\frac{1}{kT} \right)^{3/2} \int_0^\infty S(E) \exp \left[-\left(\frac{E_G}{E} \right)^{1/2} - \frac{E}{kT} \right] dE$$

By writing the rate equation in this form, the energy-dependence of the reaction rate is made explicit. However, this is still a non-trivial equation, and not many people will be able easily to picture what the function looks like. We simplify it in this section.

■   Write down what physics has contributed to each term in Phillips Equation 4.22.

❑   The following terms may be highlighted:

- $n_A n_B$ is the number of possible reactions;
- $(1/kT)^{3/2}$ comes from the Maxwellian distribution of relative speeds;
- $S(E)$ conveys the strength of the nuclear interaction;
- (E_G/E) indicates the strength of the Coulomb barrier to be penetrated;
- E/kT represents the Maxwellian thermal energy distribution. ■

The energy dependence of the rate R_{AB} is all contained in the integral

$$\int_0^\infty S(E) \exp \left[-\left(\frac{E_G}{E} \right)^{1/2} - \frac{E}{kT} \right] dE$$

Recall that $\exp(A + B) = \exp(A) \times \exp(B)$, so the integral can also be written

$$\int_0^\infty S(E) \exp \left[-\left(\frac{E_G}{E} \right)^{1/2} \right] \exp \left(-\frac{E}{kT} \right) dE$$

The nuclear factor $S(E)$ varies only slowly with energy (apart from near low-energy resonances), so essentially all of the energy-dependence comes from the exponential terms. The term $\exp[-(E_G/E)^{1/2}]$ increases as nuclei energy E increases, but the other term $\exp(-E/kT)$ decreases, so the product of the two is small at high and low energies, and becomes significant only over some range of intermediate energies. Phillips shows this behaviour in Fig. 4.3, and indicates that the distribution peaks at an energy (called the Gamow peak)

$$E_0 = \left(\frac{E_G (kT)^2}{4} \right)^{1/3} \qquad \text{(Phillips 4.23)}$$

Question 14

Consider the energy integral $\int_0^\infty S(E) \exp\left[-\left(\frac{E_G}{E}\right)^{1/2} - \frac{E}{kT}\right] dE$.

The integrand, $S(E) \exp\left[-\left(\frac{E_G}{E}\right)^{1/2} - \frac{E}{kT}\right]$, conveys the energy dependence of the thermonuclear fusion rate. Show that this integrand has a peak at $E_0 = [(1/4)E_G(kT)^2]^{1/3}$.

Hint 1: A function $f(x)$ has a maximum or minimum when $df/dx = 0$.

Hint 2: By the chain rule for differentiation,

$$\frac{d}{dx}\exp(f(x)) = \frac{d\exp(f(x))}{df(x)}\frac{df(x)}{dx} = \exp(f(x))\frac{df(x)}{dx} \blacksquare$$

A Taylor expansion about the energy of the probability peak, E_0, clarifies the function in the energy region of interest. The expansion expresses the value *near* the peak in terms of the value and derivatives *at* the peak. In this case, expanding to second order, we would write

$$f(E) \approx f(E_0) + (E - E_0)f'(E_0) + (1/2)(E - E_0)^2 f''(E_0)$$

where f is the energy function, in our case $f = \exp[-(E/kT) - (E_G/E)^{1/2}]$, and f' and f'' are the first and second derivatives.

It is possible to calculate the first and second derivatives of the expression

$$f(E) = \exp\left[-\left(\frac{E_G}{E}\right)^{1/2} - \frac{E}{kT}\right]$$

and show via a second-order Taylor expansion that this can be re-written as

$$f(E) \approx \exp\left[-3\left(\frac{E_G}{4kT}\right)^{1/3}\right]\exp\left[-\left(\frac{E - E_0}{\Delta/2}\right)^2\right] \qquad \text{(Phillips 4.24)}$$

In the process, this gives the Gamow width

$$\Delta = \frac{4}{3^{1/2}2^{1/3}} E_G^{1/6}(kT)^{5/6} \qquad \text{(Phillips 4.25)}$$

which can also be written

$$\Delta \approx 1.8 E_G^{1/6}(kT)^{5/6} = 1.8(E_G/kT)^{1/6}kT$$

However, it requires several pages of algebra and would distract you from the astrophysics, so will not be shown here and you will not be assumed to have done it.

Note that the energy dependence of the fusion reaction, the last term of Equation 4.24, resembles the form $\exp\left(-\frac{(x - \bar{x})^2}{2\sigma^2}\right)$. This is symmetric about E_0, and has the shape known as a **bell curve**, a **normal distribution**, or a **Gaussian distribution**.

The width of the fusion window is described by Phillips 4.25. Its physical

The symbol σ which appears in the exponential term of the Gaussian is called the standard deviation, and is unrelated to the fusion cross-section (or the Stefan–Boltzmann constant) which use the same symbol for different quantities. The standard deviation determines the rate at which the exponential decreases as x deviates from $\bar{x}$.

significance can be seen as follows: at $E = E_0 \pm \Delta/2$, the Gaussian term equates to

$$\exp\left[-\left(\frac{E_0 \pm (\Delta/2) - E_0}{\Delta/2}\right)^2\right] = \exp\left[-\left(\frac{\pm(\Delta/2)}{\Delta/2}\right)^2\right] = \exp[-1] = 1/e$$

That is, $\Delta/2$ is the e-folding energy width, which is to say that the fusion probability falls by a factor $1/e$, ≈ 0.37, over the interval $E_0 \pm \Delta/2$.

Consider again the fusion rate equation (Phillips 4.22)

$$R_{AB} = n_A n_B \left(\frac{8}{\pi m_r}\right)^{1/2} \left(\frac{1}{kT}\right)^{3/2} \int_0^\infty S(E) \exp\left[-\left(\frac{E_G}{E}\right)^{1/2} - \frac{E}{kT}\right] dE$$

Since (as given in Phillips 4.24),

$$\exp\left[-\left(\frac{E_G}{E}\right)^{1/2} - \frac{E}{kT}\right] \approx \exp\left(-3\left(\frac{E_G}{4kT}\right)^{1/3}\right) \exp\left(-\left(\frac{E - E_0}{\Delta/2}\right)^2\right)$$

we can rewrite the fusion rate equation as

$$R_{AB} = n_A n_B \left(\frac{8}{\pi m_r}\right)^{1/2} \left(\frac{1}{kT}\right)^{3/2}$$

$$\times \int_0^\infty S(E) \exp\left[-3\left(\frac{E_G}{4kT}\right)^{1/3}\right] \exp\left[-\left(\frac{E - E_0}{\Delta/2}\right)^2\right] dE \qquad (19)$$

■   The revised form of the fusion rate Equation 19 still looks daunting, but in fact just a few physical variables determine its value. What are they?

❑   Note that:

   •   the energy of the Gamow peak, $E_0 = [E_G(\frac{1}{2}kT)^2]^{1/3}$ (Phillips 4.23), and
   •   the width $\Delta \approx 1.8 E_G^{1/6}(kT)^{5/6}$ (Phillips 4.25)
   are primarily determined by two variables:

   1   the temperature T which governs the energy of the nuclei, and
   2   the Gamow energy E_G which characterizes the Coulomb barrier to be penetrated. ($E_G = (\pi \alpha Z_A Z_B)^2 2m_r c^2$, so depends on the charge of the nuclei and their reduced mass.)

Another factor, which we have assumed is only weakly dependent on energy is the $S(E)$ factor which encapsulates the nuclear physics of the strength of the fusion interaction. The remaining variables are the particle densities and their reduced mass.

These few quantities summarize the physics underlying thermonuclear fusion; don't lose sight of this when confronted by the algebra and calculus. ■

The first exponential term in Equation 19 is independent of energy, so can be taken out of the integral, and $S(E)$ usually varies so little over the width of the Gaussian that it can safely be replaced by its value at the peak, $S(E_0)$. The rate equation Equation 19 then becomes

$$R_{AB} = n_A n_B \left(\frac{8}{\pi m_r}\right)^{1/2} \left(\frac{1}{kT}\right)^{3/2}$$

$$\times S(E_0) \exp\left[-3\left(\frac{E_G}{4kT}\right)^{1/3}\right] \int_0^\infty \exp\left[-\left(\frac{E-E_0}{\Delta/2}\right)^2\right] dE$$

where the integration is now only over the Gaussian distribution. That integration is straightforward, but is a mathematical distraction outside the scope of this course. The result of performing it is (Phillips 4.27)

$$R_{AB} = 6.48 \times 10^{-24} \frac{n_A n_B}{A_r Z_A Z_B} S(E_0) \left(\frac{E_G}{4kT}\right)^{2/3} \exp\left[-3\left(\frac{E_G}{4kT}\right)^{1/3}\right] \, \text{m}^{-3}\,\text{s}^{-1}$$

where $S(E_0)$ is specified in keV barns. A_r is the reduced mass in atomic mass units: $A_r = m_r/u$. Since $m_r = m_A m_B/(m_A + m_B)$, u can be divided into each mass separately to write $A_r = A_A A_B/(A_A + A_B)$.

Note again that Phillips Equation 4.27 is determined by:

- the temperature T which governs the thermal energy of the nuclei,
- the Gamow energy E_G which characterizes the Coulomb barrier to be penetrated, and
- the $S(E)$ factor, which encapsulates the strength of the fusion interaction.

3.3.5 The temperature dependence of the fusion rate

As just given, Phillips shows that the integral can be simplified and the fusion rate expressed as in Equation 4.27.

The Gamow energy appears in two $E_G/4kT$ terms, of which the exponential rather than the (2/3)-power term dominates. An increase in the temperature increases the kinetic energy of the nuclei, increasing the probability that they will penetrate the Coulomb barrier, thus increasing the fusion rate. This physics is captured in the exponential term, where an increase in T decreases the *magnitude* of the argument to the exponential function, $-3(E_G/4kT)^{1/3}$, but since the argument is negative, the exponential function gives a higher value.

A more complete view of the temperature dependence is found by examining the derivative of the rate with respect to temperature.

(a) Calculate the temperature derivative of the fusion rate (Phillips 4.27)

$$R_{AB} = 6.48 \times 10^{-24} \frac{n_A n_B}{A_r Z_A Z_B} S(E_0) \left(\frac{E_G}{4kT}\right)^{2/3} \exp\left[-3\left(\frac{E_G}{4kT}\right)^{1/3}\right] \text{m}^{-3}\,\text{s}^{-1}$$

to obtain dR_{AB}/dT in terms of R_{AB}, the Gamow energy and the temperature (and some constants).

Hint 1: You may find the algebra is tidier if you rewrite the non-temperature-dependent term as a single constant a such that $a = 6.48 \times 10^{-24} \frac{n_A n_B}{A_r Z_A Z_B} S(E_0)$.

Hint 2: Recall, from the product rule, that $\frac{duv}{dx} = u\frac{dv}{dx} + v\frac{du}{dx}$. To exploit this, make the definitions

$$u = a\left(\frac{E_G}{4kT}\right)^{2/3} \quad \text{and} \quad v = \exp\left[-3\left(\frac{E_G}{4kT}\right)^{1/3}\right], \quad \text{so } R_{AB} = uv.$$

Hint 3: Note, from the chain rule, that $\frac{d\exp(y)}{dx} = \frac{d\exp(y)}{dy}\frac{dy}{dx} = \exp(y)\frac{dy}{dx}$.

(b) Use the relation $dx/x = d\ln x$ to rewrite dR_{AB}/dT as $d\ln R_{AB}/d\ln T$. ($\ln x$ is the natural logarithmic function and $d\ln x$ is an infinitesimal increment in $\ln x$.) ∎

In Question 15(b) you computed $d\ln R_{AB}/d\ln T$. The significance is that if $d\ln R_{AB}/d\ln T = v$, then $R_{AB} \propto T^v$. That is, v indicates the sensitivity of the fusion rate to temperature.

The proof is straightforward. If $R_{AB} \propto T^v$, with some unknown constant of proportionality, we can write $R_{AB} = \text{const} \times T^v$. We can take natural logarithms of both sides, to give

$$\ln R_{AB} = \ln \text{const} + \ln T^v = \ln \text{const} + v\ln T$$

Differentiating with respect to $\ln T$ gives

$$\frac{d\ln R_{AB}}{d\ln T} = v$$

That is, the statement $\dfrac{d\ln R_{AB}}{d\ln T} = v$ implies that $R_{AB} \propto T^v$.

The logarithmic derivative $\dfrac{d\ln R_{AB}}{d\ln T} = \left[\left(\dfrac{E_G}{4kT}\right)^{1/3} - \dfrac{2}{3}\right]$ (see Question 15) therefore indicates that a variation in temperature leads to a rate change of the form

$$R_{AB} \propto T^{\left[(E_G/4kT)^{1/3} - (2/3)\right]}$$

Note that the exponent (power) of the temperature, commonly given the symbol v, depends on the ratio of the Gamow energy to the temperature. It can be expanded as

$$v \equiv \frac{d\ln R_{AB}}{d\ln T} = \left(\frac{E_G}{4kT}\right)^{1/3} - \frac{2}{3} = \left(\frac{2m_r c^2 (\pi\alpha Z_A Z_B)^2}{4kT}\right)^{1/3} - \frac{2}{3} \qquad (20)$$

which shows the dependence of the temperature-exponent ν on the mass and charge of the nuclei. Clearly, reactions involving heavier particles with greater atomic number depend much more strongly on temperature.

Question 16

Calculate the power of the temperature-dependence of the fusion rate for the following reactions at the core of the Sun:

(a) $p + p \rightarrow d + e^+ + \nu_e$

(b) $p + {}^{14}N \rightarrow {}^{15}O + \gamma$

Hint 1: Use the solar centre values from Table 1.2 of Phillips (page 19).

Hint 2: For part (b), assume the mass of a proton is 1 amu, and of ^{14}N is $14u$.

Hint 3: The atomic number of nitrogen is 7. ■

Question 16 shows that, $R_{pp} \propto T^{3.8}$ and $R_{p14N} \propto T^{19.6}$, i.e. the $p + {}^{14}N$ reaction is far more sensitive to temperature. The temperature sensitivity of reactions governs the extent of the energy-generating region of a star. In low-mass stars ($M \lesssim 1M_\odot$), hydrogen burning occurs primarily by the $p + p$ reaction, whereas in higher mass ($M \gtrsim 1.5M_\odot$) stars a reaction cycle that includes $p + {}^{14}N$ dominates. Because of the *very* steep temperature dependence of the latter, energy generation in that cycle is highly concentrated, leading to a steep temperature gradient and the onset of convection. Higher mass stars with the $p + {}^{14}N$ reaction activated have convective cores, whereas low-mass stars, in which the $p + p$ reaction dominates, do not.

3.4 Summary of Section 3

1   Nuclei have radii of order 10^{-15} m ($R = r_0 A^{1/3}$, where $r_0 = 1.2 \times 10^{-15}$ m), a factor 10^5 times smaller than atoms (i.e. including the electrons) which have radii around 10^{-10} m.

2   In quantum mechanics, particles are described (in one dimension) by wave functions $\psi(x, t)$ which are solutions to the time-independent Schrödinger's equation,

$$\left[-\frac{\hbar^2 \nabla^2}{2m_r} + V(x) \right] \psi(x) = E\psi(x)$$

where the operator ∇^2 becomes, in one dimension, $\partial^2/\partial x^2$. The solutions are often of the form $\cos(ax)$ or $\sin(ax)$, which behave like waves and give the wave functions their name. The wave function can be calculated but not measured, but the squared amplitude $|\psi|^2$ can be measured and is the probability that the particle described by the wave function ψ is located between x and $x + dx$.

3   The quantum properties of particles lead to barrier penetration/quantum tunnelling. The amplitude of a wave function encountering a potential barrier goes to zero only for an *infinite* potential; in realistic *finite* barriers, there is a finite probability that a particle represented by the wave function will pass through the barrier even though this would be forbidden under classical (non-quantum) mechanics.

4   For fusion reactions, the barrier results from the Coulomb repulsion of (positively charged) nuclei. The height of the barrier is characterized by the Gamow energy $E_G = 2m_r c^2 (\pi \alpha Z_A Z_B)^2$, where α is the fine structure constant $\approx 1/137.0$.

5   The reaction cross-section σ is the product of the geometrical cross-section with the reaction probability, and thus has units of area. For nuclear reactions, the standard unit is the barn = $10^{-28} \, \mathrm{m}^2$. The reaction probability, and therefore also the cross-section, depends on the projectile energy and the strength of the interaction. The mean free path of a projectile travelling through a target with n particles per unit volume is $l = 1/n\sigma$.

6   The fusion cross-section may be written

$$\sigma(E) = \frac{S(E)}{E} \exp\left[-\left(\frac{E_G}{E}\right)^{1/2}\right]$$

where the exponential indicates that the barrier-penetration probability is higher at higher energies, and $S(E)$ is the S-factor which indicates the strength of the interaction.

7   The velocity-averaged cross-section leads to the following formulae for the fusion rate:

$R_{AB} = n_A n_B \langle \sigma v_r \rangle$ for fusion of dissimilar nuclei and

$R_{AA} = (n^2/2) \langle \sigma v_r \rangle$ for fusion of identical nuclei.

For a Maxwellian speed distribution, the former becomes

$$R_{AB} = n_A n_B \left(\frac{8}{\pi m_r}\right)^{1/2} \left(\frac{1}{kT}\right)^{3/2} \int_0^\infty S(E) \exp\left[-\left(\frac{E_G}{E}\right)^{1/2} - \frac{E}{kT}\right] dE$$

The energy-dependence of the integrand has one term increasing with energy – the Coulomb barrier-penetration probability – and one term decreasing with energy – reflecting the fact that (for the given temperature) there are fewer particles possessing higher energy. This gives the rate R_{AB} an approximately Gaussian form, with a local maximum at an energy $E_0 = (E_G(kT)^2/4)^{1/3}$ called the Gamow peak.

The rate falls to a value $1/e \approx 0.37$ of the peak at an energy

$$E_0 \pm \Delta/2 = E_0 \pm \frac{2}{3^{1/2} 2^{1/3}} E_G^{1/6} (kT)^{5/6} \approx E_0 \pm \left(\frac{E_G}{kT}\right)^{1/6} kT$$

8   The integrated reaction rate

$$R_{AB} = 6.48 \times 10^{-24} \frac{n_A n_B}{A_r Z_A Z_B} S(E_0) \left(\frac{E_G}{4kT}\right)^{2/3} \exp\left[-3\left(\frac{E_G}{4kT}\right)^{1/3}\right] \mathrm{m}^{-3} \, \mathrm{s}^{-1}$$

can be differentiated with respect to temperature to obtain the temperature-sensitivity of the reactions, dR_{AB}/dT. The *logarithmic* derivative

$$\nu \equiv \frac{d \ln R_{AB}}{d \ln T} = \left(\frac{E_G}{4kT}\right)^{1/3} - \frac{2}{3} = \left(\frac{2m_r c^2 (\pi \alpha Z_A Z_B)^2}{4kT}\right)^{1/3} - \frac{2}{3}$$

where $R_{AB} \propto T^\nu$ indicates that the temperature-sensitivity increases for reactions involving higher charged and heavier nuclei. The reaction p + p depends on $\sim T^4$, and the reaction p + ^{14}N depends on $\sim T^{20}$ (at the solar central temperature).

4 MAIN-SEQUENCE STARS

In the previous section, you studied the physics of nuclear fusion from a nuclear physics viewpoint. In this section you will begin to examine those reactions in their astrophysical context, in particular their role in stellar evolution. Nucleosynthesis and stellar evolution are inseparable topics: nuclear fusion provides the source of energy that keeps a star shining, while changes in the structure of a star as it ages alter the reactions that occur. The energy liberated in the star changes, the stellar structure is modified, and nuclear reactions change further. All the while, heavier elements are produced, and the chemical composition of the star changes.

In the remaining sections of this block we follow the various nuclear fusion phases through which a star passes as it ages, depending on its mass. Hydrogen burning is treated in Sections 4 and 5, followed by helium burning and advanced stages of evolution in Sections 6 and 7. We will then examine the fate of stars in Sections 7 and 8.

4.1 A 1M$_\odot$ star on the main sequence

Although it would be wrong to get the idea that all stars are like the Sun, it is the star which people know best, and so it is a useful reference point. We will briefly consider the structure of the Sun, to help illustrate the end points of pre-main-sequence evolution.

Activity 20   **30 minutes**

The Sun

Read Section 1.4 of Phillips, to the end of the subsection 'Solar radiation' (pages 19–23).

Keep in mind the distinction between surface properties, central properties and average properties in the Sun. Only the *surface* properties are *directly* observable, so to infer the conditions in the interior or the core, we must rely upon our knowledge of the physics at work. Some of that physics (e.g. the state of hydrostatic equilibrium) has been introduced in our study of pre-main-sequence evolution, and you will meet more soon. We can also probe the internal structure of the Sun by **helioseismology**, i.e. observing oscillations of the surface which result from waves that propagate through the interior.

Even without detailed models, estimates can be made of the average density $\langle \rho \rangle = M_\odot / \frac{4}{3}\pi R_\odot^3$, pressure (Phillips 1.29), and a typical internal temperature (Phillips 1.31).

Keywords: **random walk** ■

■ Phillips derived the mean free path of photons in the Sun as ≈ 1 mm. Will this be the mean free path everywhere?

❑ The value 1 mm was derived as typical for the Sun as a whole, but you might expect it to be less in the core where the density is highest, and greater further out. In fact Phillips shows later (page 92) that it varies from ≈ 0.1 mm in the core to ≈ 8 mm near the surface. This range is always within a factor of ten of the typical value. ■

4.2 An overview of nucleosynthesis

Fusion reactions are initiated in conditions of high temperature and density. You should be familiar with some of the thermonuclear reactions involved, such as the proton-proton chain for hydrogen burning in the Sun, or the CNO cycle found in more massive main-sequence stars. In this section, you will learn about the nuclear physics that underlies these reaction sequences. It would be possible to present you with a list of facts about nuclei, but you would not understand where those results came from or the physics underlying them. Instead, this block will lead you through the process of deriving many of the important results *yourself*.

| Activity 21 | 20 minutes |

Stellar nucleosynthesis

Read Section 1.5 of Phillips (pages 25–28). This provides an introduction to the topics that follow.

Keywords: **nuclear fusion**, **nucleosynthesis**, **binding energy**, **Periodic Table**, **proton-proton chain**, **helium burning**, **photodisintegration**, **neutron capture**, **s-process**, **r-process** ■

- ■ The last reading, though short, covers quite a few concepts, most of which we explore in greater depth later in this block. By moving on from the activity you have signalled that you understand each of the keywords highlighted above. Write a short definition of each one, no more than two or three sentences for each.

- ❑ Check your definitions against the entries in Collins or in the S381 *Glossary*. If you have misunderstood something, or missed key issues, rewrite your explanations to improve them. ■

4.3 The proton-proton (p-p) chain

With hydrogen being the most abundant element in the Universe and its nucleus having the lowest Coulomb barrier, it is understandable that hydrogen is both the starting point for stellar nuclear burning and the longest-lasting nuclear fuel. In this subsection we examine the first of two hydrogen-burning processes.

4.3.1 Reactions and the three branches

The symbol 'd' is used to describe the deuterium *nucleus*, or deuteron, consisting of one proton and one neutron. In contrast, the symbol 'D' is used to refer to the *atom* of the heavy isotope of hydrogen that is formed when a deuteron pairs with an orbital electron. A similar distinction is made with hydrogen, where 'p' refers to the nucleus – a proton – and 'H' refers to the *atom* when it pairs with an electron.

As a contracting pre-main-sequence star heats up, a temperature is reached at which two hydrogen nuclei can penetrate their Coulomb barrier (assisted by quantum tunnelling), initiating the reaction $p + p \rightarrow d + e^+ + \nu_e$. A crucial step in the reaction is an endothermic (energy-absorbing) β^+-**decay** (sometimes called the **inverse beta-decay**), $p \rightarrow n + e^+ + \nu_e$, of one of the protons. The neutron produced then combines with the second proton to form the deuteron. The deuteron then rapidly combines with a third proton to form ^{3}He via $p + d \rightarrow \,^3$He $+ \gamma$. Two such ^{3}He nuclei can combine to produce ^{4}He and liberate two protons: ^{3}He $+ \,^3$He $\rightarrow \,^4$He $+ 2p$. Although this is the main way of burning hydrogen to helium in the Sun, it is one of only three ways. All three are described in the next reading from Phillips.

The proton-proton chain

Read Section 4.2 of Phillips to the end of the subsection 'The proton-proton chain' (pages 117–121). A more detailed account of the energetics is given next in this Study Guide.

Note that there are some typographical errors in Phillips Fig. 4.4 (page 119), in the reaction flow of branch III of the p-p chain, where '+' and '→' signs have been transposed. The final two reactions should be:

$$^8B \rightarrow {}^8Be^* + e^+ + \nu_e$$

$$^8Be^* \rightarrow {}^4He + {}^4He$$

The * symbol is used to signify that a nucleus is in an excited state, i.e. its energy is higher than the ground-state energy of the nucleus.

We will occasionally use the notation 'p-p I' to refer to the first branch of the proton-proton chain. Similar abbreviations, p-p II and p-p III, will be used for the other branches.

Keywords: **proton-proton chain branches I, II and III** ▪

▪   The proton-proton chain comprises nine reactions in three branches (e.g. Phillips Fig. 4.4), but just one reaction determines the overall rate at which hydrogen burning proceeds. Which reaction is the bottleneck and why?

❑   The slowest reaction in the series is the first one, $p + p \rightarrow d + e^+ + \nu_e$, and this is slowest because during the collision of the protons, one of them must undergo a β^+-decay, $p \rightarrow n + e^+ + \nu_e$. The β^+-decay is moderated by the weak-nuclear force, so has a very low probability of occurring. In technical terms, its S-factor is incredibly low. ▪

4.3.2 The mass defect

The proton-proton chain converts four hydrogen nuclei (protons) into a ^{4}He nucleus, two positrons which quickly collide with electrons and are annihilated, and two neutrinos. Branch I of the p-p chain may be summarized in two ways:

(a) $4p \rightarrow {}^4He + 2e^+ + 2\nu_e + 2\gamma_{pd}$

followed quickly by two occurrences of

$$e^+ + e^- \rightarrow 2\gamma_e$$

as each positron annihilates in a collision with an electron causing the emission of two 0.511 MeV γ_e-rays.

(b) $2e^- + 4p \rightarrow {}^4He + 2\nu_e + 2\gamma_{pd} + 4\gamma_e$

(The *unconventional* subscripts used here on the γ-rays are to distinguish the γ-rays from the p + d reaction from those from the electron–positron annihilation.)

The energy released in these reactions can be assessed from the differences in the masses of the particles. We will examine expressions (a) and (b) separately.

Reaction path (a)

The masses of the nuclei can be obtained from the atomic masses of their isotopes. We use the atomic mass unit (amu) scale where

$$m(^{12}C) = 12 \text{ amu exactly, so } 1 \text{ amu} = 1.660\,540 \times 10^{-27}\,\text{kg}$$

Isotope tables give the atomic masses:

$$m(^{1}H) = 1.007\,825 \text{ amu} = 1.673\,534 \times 10^{-27}\,\text{kg}$$

and $\quad m(^{4}He) = 4.002\,60 \text{ amu} = 6.646\,478 \times 10^{-27}\,\text{kg}$

These include one electron for hydrogen and two electrons for helium, where $m(e^-) = 9.109 \times 10^{-31}\,\text{kg}$, so subtracting the electronic component gives $1.672\,623 \times 10^{-27}\,\text{kg}$ for the ^{1}H *nucleus* and $6.644\,656 \times 10^{-27}\,\text{kg}$ for the ^{4}He *nucleus*.

Reaction sequence (a) has the following energy release. The first step has a net mass decrease

$$
\begin{aligned}
\Delta m &= \text{initial mass} - \text{final mass} \\
&= m(4p) - m(^{4}He) - m(2e^+) - m(2\nu_e) - m(2\gamma_{pd}) \\
&= 6.690\,492 \times 10^{-27} - 6.644\,656 \times 10^{-27} - 1.8218 \times 10^{-30} - 0 - 0 \\
&= 4.4014 \times 10^{-29}\,\text{kg}
\end{aligned}
$$

This mass difference is called the **mass defect**. Note for future reference that this corresponds to the fraction ≈ 0.0066 of the original mass of four protons.

Einstein's famous equation $E = mc^2$ expresses the mass-energy equivalence and gives the energy released from this change in mass. The energy associated with the mass defect is given the symbol Q, and in our example is $Q = (\Delta m)c^2 = 3.9558 \times 10^{-12}\,\text{J}$ or 24.69 MeV. This includes the energy of the two γ_{pd}-rays, which are quickly absorbed by the surrounding particles. The energy appears as the increased kinetic energy of the gas. However, the two neutrinos do not interact with the local gas, and escape from the star unimpeded. Therefore they carry off a small amount of energy, on average 0.26 MeV each, reducing the effective energy contribution to the star to $24.69 - 2 \times 0.26 = 24.17$ MeV. A similar mass equation can be written for the two electron–positron annihilations that follow the p + p reaction:

$$
\begin{aligned}
\Delta m &= 2[m(e^+) + m(e^-) - m(2\gamma_e)] \\
&= 2(9.109 \times 10^{-31}\,\text{kg} + 9.109 \times 10^{-31}\,\text{kg} - 0) \\
&= 2 \times 1.8218 \times 10^{-30}\,\text{kg}
\end{aligned}
$$

so $\quad E = (\Delta m)c^2 = 3.2747 \times 10^{-13}\,\text{J} = 2.044\,\text{MeV}$

Consequently, the total energy liberation by branch I of the p-p chain (p-p I) is $24.17 + 2.04 = 26.21$ MeV.

Reaction path (b)

A similar analysis can be made using reaction sequence (b), which includes the electron–positron annihilation already:

$$
\begin{aligned}
\Delta m &= \text{initial mass} - \text{final mass} \\
&= 2m(e^-) + 4m(p) - m(^{4}He) - m(2\nu_e) - m(2\gamma_{pd}) - m(4\gamma_e) \\
&= 1.8218 \times 10^{-30} + 6.690\,492 \times 10^{-27} - 6.644\,656 \times 10^{-27} - 0 - 0 - 0 \\
&= 4.7658 \times 10^{-29}\,\text{kg}
\end{aligned}
$$

The energy equivalent $E = (\Delta m)c^2$ is $4.2833 \times 10^{-12}\,\text{J}$ or 26.74 MeV.

This includes the energy that goes into the γ-rays, which is then absorbed by the surrounding gas. As before, the two neutrinos escape the star without depositing their energy, which removes $2 \times 0.26\,\mathrm{MeV}$, leaving $26.74\,\mathrm{MeV} - 0.52\,\mathrm{MeV} = 26.22\,\mathrm{MeV}$ for the star.

The analyses for reaction paths (a) and (b) give the same result (within rounding errors). Of course, both analysis routes *must* lead to the same conclusion as to the energy contribution to the star, but you may find it easier to follow what is going on one way more than another. You could, if you wish, perform a similar calculation for the other branches of the p-p chain.

■ In most of the problems in this block only four significant figures are given for most of the physical constants. However, in the calculation above we have used seven for the atomic and nuclear masses. Why?

❑ Whenever you have to subtract nearly equal quantities, the number of significant figures decreases. Consider $4m(\mathrm{p}) - m(^4\mathrm{He}) = 6.690\,492 \times 10^{-27} - 6.644\,656 \times 10^{-27}$ $= 0.045\,836 \times 10^{-27}\,\mathrm{kg}$. Although the nuclear masses are quoted to 7 significant figures, the numbers are so similar that only 5 significant figures remain after the subtraction. If we had begun with only 4 figures, we would have been left with only 2, and numerical accuracy would have been lost. (*Note*: This issue can arise in any subtraction, and is something that computer programmers must avoid.) ■

4.3.3 Reaction timescales

The timescale of hydrogen burning in the p-p chain is set by the slowest reaction in that chain, the $\mathrm{p} + \mathrm{p} \to \mathrm{d} + \mathrm{e}^+ + \nu_\mathrm{e}$ reaction, which takes $\approx 6 \times 10^9$ years for any given proton. This reaction is moderated by the weak nuclear force, which governs the β^+-decay of a proton to form the neutron required to synthesize the deuteron. Note again Phillips' footnote 1 on page 118 regarding timescales. His point is that switching to a faster (more probable) reaction would *not* change the burning timescale of stars. Rather, hydrogen burning then would have set in earlier in the star's life when the core temperature and density were much lower. That is, the fusion probability for the bottleneck reaction determines the *state* (temperature and density) of the star *required* for burning hydrogen, but the *rate* at which fuel is consumed in the star is governed by the rate at which the liberated energy can be removed, i.e. lost from the star, which depends on the opacity of the material.

Question 17	15 minutes

Following the guidelines given by Phillips on page 118, calculate the reaction rate R_{pp} and mean lifetime of a proton in the first step of the p-p chain (Phillips Figure 4.4) at the solar centre.

Hint 1: Use Phillips Table 1.2 (page 19) for solar-centre values, and assume that the mass fraction of hydrogen is 0.5. $S_{\mathrm{pp}}(0) = 3.8 \times 10^{-22}\,\mathrm{keV\ barns}$.

Hint 2: The number-density (number of atoms [or nuclei] per unit volume) of some isotope Z is given by $n_\mathrm{Z} = \rho X_\mathrm{Z}/m_\mathrm{Z}$, where ρ is the matter density (typically in $\mathrm{kg\,m^{-3}}$), X_Z is the mass fraction of the isotope Z, and m_Z is the mass of each atom of the isotope (typically in kg).

Hint 3: Don't forget that each $\mathrm{p} + \mathrm{p}$ reaction consumes two protons, so the mean lifetime of a single proton is half the mean lifetime of each proton pair.

Hint 4: The mean lifetime is related to the fusion rate by Phillips Equations 4.18, 4.19. ■

4.4 Why are stars hot? Putting fusion in its place

You have now seen how to calculate thermonuclear fusion reaction rates, and have seen that hydrogen fusion provides the power that is radiated by the Sun. Before we go any further, we pause to consider exactly what fusion is and is *not* responsible for.

Take note of Phillips' estimate of the power output of the material in the solar centre, which he gives following Equation 4.36 on page 120. The astonishing figure is $120\,\text{W}\,\text{m}^{-3}$.

■   Think about this number: $120\,\text{W}\,\text{m}^{-3}$. Imagine putting two 60 W lightbulbs in a broom cupboard whose volume is about 1 cubic metre. Would that make the cupboard as bright and hot as the Sun?

❑   No, clearly it would *not*. Yet 120 W seems like a pathetically tiny power output for a volume as large as $1\,\text{m}^3$, especially in something as hot as the centre of the Sun! Is the calculation grossly wrong? No, the power output per cubic metre really is that small. Clearly hydrogen burning by the proton-proton chain is *not* much of a *power* house! (But it is a big *energy* reservoir!) ■

So, why is the Sun so hot and bright? The topic missing from this discussion so far is opacity. The solar material is very opaque, with a mean-free path of order only 1 mm. Even though the power generating rate is very small, the heat produced by it does not easily escape. Energy released from a light bulb, on the other hand, easily escapes.

■   The Sun radiates with a power given by $L_\odot = 3.83 \times 10^{26}\,\text{W}$. If only 120 W is generated by nuclear fusion per cubic metre, how many cubic metres of the Sun must be involved in fusion, and what fraction of the mass of the Sun would this be? (Assume uniform density = ρ_c from Table 1.2 of Phillips.)

❑   The volume would be $3.83 \times 10^{26}\,\text{W}/120\,\text{W}\,\text{m}^{-3} = 3.19 \times 10^{24}\,\text{m}^3$. At a density of $1.48 \times 10^5\,\text{kg}\,\text{m}^{-3}$, this corresponds to a mass of $3.19 \times 10^{24}\,\text{m}^3 \times 1.48 \times 10^5\,\text{kg}\,\text{m}^{-3} = 4.72 \times 10^{29}\,\text{kg}$ or $4.72 \times 10^{29}\,\text{kg}/1.989 \times 10^{30}\,\text{kg}\,\text{M}_\odot^{-1} = 0.2\text{M}_\odot$. That is, about 20% of the Sun must be involved in fusion (on the assumption of uniform density). ■

You might be tempted at this stage to think that, even though the *power* release in fusion is very small, the *energy* released heats up the core of the Sun, and this is why stars are hot. The energy released is indeed very important, but it is *not* the reason that stars heat up. In fact the opposite is true: fusion *prevents* a star from getting hotter!

Confused? Recall from your study of the pre-main-sequence evolution of stars that the Sun got to the main sequence without any help from nuclear burning, and moreover it had a higher luminosity *before* it started nuclear burning! This should begin to warn you that *the Sun's temperature and luminosity are not determined by nuclear burning*. However, they are *maintained* by nuclear burning. Irrespective of whether heat arises from the release of gravitational potential energy during the Kelvin–Helmholtz collapse or nuclear energy through fusion, that heat leaks out of the core only slowly. Nuclear fusion now *replenishes* that slow leakage from the solar core and eventually from the surface of the Sun. The release of gravitational potential energy can do exactly the same thing, as it did during the Kelvin–Helmholtz contraction, but the nuclear fusion *energy* source has the advantage that it lasts for much longer. That is, nuclear fusion greatly delays the gravitational collapse of a star.

You have already encountered one example of fusion greatly delaying the gravitational collapse of a star. Figure 16b shows the contracting radius and increasing central temperature of a $1M_\odot$ protostar. Around an age of 10^5 yr, the radius and central temperature stop changing for a while before continuing their previous evolution. This is due to nuclear fusion. Pre-main-sequence stars contain a small amount of deuterium, which is easily ignited and undergoes fusion long before the proton-proton chain is activated. There is not much deuterium, so this episode of nuclear burning is very short, but nevertheless you can see in the figure that it does delay the contraction of the star. You can also see that nuclear burning during this phase does not heat the star. In fact, you could argue correctly that nuclear fusion *stops* the star getting hot, because it would have become hotter sooner if the nuclear fusion had not occurred.

If someone had asked you at the beginning of this course, 'What makes stars hot?', you could have been forgiven for answering 'It is because they have thermonuclear reactions in their cores.' That answer *sounds* plausible, but hopefully now you can see that it is incorrect. Stars are hot because they have collapsed from large diffuse clouds, and half of the gravitational potential energy that has been liberated has been converted into kinetic energy. *That* is why stars are hot. It is explained by the virial theorem; nuclear fusion does not even enter the picture. The role of nuclear fusion is to delay the collapse for long enough that planets, human life, and distance education courses could develop. Nuclear fusion in stars is also responsible for the production of most of the elements heavier than helium.

In the next section you will return to the study of stellar fusion processes, but now you will be able to resist the temptation to think that fusion makes stars hot. Fusion happens *because* stars are hot, rather than the other way round.

4.5 The carbon–nitrogen–oxygen (CNO) cycle

The proton-proton chain is the main fusion reaction in the Sun, but it is *not* the main one in many *more-massive* stars. The second major reaction is studied in this subsection.

Activity 23   15 minutes

The carbon–nitrogen cycle

Read the subsection 'The carbon–nitrogen cycle', Phillips pages 121–123.

Keywords: **Sirius, carbon–nitrogen cycle** ■

REACTION NOTATION

Reactions can be written in several forms. Probably the first form you encountered was:

$$p + {}^{12}C \rightarrow {}^{13}N + \gamma$$

where the + signs indicate what the reaction began with on the left-hand side of the arrow and what it finished with on the right-hand side. If you saw several nuclear reactions written in this form, you might notice similarities between several of them, such as fusion with a proton resulting in the emission of a γ-ray which is common in the CNO cycle, or the fusion of a proton resulting in the ejection of an α-particle which is how the p-p chain and the CNO cycle finish. A second form of notation makes this similarity more obvious, by placing the high-speed particles inside brackets between the initial and final nuclei. For example, the reaction above would be written:

$${}^{12}C(p, \gamma){}^{13}N$$

Not only is this more compact, but it clarifies what class of reaction it is. The particle before the comma (if there is one) is an incident particle, and particles after the comma are products. The β^+-decay of an unstable ${}^{13}N$ nucleus in the CNO cycle can therefore be written either:

$${}^{13}N \rightarrow {}^{13}C + e^+ + \nu_e \quad \text{or} \quad {}^{13}N(\beta^+ \nu_e){}^{13}C$$

(Of course, e^+ and β^+ are alternative symbols for the same particle, the positron.) Notice here that there is no comma between the particles inside the bracket. This is because both are products of the reaction.

In contrast to the proton-proton chain, where all nuclei involved flow through to become heavier species, the **carbon–nitrogen (CN) cycle** uses ${}^{12}C$ as a catalyst. That is, if the CN cycle completes, ${}^{12}C$ is involved in the reaction sequence without being consumed. Phillips lists the reaction steps in his Fig. 4.5. An alternative view emphasizing the cyclical nature, and also showing the associated **oxygen–nitrogen (ON) cycle** which requires higher temperatures, is shown in Figure 29. Collectively these two are known as the carbon–nitrogen–oxygen cycle or **CNO cycle**.

Figure 29 The CNO cycle is made up of two parts: the CN cycle which operates at lower temperatures, and the ON cycle which becomes more important at higher temperatures. The cycles contain essentially only three types of reactions: (p, γ) captures of protons with the emission of a γ-ray, which increase the atomic number and atomic mass number by one, β^+-decays (accompanied by neutrino emission) when unstable isotopes (${}^{13}N$, ${}^{15}O$, and ${}^{17}F$) are reached – the nuclei in the middle row of the figure, and a final (p, α) reaction that closes each cycle with the capture of a fourth proton, followed by the emission of a helium nucleus (α-particle) and the recovery of the starting nucleus.

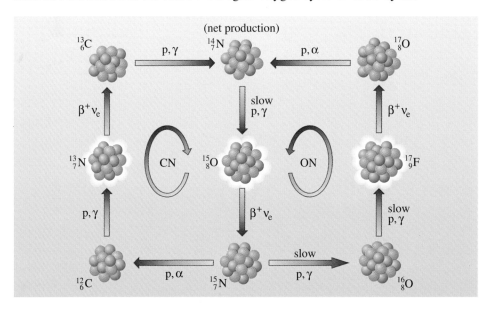

4.5.1 Reaction rates and the ^{14}N bottleneck

You can now use some of what you learnt about nuclear fusion in Section 3 to investigate the CN cycle. We examine the rates of the reactions in Example 5 and Question 18, and then look at the isotope ratios that the CN cycle produces.

Example 5

Work out the fusion rate R_{p12C} per unit mass fraction X_{12C}, given as R_{p12C}/X_{12C}, for the fusion reaction

$$p + {}^{12}_{6}C \rightarrow {}^{13}_{7}N + \gamma$$

for conditions in the centre of the Sun. Assume a hydrogen mass fraction $X_p = 0.5$.

Hint 1: Use the solar-centre values from Phillips' Table 1.2 (page 19).

Hint 2: Use the S-factors from Phillips Fig. 4.5 (page 121).

Hint 3: Use the approximation that the mass of a nucleus Z is $m_Z = A_Z u$ where A_Z is the atomic mass number and $u = 1$ amu.

Solution

The fusion rate for *dissimilar* particles is (Phillips 4.27)

$$R_{AB} = 6.48 \times 10^{-24} \frac{n_A n_B}{A_r Z_A Z_B} S(E_0) \left(\frac{E_G}{4kT}\right)^{2/3} \exp\left[-3\left(\frac{E_G}{4kT}\right)^{1/3}\right] \text{m}^{-3}\,\text{s}^{-1}$$

The number density n_A of some type of particle A in a star is given by its contribution to the mass density ρ_A divided by the mass m_A of each particle of that type: $n_A = \rho_A/m_A$.

Furthermore, its contribution to the mass density, ρ_A, is just the total density ρ multiplied by its mass fraction X_A, $\rho_A = \rho X_A$.

That is, $\quad n_A = \rho X_A/m_A$ (21)

To analyse the reaction $p + {}^{12}C$, we consider particle A to be protons p, and particle B to be ^{12}C. Writing $n_p = \rho X_p/m_p$ and $n_{12C} = \rho X_{12C}/m_{12C}$, we can rewrite the fusion-rate equation as

$$R_{p12C} = 6.48 \times 10^{-24} \frac{n_p n_{12C}}{A_r Z_p Z_{12C}} S(E_0)\left(\frac{E_G}{4kT}\right)^{2/3}\exp\left[-3\left(\frac{E_G}{4kT}\right)^{1/3}\right]\text{m}^{-3}\,\text{s}^{-1}$$

$$= 6.48 \times 10^{-24} \frac{\rho X_p(1/m_p)\rho X_{12C}(1/m_{12C})}{A_r Z_p Z_{12C}}$$

$$\times S(E_0)\left(\frac{E_G}{4kT}\right)^{2/3}\exp\left[-3\left(\frac{E_G}{4kT}\right)^{1/3}\right]\text{m}^{-3}\,\text{s}^{-1}$$

We can divide both sides by X_{12C} to give the fusion rate per unit mass fraction of ^{12}C, R_{p12C}/X_{12C}. At the same time, we recall that the reduced atomic mass is

$$A_r = \frac{A_p A_{12C}}{A_p + A_{12C}}:$$

$$\frac{R_{p12C}}{X_{12C}} = 6.48 \times 10^{-24} \frac{\rho^2 X_p}{\dfrac{A_p A_{12C}}{A_p + A_{12C}} Z_p Z_{12C} m_p m_{12C}}$$

$$\times \frac{S(E_0)}{[\text{keV barns}]}\left(\frac{E_G}{4kT}\right)^{2/3}\exp\left[-3\left(\frac{E_G}{4kT}\right)^{1/3}\right]\text{m}^{-3}\,\text{s}^{-1}$$

Using $m_Z = A_Z u$, we can substitute for m_p and m_{12C} and write

$$\frac{R_{p12C}}{X_{12C}} = 6.48 \times 10^{-24} \frac{(A_p + A_{12C})\rho^2 X_p}{(A_p A_{12C} u)^2 Z_p Z_{12C}}$$

$$\times \frac{S(E_0)}{[\text{keV barns}]} \left(\frac{E_G}{4kT}\right)^{2/3} \exp\left[-3\left(\frac{E_G}{4kT}\right)^{1/3}\right] \text{m}^{-3}\,\text{s}^{-1}$$

We evaluate $E_G/4kT$ separately for convenience: recall that $E_G = (\pi \alpha Z_A Z_B)^2 2 m_r c^2$, so

$$\frac{E_G}{4kT} = (\pi \alpha Z_p Z_{12C})^2 2 \frac{m_p m_{12C}}{m_p + m_{12C}} \frac{c^2}{4kT}$$

$$= (\pi \times \tfrac{1}{137.0} \times 1 \times 6)^2 \times 2 \times \frac{1u \times 12u}{1u + 12u} \frac{(2.998 \times 10^8\,\text{m s}^{-1})^2}{4 \times 1.381 \times 10^{-23}\,\text{J K}^{-1} \times 15.6 \times 10^6\,\text{K}}$$

$$= 3.645 \times 10^{30} u \frac{(\text{m s}^{-1})^2}{\text{J}}$$

$$= 3.645 \times 10^{30} \times 1.661 \times 10^{-27}\,\text{kg} \frac{\text{m}^2\,\text{s}^{-2}}{\text{kg}\,\text{m}^2\,\text{s}^{-2}} = 6054$$

Since both E_G and kT have energy units, the ratio is dimensionless. Four significant figures have been retained to minimize rounding errors in the next computation. Hence

$$\frac{R_{p12C}}{X_{12C}} = 6.48 \times 10^{-24} \frac{(1+12) \times (1.48 \times 10^5\,\text{kg m}^{-3})^2 \times 0.5}{(1 \times 12 \times 1.661 \times 10^{-27}\,\text{kg})^2 \times 1 \times 6}$$

$$\times \frac{1.5\,\text{keV barns}}{[\text{keV barns}]} (6054)^{2/3} \exp\left[-3(6054)^{1/3}\right] \text{m}^{-3}\,\text{s}^{-1}$$

$$= 3.5 \times 10^{17}\,\text{m}^{-3}\,\text{s}^{-1}$$

That is, there are $3.5 \times 10^{17} \times X_{12C}$ proton-capture p + ^{12}C reactions every second in one cubic metre at the centre of the Sun. ■

Question 18	30 minutes

Following the example above, compute the fusion rate R_{pZ} per unit mass fraction X_Z, for the following p + Z reactions:

(a) R_{p13C}/X_{13C} for $\text{p} + {}^{13}_{6}\text{C} \rightarrow {}^{14}_{7}\text{N} + \gamma$

(b) R_{p14N}/X_{14N} for $\text{p} + {}^{14}_{7}\text{N} \rightarrow {}^{15}_{8}\text{O} + \gamma$

(c) R_{p15N}/X_{15N} for $\text{p} + {}^{15}_{7}\text{N} \rightarrow {}^{12}_{6}\text{C} + \alpha$

for conditions in the centre of the Sun. Assume a hydrogen mass fraction $X_p = 0.5$.

Hint 1: Use the solar-centre values from Phillips Table 1.2 (page 19).

Hint 2: Use the S-factors from Phillips Fig. 4.5 (page 121).

Hint 3: Use the approximation that the mass of a nucleus Z is $m_Z = A_Z u$ where A_Z is the atomic mass number and $u = 1$ amu. ■

The reaction rates per unit mass fraction, R_{pZ}/X_Z, for the four proton-capture reactions in the CN cycle, which you have calculated in Example 5 and Question 18 are summarized in Table 1. As noted by Phillips, they indicate that the ^{14}N(p, γ)^{15}O step is the slowest and hence is the bottleneck in the CN cycle.

Since the $^{14}\mathrm{N}(p, \gamma)^{15}\mathrm{O}$ rate is so much slower than the others, you might expect that the bottleneck causes a build-up of $^{14}\mathrm{N}$ as the cycle proceeds. You would be right! In fact, the CN cycle is believed to be a major source of nitrogen in the Universe.

4.5.2 Equilibrium isotope ratios

When the CN cycle reaches equilibrium, the abundances of the isotopes cease changing. From then on, the rates of all reactions in the cycle are equal:

$$R_{p12C} = R_{p13C} = R_{p14N} = R_{p15N}$$

and the equilibrium isotope ratios are readily found from Table 1.

For example,

$$R_{p12C} = 3.5 \times 10^{17} X_{12C}\,\mathrm{m^{-3}s^{-1}}$$

and $\quad R_{p13C} = 10 \times 10^{17} X_{13C}\,\mathrm{m^{-3}s^{-1}}$

but since in equilibrium $R_{p12C} = R_{p13C}$, it follows that $3.5 \times 10^{17} X_{12C} = 10 \times 10^{17} X_{13C}$, and hence $X_{12C}/X_{13C} = 10 \times 10^{17}/3.5 \times 10^{17} = 2.9$.

That is, the isotope ratio *by mass* of $^{12}\mathrm{C}$ to $^{13}\mathrm{C}$ is 2.9.

The isotope ratio *by number* of nuclei, n_{12C}/n_{13C}, which is more commonly written $^{12}\mathrm{C}/^{13}\mathrm{C}$, differs by the ratio of their atomic masses, a factor 13/12:

$$n_{12C} = \rho X_{12C}/m_{12C} \quad \text{and} \quad n_{13C} = \rho X_{13C}/m_{13C}$$

so $\quad \dfrac{^{12}\mathrm{C}}{^{13}\mathrm{C}} \equiv \dfrac{n_{12C}}{n_{13C}} = \dfrac{\rho X_{12C}/m_{12C}}{\rho X_{13C}/m_{13C}} = \dfrac{X_{12C}}{X_{13C}}\dfrac{m_{13C}}{m_{12C}} = \dfrac{X_{12C}}{X_{13C}}\dfrac{13u}{12u} = \dfrac{X_{12C}}{X_{13C}}\dfrac{13}{12}$

i.e. $\quad {}^{12}\mathrm{C}/^{13}\mathrm{C} = 2.9 \times 13/12 = 3.1$

Question 19

Compute the equilibrium isotope ratios by mass and by number for the CN cycle at the conditions of the solar centre, for

(a) $^{14}\mathrm{N}$ relative to $^{12}\mathrm{C}$,

(b) $^{14}\mathrm{N}$ relative to $^{15}\mathrm{N}$. ∎

As you will discover later in this section, most $^{12}\mathrm{C}$ is produced by helium burning, whereas $^{13}\mathrm{C}$ is produced only by hydrogen burning when $^{12}\mathrm{C}$ already exists and where temperatures are high enough to overcome (via quantum tunnelling) the substantial Coulomb barrier. In general, then, $^{12}\mathrm{C}$ is abundant in the Universe, but $^{13}\mathrm{C}$ is produced copiously only where the CN cycle has operated. For this reason, measurements of the $^{12}\mathrm{C}/^{13}\mathrm{C}$ isotope ratio are important diagnostics of CN-cycle activation. We will return to this later, when we discuss giant star evolution.

To conclude this subsection, the results of Question 19 are summarized in Table 2.

■ The bottleneck in the proton-proton chain was the first step. Which step is the bottleneck in the CN, and what is the consequence of this?

❏ The bottleneck of the CN cycle is the fourth reaction, $p + {}^{14}\mathrm{N} \rightarrow {}^{15}\mathrm{O} + \gamma$. The consequence of this being in the middle of the cycle is that some of the original $^{12}\mathrm{C}$ is burnt but doesn't progress beyond $^{14}\mathrm{N}$, so the cycle sees the net conversion of $^{12}\mathrm{C}$ to $^{14}\mathrm{N}$. ∎

Table 1 Reaction rates per unit mass fraction, R_{pZ}/X_Z, for the four proton-capture reactions in the CN cycle at the solar central temperature.

$^{12}\mathrm{C}$	$3.5 \times 10^{17}\,\mathrm{m^{-3}\,s^{-1}}$
$^{13}\mathrm{C}$	$10 \times 10^{17}\,\mathrm{m^{-3}\,s^{-1}}$
$^{14}\mathrm{N}$	$0.015 \times 10^{17}\,\mathrm{m^{-3}\,s^{-1}}$
$^{15}\mathrm{N}$	$0.30 \times 10^{17}\,\mathrm{m^{-3}\,s^{-1}}$

Table 2 Equilibrium isotope ratios from the CN cycle for $T = 15.6 \times 10^6\,\mathrm{K}$, the temperature of the solar centre.

Isotope ratio	Ratio (by number)
$^{12}\mathrm{C}/^{13}\mathrm{C}$	3.1
$^{14}\mathrm{N}/^{12}\mathrm{C}$	200
$^{14}\mathrm{N}/^{15}\mathrm{N}$	21

4.6 The dependence of hydrogen burning on stellar mass

You have learnt that there are two hydrogen-burning reactions, the proton-proton chain and the CNO cycle. Which is more important, and in what circumstances? In this section you will discover that their different sensitivity to temperature has major consequences.

In the previous section, you studied fusion from a nuclear physics perspective, and in Section 3.3.5 you calculated the temperature-dependence (Equation 20), showing that

$$v \equiv \frac{d \ln R_{AB}}{d \ln T} = \left(\frac{E_G}{4kT} \right)^{1/3} - \frac{2}{3}$$

where the fusion rate is $R_{AB} \propto T^v$. That is, the temperature dependence increases as the Coulomb barrier, characterized by the Gamow energy, becomes more impenetrable. In Question 16 you showed that whereas the reaction rate R_{pp} of the p-p chain reaction $p + p \rightarrow d + e^+ + v_e$ varies as $R_{pp} \propto T^{3.8}$, the rate R_{p14N} of the CNO cycle stage $p + {}^{14}N \rightarrow {}^{15}O + \gamma$ varies as $R_{p14N} \propto T^{19.6}$. Strictly, those calculations were for solar conditions. Calculations for other stars lead to typical values for the p-p chain and CNO cycle rates $R_{pp} \propto T^4$ and $R_{CNO} \propto T^{16 \text{ to } 17}$ being quoted in textbooks.

The cores of more massive stars have higher temperatures. Low-mass stars have core temperatures too low to initiate the CNO cycle to any significant degree, so for them energy generation increases slowly with stellar mass, according to T^4. However, once a mass is reached at which CNO processing is initiated, it rapidly becomes important due to the much stronger temperature dependence of this reaction. Consequently:

> The proton-proton chain dominates in low-mass main-sequence stars, and the CNO cycle dominates in higher-mass stars.

The nuclear energy generation rate per unit volume, ε_{nuc}, measures the amount of energy liberated per second in one cubic metre of material,[4] and hence has units of joules per second per cubic metre, or watts per cubic metre (W m^{-3}). As you already know, R_{AB} is the fusion rate, i.e. the number of reactions per cubic metre per second. Therefore ε_{nuc} is just $R_{AB} \times$ the energy released per reaction, which you can calculate from the mass defect Δm using $E = \Delta mc^2$:

$$\varepsilon_{nuc} = \Delta mc^2 \times R_{AB} \tag{22}$$

---

[4] An alternative definition of ε as the energy generation rate per unit *mass*, rather than per unit *volume*, may be found in some books. Either can be used, but the distinction must be noted and the two must not be mixed or confused. For example, the luminosity gradient in a star, which Phillips (Equation 3.26) gives as $dL/dr = 4\pi r^2 \varepsilon(r)$ in terms of the energy generation rate per unit volume becomes $dL/dr = 4\pi r^2 \rho(r)\varepsilon(r)$ in terms of the energy generation rate per unit mass.

The best advice for now is to adopt one form and stick with it. In this block, we use the definition per unit volume.

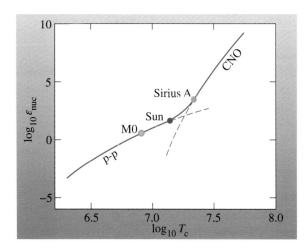

Figure 30 Stellar energy generation rate $\varepsilon_{\mathrm{nuc}}$ as a function of core temperature, for the proton-proton chain and the CNO cycle. Three stars are shown: a cool M0 dwarf, the Sun (a G2 dwarf), and Sirius A (an A0 dwarf).

Therefore, just as we have written the *temperature*-dependence of the rate as $R_{\mathrm{AB}} \propto T^{\nu}$, we can also write the *temperature*-dependence of $\varepsilon_{\mathrm{nuc}} \propto T^{\nu}$. Figure 30 shows the nuclear energy generation rate as a function of core temperature, for the proton-proton chain and the CNO cycle. The cross-over point is in stars slightly more massive than the Sun.

A final comment needs to be made about the expression $R_{\mathrm{AB}} \propto T^{\nu}$. In deriving this in Section 3.3.5 we assumed that the number-density of particles was constant, but in later work we relax that constraint and permit variations in the density of particles. Particle densities appear in R_{AB} as the product $n_{\mathrm{A}}n_{\mathrm{B}}$. Since $n_{\mathrm{A}} = \rho_{\mathrm{A}}/m_{\mathrm{A}} = X_{\mathrm{A}}\rho/m_{\mathrm{A}}$ and $n_{\mathrm{B}} = \rho_{\mathrm{B}}/m_{\mathrm{B}} = X_{\mathrm{B}}\rho/m_{\mathrm{A}}$, we can write more generally that $R_{\mathrm{AB}} \propto \rho^2 T^{\nu}$, and hence

$$\varepsilon_{\mathrm{nuc}} \propto \rho^2 T^{\nu} \tag{23}$$

Question 20

You have shown that the rate R_{pp} of the p-p chain reaction $\mathrm{p} + \mathrm{p} \rightarrow \mathrm{d} + \mathrm{e}^+ + \nu_{\mathrm{e}}$ varies as $R_{\mathrm{pp}} \propto T^{3.8}$ (for solar conditions), while the rate R_{p14N} in the CNO cycle varies as $R_{\mathrm{p14N}} \propto T^{19.6}$. On Figure 30, draw lines corresponding to $\varepsilon \propto T^{3.8}$ and $\varepsilon \propto T^{19.6}$ through the point for the Sun. You will see that your lines are a good match to the slope of the calculations shown in the figure.

Hint: Figure 30 plots ε versus T on log–log scales, i.e. it plots $\log_{10} \varepsilon$ against $\log_{10} T$. If you have a function $y = x^{\alpha}$, then taking logs of each side gives $\log_{10} y = \alpha \log_{10} x$, i.e. a straight line of slope α. So, a function $\varepsilon \propto T^{\nu}$ will appear on the log–log graph as a straight line with slope ν. ∎

4.7 The lower mass limit for stars

We have discussed hydrogen burning in stars, but have not considered which self-gravitating objects attain stardom and which do not. If the temperature in the core of a protostar continued to increase as it contracted, ultimately the ignition temperature for hydrogen burning would be reached. However, the temperature cannot always increase, due to the onset of **electron degeneracy**. The consequences are examined in this subsection.

The temperature T_{deg} at which degeneracy could set in depends on the mass of the star according to $T_{\text{deg}} \propto M^{4/3}$ (as you will soon see from Phillips Equations 1.28 and 5.52). Successful stars reach the hydrogen ignition temperature before degeneracy sets in, but objects of sufficiently low mass become degenerate whilst cooler. For the latter objects, further contraction does not increase the temperature, so they fail to initiate thermonuclear reactions at a sufficiently high rate. Detailed computations show that the limit between successful stars and unsuccessful brown dwarfs occurs at $M \approx 0.08 M_{\odot}$.

Activity 24	15 minutes

Conditions for stardom

Read the subsection 'Conditions for stardom', in Phillips (pages 17–19). In this reading, Phillips notes that pressure generated by a hot ideal gas at the centre of a star is not the only way to support a star against collapse, and that the pressure of degenerate electrons can also do this. However, unlike an ideal gas, the pressure of degenerate particles does not depend on temperature.

Keywords: **degenerate matter**, **de Broglie wavelength** ■

The main aim of the following question is for you to estimate the mass limit between objects which become stars and those which become brown dwarfs. You may be thinking, 'I've never done that before; where do I start?' You may also be thinking, 'I know the answer is about $0.1 M_{\odot}$', but then you should ask, 'Why is it about $0.1 M_{\odot}$?' This problem has been structured to cover all three questions:

*   where do I start?
*   what is the answer?
*   why is the answer what it is?

It is fairly long, but it has been broken into steps to lead you through it quite gradually. Here lies the second aim of the problem: to show you that even a seemingly long and unfamiliar question can often be broken into a number of concise, quite straightforward steps. In fact, this technique can be applied to solving many scientific problems: break it down into smaller, more-manageable pieces, while keeping the end goal in sight. It is important, therefore, that you try to do this problem. It isn't a test of your ability to remember equations, so go back through the text of this Study Guide to find the ones you need. If you get stuck, have a look at the solution for the step you are up to, and when you have it sorted out, go on to the next step.

Question 21	45 minutes

To simplify this estimate, assume that a star may be treated as a sphere of uniform density.

(a) Use the virial theorem to express the relationship between the kinetic energy and gravitational energy of an ideal gas of self-gravitating, non-relativistic particles in hydrostatic equilibrium.

(b) The principle of equipartition of energy states that in an ideal gas having s degrees of freedom, each particle has (on average) a kinetic energy $(s/2)kT$. Treating stellar material as ionized hydrogen with three (translational) degrees of freedom, write the kinetic energy of the gas in terms of the number of protons N_{p} and the typical internal temperature, T_{I}.

Hint: Despite being fully ionized, the material has no net charge.

(c) Restate the result from (b), using the relation between the mass M of the star and the proton mass m_p to substitute for the number of protons in the star.

(d) State the gravitational potential energy of a self-gravitating sphere of uniform density (see Example 1).

(e) Use the results (a), (c) and (d) to derive an expression for the typical thermal energy kT_1. Use the relation between the mean density ρ, mass, and radius of a star to write kT_1 in terms of the mean density and mass.

(f) Use the equipartition theorem to write the kinetic energy of an electron in the core of the star (at a temperature T_c), and by equating this to $(1/2)m_e v^2$, derive an expression for its momentum and its de Broglie wavelength.

(g) Electrons become degenerate if their separation becomes comparable with their de Broglie wavelength. The mean separation between electrons is the same as the mean separation l between protons (by charge neutrality), where $\rho = m_p/l^3$. Write the core density limit ρ_c corresponding to non-degeneracy in the stellar core, in terms of the core temperature T_c and particle masses.

(h) Inserting the condition to avoid degeneracy from (g) into your result from (e), find an expression for the core thermal energy kT_c in terms of the mass of the star. Assume that the core of the star is seven times hotter than the typical internal temperature T_1 calculated at (e), and that the core density is 100 times the average density, as is the case for the Sun.

(i) Finally, compute the minimum mass for a star to ignite hydrogen burning in its core and avoid becoming a degenerate brown dwarf. Adopt $T_{ign} = 1.5 \times 10^6$ K as the ignition temperature for hydrogen burning (Phillips page 162). ∎

The result obtained in Question 21 is that the minimum stellar mass which can avoid electron degeneracy and achieve hydrogen ignition is about $0.22 M_\odot$. More rigorous estimates of the minimum mass for a star give $M_{min} \approx 0.08 M_\odot$.

◼   The calculation used in Question 21 was performed to three significant figures, yet our answer is apparently incorrect by a factor of ≈ 3! Why? Was it all a waste of time?

❑   Think about the physics, not the mathematics. We began by assuming the virial theorem and the equipartition theorem, which are fine, but then we used a result (d) for the gravitational potential energy of a sphere of *uniform density*. We know this estimate has to be wrong, because stars are denser in the centre, but the essential physics is correct: the gravitational potential energy of a star comes from the sum of the potentials of all the particles. We simply used a short-cut to describe that sum. Next, we described the kinetic energy in terms of the temperature of the gas, but we know that the temperature varies through the star, and we simply used the solar ratio for T_c/T_1. Nevertheless, the essential physics is correct: the kinetic energy of its particles are based on the sum of the kinetic energies of all the particles. We simply used a short-cut to describe that sum. We correctly described the density limit corresponding to the avoidance of degeneracy, but in reality the stellar density varies through the star, and we simply used the solar ratio for $\rho_c/\langle \rho \rangle$. Even so, the equation we used captures the key physics: the density at which particles become degenerate depends on their temperature and mass. So, *was* it all a waste of time? Hopefully you do not think so. In learning the essential physics that affects a given situation, it is usually helpful to begin by simplifying the problem, so you can see what is causing what to happen. You can then add more of the details later to see how they modify your initial impressions. ■

■ In simple words, what provides the pressure support for a main-sequence star, and what provides the pressure support for a brown dwarf? Why doesn't a brown dwarf become a star?

❑ A main-sequence star is supported by the pressure of a hot classical gas in its core, while a brown dwarf is supported by the pressure of degenerate electrons. A brown dwarf does not become a star because material supported by the pressure of degenerate electrons does *not* continue to heat up as the density increases, and hence fails to ignite the hydrogen (to a degree needed to replenish radiation losses). ■

4.8 Neutrinos from hydrogen burning

In addition to electromagnetic radiation coming from the outer layers of a star, there are three additional diagnostics of the Sun: the **solar wind**, wave propagation (also called helioseismology), and **neutrinos**. We will not study the first two, but neutrinos have presented such a consistently unusual picture we cannot bypass them, and study them here.

Three types of neutrino are known:

• electron neutrinos ν_e, associated with reactions involving electrons,

• mu neutrinos ν_μ, associated with reactions involving **muons**,

• tau neutrinos ν_τ, associated with reactions involving **tauons** (= **tau leptons**),

each with its antiparticle (the electron antineutrino, mu antineutrino and tau antineutrino). The following reading describes measurements of electron neutrinos from fusion reactions in the Sun. The problem is that many fewer neutrinos are detected than expected.

Activity 25	40 minutes

Solar neutrinos

Read the subsection 'Solar neutrinos' in Phillips (pages 123–127).

Phillips 4.42 gives the results from one of the neutrino experiments as:

observed rate = $(2.55 \pm 0.17 \pm 0.18)$ SNU

In some experimental work it is common to track *systematic* uncertainties separately from *random* uncertainties. Where you see two uncertainties given, as here, that is what is being done, though it is advisable to state explicitly which is which!

Keywords: **solar neutrino problem**, **solar neutrino unit (SNU)**, **Čerenkov radiation** ▪

As the reading from Phillips indicates, experiments aimed at solving the solar neutrino problem will provide results during the first few years of the decade. It is likely, therefore, that our views on this topic will evolve over this period. When

Phillips wrote his textbook, the expectation was that neutrino oscillations – changes of the solar neutrinos from electron neutrinos ν_e at production to tau and mu neutrinos ν_τ and ν_μ – would explain the low detection rates.

Note added in proof: As this Study Guide went to print, new results from neutrino measurements seemed to show that the solar neutrino problem could indeed be solved by oscillations. See the S381 website for updates.

■ The *predicted* neutrino flux from branch I of the p-p chain is $6 \times 10^{14}\,\mathrm{m^{-2}\,s^{-1}}$, while the expected flux from branch III of the p-p chain is much lower at $5.8 \times 10^{10}\,\mathrm{m^{-2}\,s^{-1}}$. However, the Homestake mine ^{37}Cl experiment detects mostly neutrinos from branch III. Why?

❑ Neutrinos from branch III extend to higher energies than branch I neutrinos, up to 15 MeV compared to 0.4 MeV. The difference in *detection* rates comes about because the ^{37}Cl detection system is more sensitive to higher energy neutrinos. Comparisons of the expected and observed fluxes show that there are many fewer neutrinos observed than expected. ■

4.9 Summary of Section 4

1 We can write for a star:
   • the mean density $\langle \rho \rangle = M/(4/3)\pi R^3$;
   • the mean (volume-averaged) pressure $\langle P \rangle = (-1/3)(E_{GR}/V)$, [using the virial theorem], and
   • the typical internal temperature $T_I \approx GM\overline{m}/3kR$, [substituting $\langle P \rangle$ into the equation of state].

2 Thermonuclear burning begins at $T_c \approx 2 \times 10^6 - 1 \times 10^7\,\mathrm{K}$ with the most abundant and least complex nucleus, the proton (hydrogen).

3 The main path (Branch I) of the proton-proton chain can be written:

   $p + p \rightarrow d + e^+ + \nu_e$

   $p + d \rightarrow {}^3\mathrm{He} + \gamma$

   ${}^3\mathrm{He} + {}^3\mathrm{He} \rightarrow {}^4\mathrm{He} + 2p$

   A crucial step in the $p + p \rightarrow d + e^+ + \nu_e$ reaction is a β^+-decay, $p \rightarrow n + e^+ + \nu_e$. This is the bottleneck in the reaction chain. Protons in the solar centre have a lifetime of $\sim 6 \times 10^9$ yr in this step.

4 The mass defect – the difference in the masses of the reactants and products of the nuclear reactions – quantifies the energy liberated into the gas, via $E = mc^2$. Branch I of the p-p chain liberates 26.7 MeV, of which 0.5 MeV is carried away from the star by the neutrinos from the two $p \rightarrow n + e^+ + \nu_e$ reactions.

5 There are three branches to the p-p chain, each delivering slightly different energy per event and occurring with different frequency. In the Sun, p-p I occurs 85% of the time, p-p II 15% of the time, and p-p III 0.02%. The average energy released per proton-proton fusion event is 15 MeV.

6 The second main hydrogen-burning process is the CNO cycle, in which C, N and O nuclei are used as catalysts while synthesizing helium from H. The CN cycle operates first, and the ON cycle comes into play at higher temperatures. Initially, not all steps of the reaction proceed at the same rate, and the cycle converts ^{12}C into ^{13}C and ^{14}N. When the CN cycle reaches equilibrium, the abundances of the isotopes cease to change, and the rates of all reactions in the

cycle will be equal. The equilibrium isotope ratios can readily be found. Two important (easily observable) isotopes ratios are, by *number*, $^{12}C/^{13}C \approx 3$ and $^{14}N/^{12}C \approx 200$.

7   The energy generation rate is given by the product of the energy associated with the mass defect multiplied by the reaction rate, $\varepsilon_{\text{nuc}} = \Delta mc^2 \times R_{\text{AB}}$.

8   The CNO cycle involves much higher Coulomb barriers (and hence a higher Gamow energy) than the p-p chain, and since

$$v \equiv \frac{\mathrm{d} \ln R_{\text{AB}}}{\mathrm{d} \ln T} = \left(\frac{E_{\text{G}}}{4kT} \right)^{1/3} - \frac{2}{3}$$

the temperature sensitivity of the energy generation rate $\varepsilon \propto T^v$ is much higher for the CNO cycle ($v \approx 16$–20) than for the p-p chain ($v \approx 4$). The p-p chain predominates in stars with $M \lesssim 1.5 M_\odot$ (the CNO cycle accounts for only 1.6% of solar energy production), whereas the CNO cycle predominates in stars with $M \gtrsim 1.5 M_\odot$.

9   In objects with $M < 0.08 M_\odot$, electrons become degenerate in the contracting core before hydrogen is ignited. Degeneracy sets in when the electron separation becomes comparable with its de Broglie wavelength. In an object supported by degenerate electrons, the temperature ceases to rise even when it contracts further. Such objects form brown dwarfs that shine by the release of gravitational potential energy, not from thermonuclear energy as in stars.

10   Neutrinos stream out from the solar centre relatively unimpeded (the interaction probability in the Sun is $\sigma n R_\odot \sim 10^{-9}$) and their flux at the Earth should be $\approx 7 \times 10^{14}\,\mathrm{m^{-2}\,s^{-1}}$. Unfortunately, they are also relatively unimpeded by Earth-bound particle detectors, and are very difficult to detect with just a few captures per second per 10^{36} target nuclei ($1\,\mathrm{s^{-1}}$ per 10^{36} targets is 1 SNU). (Note that even 610 tons of perchloroethylene (= carbon tetrachloride) – C_2Cl_4 – contains only 2×10^{30} ^{37}Cl targets!)

11   Neutrinos from p-p III have been detected since 1968 via $v_e + {}^{37}Cl \rightarrow {}^{37}Ar + e^+$, along with a small component from p-p II and the CNO cycle, but these are minor parts of solar energy production. We observe 2.6 ± 0.3 SNU, compared with 7.9 ± 2.6 SNU predicted. Kamiokande measures Čerenkov radiation from similar-energy neutrinos with similar results. The SAGE and GALLEX experiments are sensitive to lower energy neutrinos from p-p I, via $v_e + {}^{71}Ga \rightarrow {}^{71}Ge + e^-$, but data taken since 1991 record 77 ± 9 SNU compared to 132 predicted for these neutrinos. It is unclear why the solar neutrino flux is so much lower than theoretical models suggest. One explanation is that neutrinos transform themselves between their three types – v_τ, v_μ and v_e – when they interact with matter, and hence some of the v_es emitted from the Sun are no longer recognizable as such when they reach Earth-bound particle detectors.

5 FROM THE MAIN SEQUENCE TO THE GIANT BRANCH

Hydrogen burning accounts for the two most obvious features of the Hertzsprung–Russell diagram: the main sequence and the giant branch. Stars spend most of their lives burning hydrogen on the main sequence, but once core hydrogen burning ceases, they expand and cool to become red giants. Nevertheless, hydrogen burning continues in a shell outside the inert core during this phase. In this section, we examine the timescales for evolution and the changes that take place when a star exhausts the hydrogen in its core. We also see what we can learn from observations of stars nearing the end of this stage of evolution.

5.1 Hydrogen-burning timescales

So far you have looked at hydrogen-burning reactions and their energy contribution to a star. Your calculations for Question 17 showed the lifetime of a *proton* in the core of the Sun during hydrogen burning by the proton-proton chain is $\approx 6 \times 10^9$ yr. In this subsection we will go from studying *particle* lifetimes to *stellar* lifetimes.

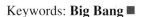 **Activity 26**

Stellar life cycles

Read Section 1.6 of Phillips, 'Stellar life cycles' up to the end of the subsection 'Rate of stellar evolution' (pages 28–30), which deals specifically with hydrogen-burning stages.

Keywords: **Big Bang** ■

■ Why does Phillips highlight the case (page 29) that $l \propto 1/\langle \rho \rangle$?

❏ Because if $l\langle \rho \rangle$ is constant, Equation 1.36 simplifies to $L_\odot = \text{const} \times M_\odot^3$ and leads to the observed mass–luminosity relation. ■

A star uses its fusion energy to replace the radiation losses at its surface, so its nuclear lifetime τ_{nuc} is given by the energy content of its fusion fuel supply E_{fusion} divided by the rate at which energy is radiated away from the star, its luminosity L:

$$\tau_{\text{nuc}} = E_{\text{fusion}}/L \tag{24}$$

Question 22

Assume that at birth, the Sun is 70% hydrogen by mass. (The Big Bang made a helium fraction close to 24% which increased to about 28% by nucleosynthesis in stars, and heavier elements account for about 2%.) Using the mass defect for hydrogen burning (Section 4.3.2), calculate how long the Sun could continue to radiate at its current rate, if it converted *all* of its hydrogen into helium. ■

Question 22 shows that if the Sun could convert all of its hydrogen into helium, it would have a lifetime around 70×10^9 yr. In reality, we find that stars finish hydrogen burning after they have used of order 10% of their hydrogen. We find a hydrogen-burning lifetime for the Sun of about 10×10^9 yr.

The fuel supply depends on the mass of a star ($\propto M$). In the previous reading, Phillips shows from the observed mass–luminosity relation that during hydrogen burning, the luminosity varies $\propto M^{3.0 \text{ to } 3.5}$, so the hydrogen-burning lifetimes vary as $M/M^{3.0 \text{ to } 3.5} = M^{-2.0 \text{ to } -2.5}$, and are therefore *longer* for *lower-mass* stars.

Hydrogen burning is the longest phase of evolution for any star. You will find out why in Section 6 on helium burning. Hydrogen burning is such a slow and stable process that a star evolves little during this period. Apart from gradually brightening by about 0.5 magnitude, stars maintain much the same conditions until they have burnt about 10% of their hydrogen.

Question 23

Use the mass-dependence of stellar lifetimes, and the approximate hydrogen-burning lifetime of the Sun (assume 10 billion years), to estimate the hydrogen-burning lifetimes of $0.5 M_\odot$ and $10 M_\odot$ stars. Assume that the observed mass–luminosity relation has an exponent of 3.5 ($L \propto M^{3.5}$). ■

5.2 Assigning ages from hydrogen-burning timescales

One of the most important and difficult tasks in astronomy is finding the ages of objects. In this subsection we see how to derive ages for stars from their hydrogen-burning timescales.

There are essentially two types of ages measurable in astronomy: radioactive decay ages, which require the measurement of elements or isotopes which undergo natural decay, and evolutionary ages, which require that we have an accurate model of stellar evolution and that we can assign an age to an object depending on how advanced its evolution is. When trying to measure ages for stars, we almost always have to rely on the latter, and the evolutionary process we measure is hydrogen burning.

■   Carbon dating, which measures the radioactive decay of ^{14}C with a half-life of 5730 yr, is often used for assigning ages of archaeological discoveries. Could ^{14}C dating be used to measure the ages of stars? Justify your answer.

❑   The half-life of ^{14}C is very short compared with stars' lives of millions or billions of years. The probability of seeing *any* short-lived isotope is extremely low; isotopes with half-lives of millions or billions of years must be measured instead. Suitable elements are technetium Tc, thorium Th, and uranium U. (There are also additional reasons besides the short half-life why ^{14}C is unsuitable.) ■

The evolutionary dating method is as follows. Hydrogen-burning lifetimes depend strongly on stellar mass, as you have seen from Question 23. You can tell the mass of a main-sequence star from its temperature and luminosity, but you can't tell easily how long ago it formed. However, you know that a star *just leaving the main sequence* to become a red giant has just finished burning its core hydrogen, and you know from its mass how long that takes. This way, you *can* assign ages to stars just leaving the main sequence.

The H–R diagram of a star cluster, a group of many stars of *different masses* that formed from the *same gas cloud* at the *same time*, clearly shows which stars are just finishing their main-sequence evolution. The age of stars at the main-sequence turnoff therefore dates the whole cluster. Cluster dating is of major importance for astrophysics, and is usually the *only* way of obtaining ages for stellar systems. Because of its importance, much effort goes into producing more realistic theoretical models of stellar evolution.

■ If you observe a star cluster with $1M_\odot$ stars at the main-sequence turnoff, approximately how old must the cluster be? Recall that the Sun is 4.5 billion years old.

❑ The *age* of the Sun sets only a lower limit on the age of a cluster with $1M_\odot$ stars at the main-sequence turnoff. Moreover, you know that the hydrogen-burning lifetime of the Sun is ≈ 10 billion years, so the cluster age must be ≈ 10 billion years. ■

Figure 31 compares the observed H–R diagrams of several **open clusters** of different ages, which have vastly different main-sequence turnoffs. A more detailed comparison between the observed H–R diagram of the old globular cluster M92 and theoretical models for a range of ages is shown in Figure 32 (overleaf). Images of these or similar clusters, which also emphasize the different *appearances* of clusters of *vastly different ages*, are shown in Figure 33 (overleaf).

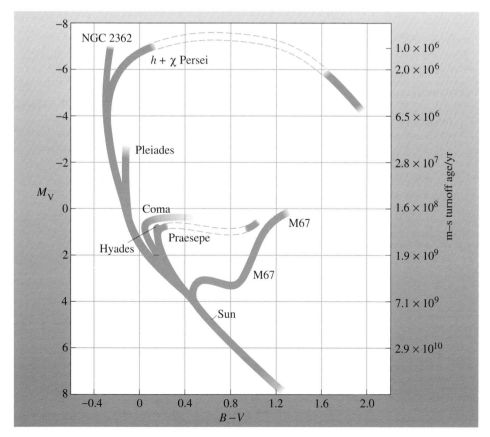

Figure 31 H–R diagram of several open clusters of different ages. The youngest clusters, e.g. NGC 2362 and the *h* and χ Persei, have main sequences populated by bright, blue stars, whereas older clusters, e.g. M67, have only cooler dwarfs and a well-developed giant branch. The main-sequence turnoffs (m-s turnoff) of older clusters are found at lower luminosities and temperatures; the ages corresponding to these turnoff luminosities are shown on the right-hand vertical axis.

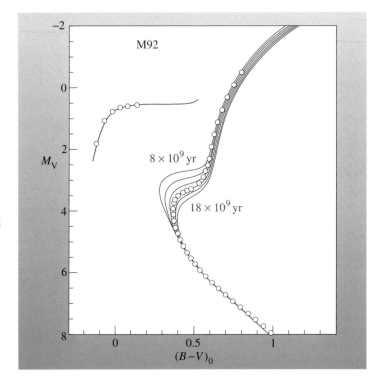

Figure 32 H–R diagram of the old globular cluster M92, showing the main sequence, subgiant branch, giant branch, and horizontal branch of the cluster (circles), and theoretical H–R diagrams for ages 8, 10, 12, 14, 16 and 18 billion years. The main-sequence turnoff indicates an age of 14 billion years for this cluster.

The theoretical H–R diagrams shown in Figure 32 are called **isochrones**. This word comes from the Greek *isos* meaning equal and *khronos* meaning time. An isochrone gives the location of many stars (having different masses) at the same time. Hence an isochrone is calculated for a specific age. The five isochrones shown in Figure 32 show the locations in the H–R diagram of stars of different masses at ages 8, 10, 12, 14 and 16 billion years. As the position of stars in the H–R diagram also depend on metal content, an isochrone is also calculated for a specific metallicity, Z.

Activity 27

Star clusters

Use the Image Archive to view images of old globular clusters and young open clusters (also known as galactic clusters). Note the different appearance and stellar content of star clusters of different age. In particular note the differences in the colours of the stars, and then consider the question below.

Keywords: none ■

■ What difference do you see in the colours of the stars in (i) young open clusters and (ii) globular clusters? How would you explain that difference from what you know about the different H–R diagrams of these types of objects?

❑ (i) Young open clusters are dominated by hot blue or white stars, whereas globular clusters have mostly yellow-red stars. Hot, blue main-sequence stars must be massive and hence very young, so open clusters must be young.
(ii) Globular clusters, on the other hand, are dominated by red giants and yellow solar-temperature stars, so they must be much older than open clusters. ■

(a)

(b)

(c)

Figure 33 Images of three star clusters of vastly different ages: (a) the Pleiades, which is sufficiently young (50×10^6 yr) that not all of the initial gas cloud has been blown away, (b) M67, one of the oldest open clusters (4×10^9 yr), and (c) NGC 6093 (M80), a globular cluster similar to M92 (14×10^9 yr).

5.3 The changing structure of main-sequence stars

In this subsection, we examine the changes in a star that drive it away from the main sequence onto the red giant branch. Of prime importance are changes in its chemical composition resulting from the conversion of hydrogen into helium.

5.3.1 Characterizing the chemical composition of stars

The composition can be described in several ways, such as by stating the mass fractions X_Z of each of its constituent elements. However, a more convenient though less detailed measure is the mean molecular weight of the material. The **mean molecular weight**, μ, is the mean mass (in amu, u) of the particles making up a gas, given by the sum of the mass of the particles, $\sum_i n_i \dfrac{m_i}{u}$, divided by the total number of particles, $N = \sum_i n_i$:

Some texts define μ in terms of the atomic mass unit, and some in terms of the hydrogen mass, which is very similar but not identical. We adopt the former convention.

$$\mu = \frac{\sum_i n_i \frac{m_i}{u}}{\sum_i n_i} \tag{25}$$

The word *molecular* is a little misleading, because the interiors of stars are too hot for molecules to exist, and even most atoms are completely ionized, but the expression has survived from its use in cooler environments. The mean molecular weight is sensitive to both the chemical composition of the gas *and* its degree of dissociation and ionization. It is an important evolutionary parameter of models besides their mass, radius, and temperature, because the chemical composition changes when a star burns hydrogen to helium. A few questions will help clarify the concept.

Example 6

Calculate the mean molecular weight for:

(a) a neutral gas of pure molecular hydrogen (H_2);

(b) a neutral gas of pure atomic hydrogen;

(c) a neutral gas of completely ionized hydrogen.

Solution

(a) Each particle in a gas of molecular hydrogen (H_2) has the mass of two hydrogen atoms, so the mean molecular weight is

$$\mu_{H2} = \frac{N_{H2} \times 2(m_p + m_e)/u}{N_{H2}} = 2(m_p + m_e)/u$$

$$= 2 \times (1.673 \times 10^{-27} \text{ kg} + 9.109 \times 10^{-31} \text{ kg})/1.661 \times 10^{-27} \text{ kg}$$

$$= 2.016 \approx 2.0$$

(b) Each particle in a gas of neutral atomic hydrogen has the mass of one hydrogen atom, so the mean molecular weight is

$$\mu_H = \frac{N_H \times 2(m_p + m_e)/u}{N_H} = (m_p + m_e)/u$$
$$= (1.673 \times 10^{-27} \text{ kg} + 9.109 \times 10^{-31} \text{ kg})/1.661 \times 10^{-27} \text{ kg}$$
$$= 1.008 \approx 1.0$$

(c) There arc two different types of particles in a neutral gas of completely ionized hydrogen: protons *and* for each one an electron. The *mean* molecular weight is therefore

$$\mu = \frac{N_p(m_p/u) + N_e(m_e/u)}{N_p + N_e}$$

but since $N_p = N_e$ for a neutral gas, we can write

$$\mu = \frac{N_p(m_p/u) + N_p(m_e/u)}{N_p + N_p} = \frac{(N_p/u)(m_p + m_e)}{2N_p}$$
$$= (m_p + m_e)/2u$$
$$= (1.673 \times 10^{-27} \text{ kg} + 9.109 \times 10^{-31} \text{ kg})/(2 \times 1.661 \times 10^{-27} \text{ kg})$$
$$= 0.5039 \approx 0.5 \blacksquare$$

Note that the mean molecular weight of ionized hydrogen is half that of neutral hydrogen, which is half that of molecular hydrogen, even though exactly the same numbers of protons and electrons are involved in each sample! In this way, the mean molecular weight depends not only on the particles present but also their state of dissociation and ionization.

Question 24   15 minutes

Calculate the mean molecular weight μ of the following samples of neutral gas:

(a) fully ionized hydrogen and helium in the Big-Bang proportions, 93% hydrogen and 7% helium by number (which is equivalent to 76% and 24% by mass);

(b) as for (a), but after 10% of the hydrogen has been converted into helium.

(*Hint*: Note that for every four hydrogen nuclei destroyed, only one helium nucleus is produced.)

(c) for fully ionized helium.

(d) Calculate the ratio of cases (b) to (a) and (c) to (a). ∎

5.3.2 Rescaling the stellar-structure equations

In Section 2.2.3 you studied the Henyey contraction of the star, and estimated that during this phase of evolution its luminosity varied as $L \propto T_{eff}^{4/5}$. That result was obtained by working out how the density, pressure, temperature, opacity, temperature gradient and luminosity varied as the radius of the star changed. These scaling relations were obtained under the assumption of homology: that the temperature, density and pressure at every point in a star scale independently of the radial position of the points. It was then possible to combine the scaling relations to isolate an expression in the parameters that interested us, in that case L and T_{eff}.

In this subsection, we apply the technique again. This time we are interested not in what happens as a star collapses, i.e. as its radius changes, but rather what happens as its chemical composition changes. We will characterize the chemical composition by the mean molecular weight μ.

Mass distribution

The first equation we will write a scaling relation for is the density. Under homologous conditions, the density $\rho(r)$ at some radius r scales in the same way as the mean density $\rho = M/(\frac{4}{3}\pi R^3)$, which clearly scales with the mass and radius as

$$\rho \propto \frac{M}{R^3} \tag{26}$$

Ideal gas law

We begin with the familiar ideal gas law $P(r) = \dfrac{\rho(r)kT(r)}{\overline{m}}$. Since $\mu = \overline{m}/u$, we can also express the ideal gas law as

$$P(r) = \frac{k}{u}\frac{\rho(r)T(r)}{\mu}$$

According to the homology assumption,

- the pressure $P(r)$ scales in the same way as the central pressure P_c,
- the density $\rho(r)$ scales in the same way as the mean density ρ, and
- the temperature $T(r)$ scales in the same way as the central temperature T_c.

Consequently we can write the scaling relation for the ideal gas law as

$$P_c \propto \frac{\rho T_c}{\mu} \tag{27a}$$

and using Equation 26,

$$P_c \propto \frac{MT_c}{R^3\mu} \tag{27b}$$

Hydrostatic equilibrium

We take the equation for hydrostatic equilibrium

$$\frac{dP}{dr} = -\frac{Gm(r)\rho(r)}{r^2} \tag{Phillips 1.5}$$

and write the scaling relations for that. As before, for a homologous change,

- the pressure interval dP scales in the same way as the central pressure P_c,
- a radial interval dr and some radius r both scale in the same way as the outer radius R,
- the mass $m(r)$ enclosed by some radius r is proportional to the total mass M,
- and the density $\rho(r)$ scales in the same way as the mean density ρ.

Consequently we can write the scaling relation for hydrostatic equilibrium as

$$\frac{P_c}{R} \propto \frac{M\rho}{R^2}$$

so

$$P_c \propto \frac{M\rho}{R} \tag{28}$$

We can now equate the two scaling relations for the central pressure, derived from the ideal gas Equation 27a and hydrostatic equilibrium Equation 28, to obtain

$$\frac{\rho T_c}{\mu} \propto \frac{M\rho}{R}$$

so
$$T_c \propto \frac{M}{R}\mu \qquad\qquad (29)$$

This gives us a relation between the core temperature, chemical composition, mass and radius of a star.

■   Consider a given star whose chemical composition is unchanging. What relation do you expect between core temperature and radius?

❑   For a given star, M is constant, and if μ is also constant then Equation 29 gives $T_c \propto 1/R$. You may recall this result from Section 2.2.3, Equation 10. Later in the present section, however, we deal with *changing* chemical composition, and then the relation $T_c \propto 1/R$ no longer holds. We need to consider additional physics to find the new relations. ■

Radiative diffusion

In Equation 6 we stated the equation for when energy transport is dominated by radiative diffusion, (as in Phillips 3.27)

$$L(r) = -4\pi r^2 \frac{4ac}{3} \frac{T^3(r)}{\rho(r)\kappa(r)} \frac{dT}{dr}$$

where $a = 4\sigma/c$.

For an homologous change,

*   the luminosity $L(r)$ at some radius r scales in the same way as the surface luminosity L,

*   a radial interval dr and some radius r both scale in the same way as the outer radius R,

*   the temperature $T(r)$ and the temperature interval dT scale in the same way as the central temperature T_c, and

*   the density $\rho(r)$ scales in the same way as the mean density $\rho \propto M/R^3$.

We will assume that the opacity in the stars is dominated by electron scattering, for which $\kappa = $ constant. This means our analysis will be more appropriate for stars with $M \gtrsim M_\odot$ than for $M \lesssim M_\odot$, but the latter are in any case affected by convection, making the adoption of the radiative diffusion equation rather dubious.

Substituting these scaling relations into the radiative diffusion equation gives

$$L \propto R^2 \frac{T_c^3}{\rho} \frac{T_c}{R} = R\frac{T_c^4}{\rho}$$

Substituting in for T_c using Equation 29 and for ρ using Equation 26 gives

$$L \propto R\frac{[(M/R)\mu]^4}{M/R^3} = R^{1-4-(-3)}M^{4-1}\mu^4$$

i.e.
$$L \propto M^3\mu^4 \qquad\qquad (30)$$

■ What does the luminosity relation say about stars that have the same chemical composition?

❑ The mean molecular weights of stars that have the same chemical composition are constant, and hence the term μ^4 is merely a constant, so $L \propto M^3$. This is, of course, the observed mass–luminosity relation for stars with $M > a$ few $M_\odot$. ■

We have now obtained relations for:

• T_c in terms of M, R and μ, and

• L in terms of M, R and μ (actually, R has cancelled out)

but we still need a relation between M, R and μ. For this we turn to a new equation in this block, the energy generation equation, and seek to express the radius as a function of the mass and composition.

Energy generation

The luminosity increases outwards from the centre of a star, as new sources of energy (or more accurately, sites of energy liberation) are encountered. The energy generation equation describes the increase in luminosity dL per step in radius dr as:

$$\frac{dL}{dr} = 4\pi r^2 \varepsilon(r) \tag{31}$$

where $\varepsilon(r)$ is the energy generation rate per unit volume, therefore having units $W\,m^{-3}$. During the stages of stellar evolution that we consider here, the luminosity is supplied mostly by fusion. Under the homology condition, we can write the scaling relation for the energy generation Equation 31 as

$$\frac{L}{R} \propto R^2 \varepsilon(r)$$

We know already from Equation 23 that

$$\varepsilon_{nuc}(r) \propto \rho(r)^2 T(r)^\nu$$

which under homology scales as $\varepsilon_{nuc} \propto \rho^2 T_c^{\,\nu}$. We make use of that relation to write

$$\frac{L}{R} \propto R^2 \rho^2 T_c^\nu$$

i.e. $\qquad L \propto R^3 \rho^2 T_c^\nu$

but we can use the results $\rho \propto M/R^3$ (Equation 26) and $T_c \propto (M/R)\mu$ (Equation 29) to write

$$L \propto R^3 \left(\frac{M}{R^3}\right)^2 \left(\frac{M}{R}\mu\right)^\nu = \frac{M^{2+\nu}}{R^{3+\nu}}\mu^\nu$$

We can then equate this with the result from homologous scaling of the radiative equilibrium equation, $L \propto M^3\mu^4$ (Equation 30) to write

$$M^{2+\nu} R^{-(3+\nu)}\mu^\nu \propto M^3\mu^4$$

which we simplify as

$$R^{-3-\nu} \propto M^{3-(2+\nu)}\mu^{4-\nu}$$

i.e. $\qquad R^{-3-\nu} \propto M^{1-\nu}\mu^{4-\nu}$

Taking the $(-3 - v)$-root of both sides gives

$$R \propto M^{\frac{1-v}{-3-v}} \mu^{\frac{4-v}{-3-v}} \propto M^{\frac{v-1}{v+3}} \mu^{\frac{v-4}{v+3}} \tag{32}$$

We can use the last of these (Equation 32) to eliminate the dependence on R in T_c (Equation 29), giving it as a function of M and μ only:

$$T_c \propto \frac{M}{R} \mu \propto \frac{M\mu}{M^{\frac{v-1}{v+3}} \mu^{\frac{v-4}{v+3}}} \propto M^{1-\frac{v-1}{v+3}} \mu^{1-\frac{v-4}{v+3}}$$

$$\propto M^{\frac{v+3-(v-1)}{v+3}} \mu^{\frac{v+3-(v-4)}{v+3}}$$

i.e.
$$T_c \propto M^{\frac{4}{v+3}} \mu^{\frac{7}{v+3}} \tag{33}$$

Taking stock

We have developed homologous scaling relations for the ideal gas law and for four other equations called the **stellar structure equations**. The three scaling laws we use below are Equations 30, 32 and 33:

$$L \propto M^3 \mu^4$$

$$R \propto M^{\frac{v-1}{v+3}} \mu^{\frac{v-4}{v+3}}$$

$$T_c \propto M^{\frac{4}{v+3}} \mu^{\frac{7}{v+3}}$$

We can use Equations 30, 32 and 33 in two ways:

*   to ask how the luminosity, radius, and central temperature of stars having the same composition depend on their mass M, and
*   to ask how a single star (i.e. of fixed mass) evolves as its chemical composition changes, for example as a result of burning hydrogen to helium.

It can be instructive to consider two cases:

*   Low-mass stars ($M \sim M_\odot$) where the proton-proton chain dominates energy production. For this case, the temperature-sensitivity of energy generation suggests $v \approx 4$.
*   Higher-mass stars ($M \gtrsim$ a few $M_\odot$) where the CNO cycle dominates energy production and $v \approx 17$.

5.3.3 Relations between stars of different mass along the main-sequence

For stars covering a range of masses but having the same composition, we can use Equations 30, 32 and 33 to derive relationships between the radius, central temperature, luminosity and mass.

Example 7

For low mass stars ($M \sim M_\odot$), use Equations 30, 32 and 33 to find expressions for the following quantities as a function of mass, assuming uniform chemical composition: (a) luminosity (i.e. the mass–luminosity relationship), (b) central temperature, (c) radius.

Solution

For low-mass stars, the proton-proton chain dominates energy production and $v \approx 4$. For stars of uniform chemical composition, μ is constant, so the μ-term can be absorbed into the unknown constant of proportionality.

(a) Equation 30 becomes $L \propto M^3 \mu^4$, i.e. $L \propto M^3$.

(b) Equation 33 becomes

$$T_c \propto M^{\frac{4}{v+3}} \mu^{\frac{7}{v+3}} \propto M^{\frac{4}{4+3}}$$

i.e. $T_c \propto M^{0.6}$.

(c) Equation 32 becomes

$$R \propto M^{\frac{v-1}{v+3}} \mu^{\frac{v-4}{v+3}} \propto M^{\frac{4-1}{4+3}}$$

i.e. $R \propto M^{0.4}$. ∎

That is, the results suggest that the luminosity increases steeply with mass, the central temperatures increases somewhat with mass, and the radius barely increases with mass.

Question 25

For high-mass stars ($M \gtrsim$ a few $M_\odot$), use Equations 30, 32 and 33 to find expressions for the following quantities as a function of mass, assuming uniform chemical composition: (a) luminosity, (b) central temperature, (c) radius. ∎

Table 3 summarizes the differences for these two mass ranges of stars having the same composition, using the results of Example 7 and Question 25. Since the main sequence is one of the few places where we can see a wide range of stellar masses at the same time, these results are useful as giving an understanding of the physics that shapes the main sequence. The mass–luminosity relation derived for the high-mass stars, $L \propto M^3$, matches the observed relation very well, but for the low-mass stars these scaling results differ from observations, which suggest $L \propto M^4$. Nevertheless, the scaling relations are useful for seeing the overall behaviour of different stars, and indicate how the energy generation mechanism (v) affects the outcome.

Table 3 Mass-dependence of luminosity, central temperature and radius for stars having the same composition.

Mass range	low mass $M \approx M_\odot$	high mass few $M \gtrsim$ a few $M_\odot$
Energy source	proton-proton chain $v \approx 4$	CNO cycle $v \approx 17$
Results from homologous scaling of stellar structure equations	$L \propto M^3$ $T_c \propto M^{0.6}$ $R \propto M^{0.4}$	$L \propto M^3$ $T_c \propto M^{0.2}$ $R \propto M^{0.8}$

5.3.4 The impact on a star of its changing composition

The second area of use for the re-scaled equations is to consider the case where M is fixed, i.e. where a single star is being considered, but now its chemical composition, characterized by the mean molecular weight, μ, is allowed to vary. We can express the luminosity, central temperature, and radius as a function of μ.

Example 8

For a low-mass star ($M \sim M_\odot$), use Equations 30, 32 and 33 to find expressions for the following quantities as a function of chemical composition, assuming constant mass: (a) luminosity, (b) central temperature, (c) radius.

Solution

For a low-mass star, the proton-proton chain dominates energy production and $v \approx 4$. For a star of constant mass, the M-term can be absorbed into the unknown constant of proportionality.

(a) Equation 30 becomes $L \propto M^3 \mu^4$, i.e. $L \propto \mu^4$.

(b) Equation 33 becomes

$$T_c \propto M^{\frac{4}{v+3}} \mu^{\frac{7}{v+3}} \propto \mu^{\frac{7}{4+3}}$$

i.e. $T_c \propto \mu^{1.0}$.

(c) Equation 32 becomes

$$R \propto M^{\frac{v-1}{v+3}} \mu^{\frac{v-4}{v+3}} \propto \mu^{\frac{4-4}{4+3}}$$

i.e. $R \propto \mu^0$, i.e. constant. ■

Note that according to these calculations for low-mass stars, the luminosity increases steeply with increasing mean molecular weight.

Question 26

For a high-mass star ($M \gtrsim$ a few $M_\odot$), use Equations 30, 32 and 33 to find expressions for the following quantities as a function of mean molecular weight, assuming constant mass: (a) luminosity, (b) central temperature, (c) radius. ■

The results of Question 26 show that the luminosity increases steeply with mean molecular weight, and the radius increases moderately, in contrast to the case for low-mass stars.

Table 4 summarizes the results of Example 8 and Question 26 for these two mass ranges of stars. These differences indicate that the different physics at work in each case produces different evolutionary effects.

Table 4 Dependence of luminosity, central temperature and radius on changing composition.

Mass range	low mass $M \approx M_\odot$	high mass $M \gtrsim$ a few $M_\odot$
Energy source	proton-proton chain $v \approx 4$	CNO cycle $v \approx 17$
Results from homologous scaling of stellar structure equations	$L \propto \mu^4$ $T_c \propto \mu^1$ $R \propto \mu^0$	$L \propto \mu^4$ $T_c \propto \mu^{0.4}$ $R \propto \mu^{0.7}$

You would not be expected to remember the contents of Table 3 and Table 4, though you might be expected to remember how you calculated them. They are tabulated here because we will make use of them shortly, and to remind you that it is possible for you to compute the impact of evolution on a star, albeit subject to some simplifying assumptions.

Before moving on to the evolution of a hydrogen-burning star away from the main sequence, complete one last question on the structure proportionalities.

In Question 24, you showed that the mean molecular weight of ionized helium was 2.3 times higher than that of ionized pre-stellar (Big-Bang) material. Using the proportionalities summarized in Table 4, calculate how much larger the radius, temperature, and luminosity of a star would be if burnt *completely* to helium via (a) proton-proton chain, (b) the CNO cycle. ∎

The main point of this subsection, as summarized by Question 27, is that objects which convert hydrogen into helium become hotter and very much more luminous. It is important to remember, however, that these changes are taking place in the *core* of the star; the *surface* temperature of a star also depends on its radius, so the *core and surface temperatures need not evolve in unison*.

5.4 The subgiant transition to shell hydrogen burning

Having studied the physical process occurring in the core of hydrogen-burning stars, we now study the transition from the main sequence to the giant branch in the H–R diagram.

5.4.1 Expansion of the envelope, contraction of the core

When stars have burnt a fraction of their hydrogen to helium, around 10% in solar-mass objects, they undergo significant changes that send them from the main sequence to the red giant branch. Numerical evolutionary models that incorporate all of the known contributing physics reproduce the observations very well, so astronomers have confirmed that they understand the process sufficiently well to be able to reproduce it on computers. However, despite this triumph, one regrettable problem persists: it has not yet proven possible to reduce those processes to just a few simple statements that encapsulate the major physics driving this phase of evolution. It is possible to point out *parts* of the contributing physics, but these on their own fail to provide a robust explanation of what takes place. This makes it difficult for students (and tutors!) to grasp the elusive key explanation of subgiant evolution. Fortunately the problem is more pedagogical (to do with teaching) than physical, since when all of the physics *is* incorporated in the numerical models, the predictions *do* agree well with the observations. In this subsection we can present *some* of the physical processes involved, but unfortunately we cannot provide a definitive and simplified explanation of this phase of evolution.

Low-mass ($M \lesssim 1.5M_\odot$), initially p-p chain dominated stars are not well-mixed, which means that the build-up of helium produced from hydrogen burning in the **core** is confined there. Material in their outer layers – the **envelope** – does not experience the same progressive increase in the mean molecular weight that occurs with the conversion of hydrogen to helium. (You will learn later about specific evolutionary phases during which mixing does occur.) So, while the core becomes helium-rich as the star sits on the main sequence, the envelope retains its original chemical composition. Nevertheless, the changing mean molecular weight in the core does alter the structure of the star, and this probably contributes to the expansion of the envelope, as we will now see.

As hydrogen is converted into helium, the mean molecular weight and central temperature increase. The higher temperatures increases the relative importance of the CNO cycle compared to the p-p chain for energy generation. As the CNO cycle has such a strong dependence on temperature ($\varepsilon \propto T^{17}$), this has the effect of concentrating energy generation in a narrow shell of hot material sandwiched between the already-burnt helium interior and the yet-to-be-burnt, cooler hydrogen envelope (Figure 34). This condition is called **shell hydrogen burning**. Under this condition, burning by the CNO cycle becomes more important than the initial p-p chain.

That is all very well for the helium-rich core, but the mean molecular weight of the hydrogen-rich envelope is unchanged from before. However, it now has a much hotter core embedded within it than previously. This increased pressure at the base of the envelope may be one factor contributing to the envelope's subsequent expansion. The expansion is gradual throughout the main sequence life, causing the star to expand slowly. This can be seen in Figure 16, where the solar radius is seen to have increased by a few per cent since it began burning hydrogen.

Detailed numerical calculations show that the expansion becomes particularly noticeable when about 10% of the star's mass is in its helium core. By this stage, the expansion of the envelope is sufficient to drive the star off the main sequence (Figure 35). (It is for this reason that, in previous main-sequence lifetime calculations, we have assumed that only 10% of the hydrogen mass would be converted into helium during the star's main-sequence lifetime.) The star maintains its luminosity during this envelope expansion, and hence moves essentially horizontally across the H–R diagram towards larger radii. Recall from Section 1 that since $L = 4\pi R^2 \sigma T_{\text{eff}}^4$, an expansion in R at constant L corresponds to a decrease in the surface temperature. The star therefore becomes cooler and larger: a red giant.

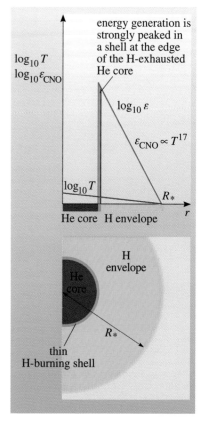

Figure 34 Schematics of (a) the steep dependence of energy generation by the CNO cycle on temperature, $\varepsilon_{\text{CNO}} \propto T^{17}$, leading to strongly peaked energy generation on the edge of the hydrogen-exhausted helium core, and (b) a star with this structure.

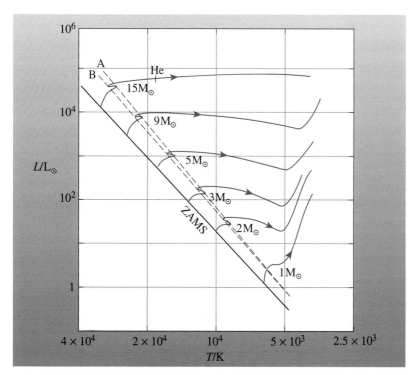

Figure 35 Evolutionary tracks of 1–9M$_\odot$ stars during hydrogen burning, i.e. from hydrogen ignition on the main sequence – the zero-age main sequence or ZAMS – to helium ignition on the red giant branch. The slow evolution from the ZAMS to 'A' is due to small structural changes during core hydrogen burning. The zig-zag in $M \gtrsim 2$M$_\odot$ stars marks (first, at 'A', the cooler turning point) the contraction of the core as gravitational energy release dominates hydrogen burning, and (second, at 'B' the hotter turning point) the transition to shell hydrogen burning. A 15M$_\odot$ star is also shown; this ignites helium (point 'He') while still close to the main sequence.

Although material from the helium-rich core is not mixed into the hydrogen-rich envelope, the envelope is not static. In particular, low-mass main-sequence stars have outer **convection zones** that circulate material through the stars' outer layers. As the star becomes cooler, it also becomes more convective as it again approaches the Hayashi limit in the H–R diagram. Recall that the Hayashi tracks correspond to fully convective stars. As the expanding envelope causes the outer layers to cool, the outer convective zone extends deeper into the star.

In stars more massive than about $2M_\odot$, core temperatures are high enough on the main sequence for the CNO cycle to be the major hydrogen-burning process. The high temperature dependence of the CNO cycle, $\varepsilon \propto T^{17}$, causes energy generation to be so centrally concentrated that a steep temperature profile is established. Consequently convection occurs in the cores of these stars, which keeps their cores well mixed. (We briefly discussed *why* a steep temperature gradient leads to convection in Section 2.2.2, and will study it again in more detail in Section 5.5.1.)

■   Figure 30 shows that energy generation in the Sun is dominated by the p-p chain, but the discussion above claims that the CNO cycle will dominate during its subgiant phase. What will cause the change, and how will Figure 30 show it?

❑   The temperature of the *core* of the Sun will increase as the mean molecular weight increases and hence *it* will move to the right in Figure 30. The relative importance of the CNO process will therefore increase. ■

Although *energy* production is strongly centrally concentrated, the CNO cycle is nevertheless active over a large radial distance within the star. This affects the *abundances* of the CNO isotopes at different depths. In particular, the CN cycle converts ^{12}C into ^{13}C and ^{14}N, and in the core of the star, the higher temperature activates the ON cycle which converts ^{16}O into ^{14}N (Figure 36). The surface of the star will not reveal this process yet, but it is important to keep in mind that it is happening below the surface.

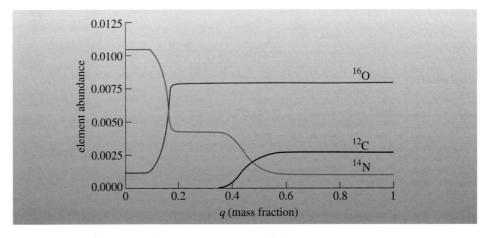

Figure 36 CNO abundances as a function of radius within a $2.5M_\odot$ star, around the end of its main-sequence evolution. When the star reaches the giant branch, the outer convective zone will deepen and may reach layers in which the CN-cycled isotopes are dredged up to the surface where they can be observed.

5.4.2 The Hertzsprung gap

The interval during which the star moves horizontally to the right across the H–R diagram is called the subgiant phase. As the envelope expansion is quite rapid, on a thermal (τ_{KH}) rather than nuclear timescale, stars are in this phase for only a relatively short period of time compared to main-sequence hydrogen burning. Consequently very few stars are seen in the subgiant stage of evolution. This gives rise to a gap in the H–R diagram between the end of the main sequence – called the main-sequence turnoff – and the base of the red giant branch. This gap is called the **Hertzsprung gap**.

Although there are relatively *few* stars in the Hertzsprung gap compared to the number on the main sequence or giant branch, some that are there are highly conspicuous. There is a roughly vertical region of the H–R diagram, extending upward from near the main-sequence turnoff of a star slightly more massive than the Sun, in which the outer layers of the star pulsate; that is, they repeatedly expand and contract. Not surprisingly, this region of the H–R diagram is called the **instability strip** (Figure 37). The changing radius of the star brings about a change in its brightness and its effective temperature, so it draws attention to itself in the same way as a flashing light on an emergency vehicle, though with a period of a few hours rather than a second. As subgiants with $M \approx 2M_\odot$ evolve off the main sequence to make the transition from the main-sequence turnoff to the giant branch, they go through the instability strip, and hence undergo a short episode of pulsation. These are called δ **Scuti stars** (after the first such star discovered) or **dwarf Cepheids** (because of their similarity to some giant stars also in the instability strip which

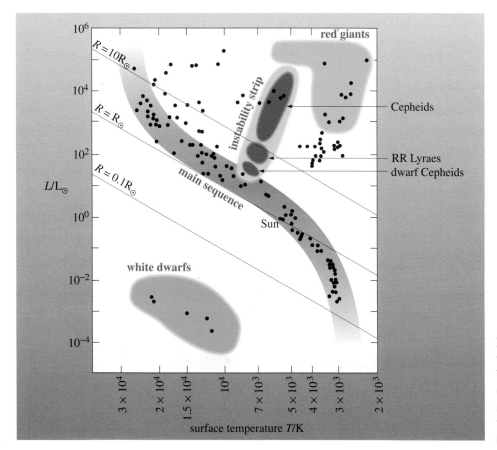

Figure 37 H–R diagram showing the instability strip that lies between the red giant branch (RGB) and the upper main sequence (MS). The locations of three classes of pulsational variable stars are indicated.

119

were named after their prototype β Cephei). These **pulsating variable stars** should be distinguished from stars with companions in a **binary system**, which may be variable due to eclipses, distortions to the shape of the stars, or the presence of matter streaming from one star to the other.

5.5 The red-giant phase: shell hydrogen burning

Once a subgiant reaches the Hayashi limit, the increasing convection does two things: it affects the energy transport through the envelope, and also transports matter from deep in the star to the surface. The results of these processes will be discussed in this subsection.

5.5.1 Convective energy transport

Before studying the effects of convection in red giants, it is important to understand why convection sets in as a subgiant cools. The following reading from Phillips and the subsequent material in the Study Guide address this issue.

Activity 28   **15 minutes**

The critical condition for convection

Read Phillips Section 3.2 (pages 93–95), to study the conditions under which convection becomes a more important energy-transport mechanism than radiative diffusion which you have already studied in Phillips Section 1.4. The condition for convection is discussed further below.

Keywords: none ■

Question 28

For a cell of material displaced adiabatically as in Phillips Fig. 3.2, show that $\Delta\rho/\rho = \Delta P/P - \Delta T/T$ (Phillips 3.19).

Hint 1: Take natural logarithms of the ideal gas law $\rho = \dfrac{\overline{m}}{k}\dfrac{P}{T}$ and differentiate with respect to pressure.

Hint 2: Note that $d\ln x/dx = 1/x$. ■

Question 29

In an adiabatic process, $P \propto \rho^\gamma$. Calculate $dP/d\rho$ and show that $\delta\rho/\rho = (1/\gamma)\delta P/P$ (Phillips 3.20).

Hint: You may find it easier if you adopt some arbitrary symbol for the unknown constant of proportionality in the equation $P \propto \rho^\gamma$, and hence write it as an equality. ■

Consider the critical temperature gradient for convection,

$$\frac{dT}{dx} < \frac{(\gamma-1)}{\gamma}\frac{T}{P}\frac{dP}{dx} \qquad \text{(Phillips 3.23)}$$

Note that since x is measured outwards in the star, both dT/dx and dP/dx are negative (T and P decrease outwards). Therefore, the statement that dT/dx is *less* than another negative number actually means that the temperature gradient is *steeper* than the pressure gradient term. Taking absolute magnitudes of the gradients, we get

$$\left| \frac{dT}{dx} \right| > \frac{(\gamma - 1)}{\gamma} \frac{T}{P} \left| \frac{dP}{dx} \right|$$

i.e. the sign switches from < to >. You may use either form, but you must be unambiguous; merely saying that the temperature gradient must be less than the pressure gradient, without adding that both are negative, could be misleading.

Question 30

Consider the critical temperature gradient for convection, given in Phillips Equation 3.23. Recall that $\gamma = \dfrac{1 + (s/2)}{(s/2)}$, where s is the number of classical degrees of freedom (Phillips 3.24). Evaluate the coefficient $(\gamma - 1)/\gamma$ for two values of s: (a) $s = 3$, and (b) $s = \infty$.

In case (b), under what circumstances is the gas unstable to convection (assuming $dT/dx < 0$)? ■

The critical temperature gradient for convection (Phillips 3.23) can be written in several different ways. Since $dx/x = d \ln x$, we can also write the critical condition for convection in terms of the logarithmic temperature and pressure gradients

$$\frac{d \ln T}{dx} < \frac{(\gamma - 1)}{\gamma} \frac{d \ln P}{dx}$$

One can even go a step further, and remove all reference to the length x, and consider the change in log temperature with log pressure:

$$\frac{d \ln T}{d \ln P} > \frac{\gamma - 1}{\gamma}$$

(Note the change of sense of the inequality from < to > because we have divided both sides by a negative quantity, $d \ln P$.) Sometimes $d \ln T/d \ln P$ is given the special symbol nabla:[5]

$$\nabla_{rad} \equiv d \ln T/d \ln P$$

where the subscript rad indicates that this is for the temperature and pressure under radiative conditions. Likewise, $(\gamma - 1)/\gamma$ is the gradient under adiabatic conditions, and is given the symbol ∇_{ad}. The critical condition for convection then becomes $\nabla_{rad} > \nabla_{ad}$.

5.5.2 The increase in luminosity on the red giant branch

When a star's envelope is in radiative mode, energy escapes from the core to the surface by a process of random walks, in which radiative energy (i.e. photons) is constantly absorbed and re-emitted. As the light is re-emitted in a random direction, it takes a long time for it to make its way to the surface. If the opacity of the material were quite low, photons could at least travel a decent distance in one step. However,

---

[5] Don't confuse this symbol with the vector differential operator grad $\nabla = (\partial/\partial x, \partial/\partial y, \partial/\partial z)$.

stellar material is generally very opaque, and a photon is absorbed and re-emitted many times before reaching the surface. In the Sun, for example, it is estimated that it takes ~50 000 years for photons to diffuse from the core to the surface.

■ How long would it take a photon to reach the surface of the Sun if it did not have to diffuse out, i.e. if it travelled in a straight line rather than being absorbed and re-emitted?

❑ The time is just the distance $R_\odot$ divided by the speed of light c, or 2.3 seconds. Radiative diffusion is a very slow process! ■

Physical transport of hot gas has the potential to be far more efficient at transporting energy to a star's surface. As the stellar envelope in a subgiant becomes fully convective, this in fact happens.

During the red-giant-branch phase, energy generation, and hence the star's luminosity, is closely related to the mass of the stellar core. The core mass steadily increases during shell hydrogen burning, as the shell progressively burns hydrogen-rich material surrounding the core. Hence the luminosity of the star increases. Convection, being a far more effective energy transport mechanism than radiative diffusion, allows the liberated energy to escape from the star far more easily than before. In evolving to higher luminosity, the star moves up the H–R diagram and makes the transition from the horizontally evolving subgiant branch to become a vertically evolving red giant branch (RGB) star (see Figure 35).

5.5.3 First dredge-up

As the convective zone deepens when the star evolves towards the Hayashi track, it may eventually reach a depth where material which has undergone hydrogen burning by the CN cycle is dredged up to the surface. This is called the **first dredge-up**. (Two more dredge-up episodes may occur during the **asymptotic giant branch (AGB)** phase of a star's evolution, which we discuss in Section 6.7.) Recall from Figure 36 that CN cycling may be active enough to modify isotopic abundances even in the intermediate zones of a star where the *energy* contribution from the CN cycle is negligible. When first dredge-up happens, the star's surface $^{12}C/^{13}C$ ratio decreases, due to the greater proportion of ^{13}C in CN-cycled material. (Recall from Question 19 that the CN cycle equilibrium $^{12}C/^{13}C$ ratio is ~3; the interstellar medium value, in contrast, is ~70.) The $^{12}C/^{13}C$ ratio observed in stars is therefore a vital diagnostic of hydrogen burning via the CN cycle and the degree of deep mixing in stars. An increase in the nitrogen abundance, due to ^{14}N production, may also be observed.

Two other diagnostics related to the $^{12}C/^{13}C$ ratio are:

- *lithium (Li) destruction*. Lithium is destroyed in stars via $^7Li(p,\alpha)^4He$ reactions, i.e. $^7Li + p \rightarrow {}^4He + {}^4He$. It survives, if at all, only in the coolest (outermost) layers, and only if the surface material is not mixed down to hotter layers where the (p,α) reactions destroy it. Observations of preserved Li provide constraints on mixing during giant-branch evolution.

- *Hydrogen-burning in the NeNa and MgAl cycles*. These hydrogen-burning reactions, that accompany the CNO cycle in sufficiently massive stars, are irrelevant for energy production but important for nucleosynthesis. They convert neon into sodium, and magnesium into aluminium at the same time as ^{16}O (the dominant O isotope) is destroyed via the ON cycle.

Carbon isotopes and lithium in red giant stars

In this activity you will download and read a short research paper from 1995 on theoretical modelling and observations of convection in red giants. As it is a research paper written for a specialist audience, there will be many terms, and possibly even entire paragraphs, unfamiliar to you. For this reason, the details of the paper will not be examinable in this course. The aim of directing you to read it is to reinforce the concepts you have just studied, and to show you that they are part of modern scientific research.

Connect to the S381 home page, and access the list of Web-based activities (under Course resources). Select Block 2, Activity 29 and follow the link to the Harvard Astrophysical Data System (ADS). Locate and retrieve the paper:

'A consistent explanation for ^{12}C/^{13}C, ^{7}Li, and ^{3}He anomalies in red giant stars', by Dr Corinne Charbonnel, published in 1995 in *The Astrophysical Journal Letters*, volume 453, page 41–44.

As you are reading, summarize the main ideas in brief note form, and write an outline for a short essay on this topic.

Keywords: none ■

Question 31

If you had to explain the research paper to another student on the course, and wanted to relate it to things he or she has studied so far, what points would you make? ■

5.6 Summary of Section 5

1   The observed mass–luminosity relation gives $L \propto M^{3.0}$ for stars with $M \gtrsim 3M_\odot$ and $L \propto M^{3.5}$ for $M \lesssim 3M_\odot$.

2   The luminosity reflects the rate of fuel consumption, and the mass reflects the fuel supply. Hence the hydrogen-burning lifetimes vary as $\tau_{nuc} = E_{fusion}/L \propto M/L \propto 1/M^{2.0 \text{ to } 2.5}$. Core hydrogen burning ends when of order 10% of the hydrogen has been burnt. Using the Sun as a reference for other stars, $\tau_{ms} \sim 10^{10}(M/M_\odot)^{-2.5}$ yr. Hence a $10\,M_\odot$ star has a main-sequence lifetime of only $\sim100 \times 10^6$ yr, whereas a $0.5M_\odot$ star lasts almost 60×10^9 yr!

3   The main-sequence lifetimes of stars are used to assign ages to stellar populations. Young star clusters have large numbers of massive stars lying on the hot (blue), luminous portion of the main sequence. Older clusters have a main sequence that terminates (the main-sequence turnoff) at lower luminosity and also have a well-developed giant branch.

4   The mean molecular weight, μ, is the mean mass (in amu) of the particles making up a gas:

$$\mu = \frac{\sum_i n_i \frac{m_i}{u}}{\sum_i n_i}$$

It characterizes both the chemical composition of the gas *and* its state of dissociation and ionization. The mean molecular weights for three forms of hydrogen are:

μ(molecular H_2) $\approx$ 2, μ(atomic H) $\approx$ 1, and μ(ionized H) $\approx$ 0.5

5   Scaling relations can be written for the stellar structure equations and the ideal gas law under the assumption of homology. These describe the dependence of the luminosity, central temperature and radius of stars on stellar mass and mean molecular weight. The equations are parametrized by ν, the temperature-exponent of the energy generation rate $\varepsilon = \varepsilon_0 \rho^2 T^\nu$.

$\nu \approx 4$ for the p-p chain; this is applicable for solar-mass stars

$\nu \approx 17$ for the CNO cycle; this is applicable for $M \gtrsim 2\ M_\odot$

6   For stars of the same composition, μ is constant, so the equations give the dependence of L, T_c and R on M.

7   For a given star, M is fixed, so the equations give the dependence of L, T_c and R on μ.

8   The luminosity increases *extremely* rapidly with increasing mean molecular weight, with $L \propto \mu^4$. The central temperature also increases. The *cores* of stars converting hydrogen to helium therefore become hotter and more luminous.

9   The increased temperature of the helium-enriched core eventually causes even p-p-chain dominated stars to initiate the CNO cycle and develop a hydrogen-burning shell around the helium-rich core. More massive stars ($M \gtrsim 2M_\odot$) are dominated by the CNO cycle, and have well-mixed cores burning hydrogen in the centre.

10   The increased temperature of the helium-enriched core ($T_c \propto \mu^{0.4 \text{ to } 1}$) increases the pressure inside the unenriched envelope. This increased internal pressure contributes to the expansion of the envelope.

11   Once ~10% of the hydrogen has been burnt to helium, expansion of the envelope becomes very significant and drives the star at roughly constant luminosity to the right across the H–R diagram, along the subgiant branch through the Hertzsprung gap. The cooling of the outer layers causes the outer convective zone to deepen as the star approaches its Hayashi track once more.

12   A stellar layer is unstable to convection if the density of a cell of gas displaced adiabatically is less than that of its new surroundings. By considering an adiabatic displacement of an ideal gas, it can be shown that convection occurs if

$$\frac{dT}{dx} < \frac{(\gamma - 1)}{\gamma} \frac{T}{P} \frac{dP}{dx}$$

Both dT/dx and dP/dx are *negative*, so convection occurs if the radiative temperature gradient is *steeper* than the pressure gradient term, i.e. if

$$\left| \frac{dT}{dx} \right| > \frac{(\gamma - 1)}{\gamma} \frac{T}{P} \left| \frac{dP}{dx} \right|$$

The condition is often written in terms of the logarithmic gradients nabla $\nabla \equiv d \ln T / d \ln P$, such that convection occurs if $\nabla_{rad} > \nabla_{ad}$.

13   The critical gradient for convection becomes less steep, i.e. is more easily exceeded, as γ is reduced below its maximum value (5/3), such as by the

appearance of additional degrees of freedom (s) in zones where hydrogen or helium is being ionized. The radiative gradient will be very steep if the material has high opacity or if the energy source is very concentrated, as when it is strongly temperature-dependent (e.g. the CNO cycle). Both effects favour the onset of convection.

14 As the star becomes more fully convective, bulk energy transport provides a much more efficient mechanism for moving energy from the core to the surface of the star. As the core mass increases, so does the energy generation rate. Efficient convection transports this energy to the surface, and the luminosity of the star increases, which drives it up the red giant branch.

15 The deepening convective zone may carry CNO-cycled material to the surface. This is called first dredge-up. Observable signatures of dredge-up include

(i) a reduction in the $^{12}C/^{13}C$ ratio *towards* the equilibrium value of the CNO cycle (≈ 3),

(ii) an increase in the nitrogen abundance due to ^{14}N production,

(iii) a reduction in the surface lithium abundance, and

(iv) possible changes in the surface abundances of O, Na, Mg and Al due to the NeNa and MgAl cycles running concurrently with the CNO cycle.

6 HELIUM-BURNING STARS

Stars spend the majority of their lives burning hydrogen, first as core-burning main-sequence stars and later as shell-burning red-giant-branch stars. Burning phases involving heavier nuclei such as helium, carbon, oxygen and silicon are no less important. In this section we study helium burning, which is the source of most of the carbon, oxygen and (indirectly) nitrogen in the Universe, and is the final phase of nuclear fusion for many stars. We begin, however, by reviewing how ineffective nucleosynthesis would be without helium burning.

6.1 Nucleosynthesis without helium burning

Hydrogen burning produces new helium nuclei from protons, but it does not contribute to the net production of heavier elements. In the CNO cycle, for example, the nitrogen abundance increases dramatically, but only at the expense of the carbon abundance as ^{12}C is converted into ^{14}N. Likewise, the NeNa and MgAl cycles introduced in the previous section *do not produce more* heavy nuclei; they *convert pre-existing nuclei*, neon into sodium, and magnesium into aluminium. The net production of elements heavier than helium, which astronomers refer to collectively as **metals**, is due to stellar nucleosynthesis beyond hydrogen burning. We will examine some of the more important reactions in this section.

Nucleosynthesis in the first few minutes of the Big Bang produced hydrogen as ^{1}H and ^{2}H, helium as ^{3}He and ^{4}He, and a tiny amount of lithium as ^{7}Li, but no significant quantity of any other isotope. Nucleosynthesis of heavier elements was prevented by three factors:

1   the greater Coulomb barriers of elements with higher atomic numbers; recall that the electrostatic repulsive force between two nuclei having charges Z_A and Z_B scales as the product $Z_A Z_B$, and that the Gamow energy scales as the square of this:

$$E_G = (\pi \alpha Z_A Z_B)^2 2 m_r c^2 \qquad \text{(Phillips 4.10)}$$

2   the lack of stable isotopes having mass number 5 and 8;

3   the decreasing density of matter as the Universe expanded.

Nucleosynthesis in the Big Bang produced the raw materials from which the first stars formed. (In fact, the composition of the interstellar medium today is still predominantly hydrogen and helium.) All other elements are produced as a consequence of stellar evolution.

Activity 30

Stellar nucleosynthesis

Read Phillips subsection 'Abundances of the chemical elements' (pages 31–33), which introduces forthcoming topics on nucleosynthesis.

Keywords: **neutron capture** ■

■   Helium makes up 28% of the Sun. Where did that helium come from?

❏   24% was made in the Big Bang, and most of the remaining 4% was made in stars that existed before the Sun formed. Both the Big Bang and the stars synthesized helium from hydrogen (protons). ■

6.2 Equilibrium and the chemical potential

The thermodynamic properties of a gas are described by its temperature T, pressure P and **chemical potential** μ'. Phillips uses the chemical potential to calculate the equilibrium ratios of nuclei involved in helium-burning reactions, so we begin this subsection by defining μ'.

The chemical potential is a measure of the internal energy that each particle in a gas brings to the total, and for non-relativistic particles may be written

Phillips uses the symbol μ in his Equation 2.21, but we add the prime ′ so you won't mistake it for the mean molecular weight. The other terms in the equation are explained below.

$$\mu' = mc^2 - kT\ln(g_s n_{QNR}/n)$$

The first term is the mass-energy (or **rest energy**) $E = mc^2$ of each particle, where we recognize that each particle is an energy reservoir by virtue of its mass. It is possible to tap that reservoir in nuclear reactions and convert some fraction of the mass into thermal energy, reducing the mass of the system but increasing the kinetic energy. Of course, this is precisely what happens in nuclear fusion, where the small mass difference between the initial and final nuclei is realized as a change in the energy of the particles. For example, recall from Section 4 that the p-p chain converts $4p \rightarrow {}^4He + 2e^+ + 2\nu_e$ (Phillips 4.31). The sum of the masses of the particles on the right-hand side is lower than the sum of the masses of the particles on the left; the decrease in mass goes hand in hand with the release of 24.69 MeV of energy.

The second term of the chemical potential equation relates the particle energy to the quantum properties discussed in more detail later in this section. It comprises a kT term, which you will by now recognize as a thermal energy, multiplied by a factor (recall that logarithms are dimensionless) which depends on:

- g_s, the number of polarizations possible for each particle (see box below), and
- the ratio between n, the number density of gas particles (i.e. the number per unit volume), and the (non-relativistic) **quantum concentration** $n_{QNR} = (2\pi mkT/h^2)^{3/2}$ which reflects the number density of quantum states available to particles of an ideal gas.

(The derivation of the quantum properties is detailed by Phillips (Section 2.1), should you wish to follow it, but you will not be expected to have read that. You should, however, *recognize* the chemical potential when you see it and know what it represents.)

We began this subsection with the statement that the thermodynamic properties of a gas are described by its temperature T, pressure P, and chemical potential μ'. When a state of thermodynamic equilibrium exists between various particles, they have the same temperature, pressure, and also *the same chemical potential*. For this reason, the chemical potential allows you to compute the relative abundances of the particles in *equilibrium* reactions. For the triple-alpha process (which you will study in the next subsection), the stage

$${}^4He + {}^4He \rightleftharpoons {}^8Be$$

is one such equilibrium reaction. (The double-headed arrow indicates that the reaction can go in both directions.)

POLARIZATIONS AND SPIN

(The information provided in this box should aid your understanding of the factor g_s that appears in the chemical potential, but you will not be expected to remember the details.)

The **spin** of a particle may be thought of as the angular momentum it possesses *about* its own centre of mass, analogous to the spin of the Earth. This distinguishes it from the angular momentum a body may possess because of the motion *of* its centre of mass, analogous to the motion of the Earth around the Sun. Spin is quantized with **quantum number** s giving the magnitude of the spin vector s.

The *number* of **polarizations** of a particle, g_s, is the number of independent spins it can have.

The values of these quantum numbers differ for massive and massless particles.

Electrons, protons and neutrons have spin $s = 1/2$. The number of polarizations g_s is given by $g_s = 2 \times \text{spin} + 1$, and thus takes the value 2. The two polarizations are sometimes referred to as spin up and spin down, with corresponding spin vectors $s = +1/2$ and $s = -1/2$.

The spin of a nucleus, usually given the symbol I, depends on the numbers of protons and neutrons.

- Where an even number of protons is present, the protons with spin $s = +1/2$ pair with those of opposing spin $s = -1/2$, and the net proton spin is zero. Similar pairing occurs for an even number of neutrons. Nuclei with an *even* number of protons and an *even* number of neutrons – called even-even nuclei – therefore have zero net spin $I = 0$, and hence $g = 2 \times \text{spin} + 1 = 1$. That is, there is only one polarization when the spin is zero.

- Nuclei with an even number of protons but an odd number of neutrons (or vice versa) – odd nuclei – must have one unpaired particle and hence non-zero spin. The spin I for such nuclei can be found from data tables.

- Odd-odd nuclei, for which both the neutron number and the proton number are odd, generally have non-zero spins, which likewise can be found from data tables.

For *massless* particles, e.g. photons and neutrinos, the relation between spin and the number of polarizations g *differs*. Photons have spin =1 but *two* possible polarizations i.e. $g_s = 2$, corresponding to their **circular polarization** axis being aligned either forwards or backwards along the photon's direction of propagation. Neutrinos have spin = 1/2, but only one polarization, i.e. $g_s = 1$; the opposite polarization is possessed by the antineutrino. (See Table 5.)

Table 5 Spins and polarizations of various particles.

	s	s	g_s
e^-, e^+, p, n	$\frac{1}{2}$	$\pm\frac{1}{2}$	2
even-even nuclei	0	0	1
odd, odd-odd nuclei	> 0	various	> 1
γ	1	± 1	2
ν	$\frac{1}{2}$	$\frac{1}{2}$	1

> The sum of chemical potentials on one side of the reaction must equal the sum of chemical potentials on the other side.

If they were not equal, the reaction would not be in equilibrium. This allows you to write

$$\mu'(^4\text{He}) + \mu'(^4\text{He}) = \mu'(^8\text{Be})$$

We will see below how to make use of this result.

■ How many polarization states, g_s, do the nuclei (i) ^4_2He and (ii) ^8_4Be possess?

❑ (i) ^4He contains $Z = 2$ protons and $A - Z = 4 - 2 = 2$ neutrons, so is even-even, which signifies zero spin and hence that $g_s = 1$.

(ii) ^8He contains $Z = 4$ protons and $A - Z = 8 - 4 = 4$ neutrons, so is even-even, which signifies zero spin and hence that $g_s = 1$. ■

6.3 The physics of helium burning

In this subsection we examine helium-burning reactions to see how much energy helium fusion can liberate, and the implications for the lifetime of a helium-burning star.

6.3.1 The triple-alpha process

We begin with a brief additional note on parity (see the box), and then proceed with readings on the helium-burning reactions.

PARITY

One property of a particle that has no classical analogue, and makes sense only in the context of a wave function, is its parity, π. The parity of a particle reflects the symmetry of the wave function, and indicates whether:

- the wave function at some point r is the *same* as the wave function at $-r$, i.e. $\psi(-r) = \psi(r)$, in which case it has *positive* parity, or
- the wave function at some point r is the *negative* of the wave function at $-r$, i.e. $\psi(-r) = -\psi(r)$, in which case it has *negative* parity.

The parity of a particle is related to its angular momentum quantum number l as $p = (-1)^l$:

- if $(-1)^l = +1$, then the parity is positive. This occurs for $l = 0$, 2, etc., i.e. even l.
- if $(-1)^l = -1$, then the parity is negative. This occurs for $l = 1$, 3, etc., i.e. odd l.

In all interactions except the weak nuclear interaction (involving emission of a neutrino or antineutrino) parity is conserved.

■ Consider the wave functions derived in Activity 15 and shown in Figure 60 (see 'Comments on activities'). Identify the parity of each.

❑ Wave functions 1 and 3 have *positive* parity, because $\psi(-x) = \psi(x)$, whereas wave functions 2 and 4 have *negative* parity, because $\psi(-x) = -\psi(x)$. ■

Activity 31   **30 minutes**

The triple-alpha process (I)

Read the section 'Helium burning' in Phillips to the end of the subsection 'Production of ^{8}Be' (pages 127–130).

Keywords: **helium burning, triple-alpha process** ■

Question 32   **20 minutes**

(a) Write the chemical potential equation for the equilibrium reaction

$$^4\text{He} + {}^4\text{He} \rightleftharpoons {}^8\text{Be}$$

(b) Using the expression for the chemical potential (Phillips 2.21), find the ratio of ^{8}Be nuclei to ^{4}He nuclei at $T = 2 \times 10^8$ K and $\rho = 10^8$ kg m^{-3}. (The Q-value for this reaction, given by the mass defect multiplied by the speed of light squared, $[m_{8\text{Be}} - (m_{4\text{He}} + m_{4\text{He}})]c^2$, is 91.8 keV.)

Hint 1: Recall that $\log_{10} a - \log_{10} b = \log_{10} a/b$, and that $\exp(\ln x) = x$.

Hint 2: Recall that $n_4 = \rho X_4/m_4$, and further assume that the gas is primarily ^{4}He. ■

Activity 32   **30 minutes**

The triple-alpha process (II)

Read the subsections 'Production of ^{12}C*' and 'Carbon production' in Phillips (pages 131–134).

Keywords: none ■

Question 33

(a) Calculate the Gamow energy for the fusion of two ^{4}He nuclei.

(b) At what temperature does the Gamow peak coincide with the 91.8 keV energy excess of the ^{8}Be nucleus?

(*Hint*: You may find it easier to use SI units for energy.)

(c) Based on your result for (b), typically what temperature is probably required for helium burning? ■

Question 34

(a) Calculate the Gamow energy for the fusion of a ^{4}He nucleus and a ^{8}Be nucleus.

(b) At what temperature does the Gamow peak coincide with the 287.8 keV energy excess of the 7.65 MeV excited state of the ^{12}C nucleus relative to ^{4}He + ^{8}Be.

(c) Based on your result for (b), typically what temperature is probably required for helium burning? ■

The results for Question 33 and Question 34, that the temperatures for the fusion of two ^{4}He nuclei, and a ^{4}He nucleus and ^{8}Be nucleus, are around 1×10^8 K and 3×10^8 K respectively indicate that helium burning in stars occurs when they attain temperatures around 10^8 K. Recall that the central temperature of the Sun is currently 1.56×10^7 K (Phillips Table 1.2), so the Sun is much too cool for helium burning to occur at present.

6.3.2 The mass defect

We can calculate the mass defect for the triple-alpha process in the same way as for the proton-proton chain.

Question 35

Calculate the mass defect for the triple-alpha process,

(a) in atomic mass units, explicitly subtracting the electron masses from the atomic masses to get nuclear masses, and

(b) in atomic mass units, ignoring the electron contributions to the mass.

(c) as a fraction of the initial atomic mass. Compare the fractional mass defect of the triple-alpha process to that for hydrogen burning (see Section 4.3.2).

(*Hint*: The *atomic* mass of $^4_2$He is 4.002 60 amu, and for $^{12}_6$C is 12 exactly (by definition).) ■

- Note that the answers to parts (a) and (b) of Question 35 are the same. Why? Why was it essential to account for the electrons when we calculated the mass defect for the p-p chain?

- ❑ In the triple-alpha process, there are the same number of electrons at the beginning of the reaction as at the end, so they make no difference to the change in mass. For that reason it does not matter whether we consider their masses or not. However, the p-p chain begins with a weak interaction $(p + p \rightarrow d + e^+ + \nu_e)$ in which one of the protons undergoes β^+-decay $(p \rightarrow n + e^+ + \nu_e)$, emitting a positron. The positron then annihilates with an electron, so there are fewer electrons left at the end of the reaction that at the beginning. Therefore we have to account for that change in mass. ■

Hydrogen burning converts 0.0066 of a star's burnable (core) hydrogen into energy (see Section 4.3.2 on the mass defect in hydrogen burning). Question 35(c) shows that for the triple-alpha process, however, the mass fraction converted into energy is a factor of ten lower, 0.000 65. One immediate implication of this is that helium burning liberates at most a tenth of the energy that hydrogen burning does. If a star had the same luminosity during both phases of evolution, its helium-burning lifetime would therefore be a factor of ten shorter. In fact, the luminosity during helium burning is even higher, which shortens the helium-burning lifetime further. This indicates why the hydrogen-burning phase, on the main sequence, is longer lasting than the helium-burning phase of stellar evolution. In fact, it is longer than any other phase of evolution.

6.3.3 The ^{12}C$(\alpha, \gamma)^{16}$O reaction

When stars undergo helium burning, the reaction

$$^4\text{He} + {}^{12}\text{C} \rightarrow {}^{16}\text{O} + \gamma$$

is also possible. This converts pre-existing and freshly synthesized carbon to oxygen. However, the nuclear S-factor for the ^{12}C$(\alpha, \gamma)^{16}$O reaction is not well known. Nevertheless it determines how much of the carbon produced by the triple-alpha process remains as carbon and how much is burnt onwards to oxygen. The C/O ratio that results in the core of a helium-burning star greatly influences its future evolution. It determines the luminosity of runaway thermonuclear burning in the white dwarfs involved in type Ia supernovae, which are used as standard candles by cosmologists. Consequently the uncertainty in this rate is one of the most important long-standing uncertainties in stellar astrophysics.

6.4 Quantum states and degeneracy

As a star on the red giant branch burns hydrogen in a shell, its contracting core continues to increase in density and pressure. As you have already seen from Table 1.3 of Phillips (page 26) and from the questions above, once the internal temperature reaches ~10^8 K, helium fusion becomes possible. However, before we discuss helium burning further, we need to understand the condition of the stellar material when it reaches that temperature.

We begin by discussing the wave properties of the particles that constitute a gas. The volume of space containing the gas may be considered to be occupied by particles whose wave properties give rise to standing waves fitting neatly within that volume. They therefore have quantized values of wavelength, and therefore also of energy and momentum. This quantization means that there is a discrete rather than continuous distribution of possible energies. The number of possible quantum states available to particles below some energy is finite; often it is very large, but nevertheless finite. In the very dense interiors of some astronomical objects, the finite number of available quantum states, though large, can be insufficient for the huge number of particles squeezed into the confined volume. Physics then takes new twists as a result, giving rise to some remarkable properties.

The critical point of having too few available quantum states for the number of particles present is reached when the separations of the gas particles become smaller than their de Broglie wavelengths. At that point, the wave properties dominate over the classical properties of the gas, and a quantum gas is said to exist.

The de Broglie wavelength of a particle of momentum p is $\lambda_{dB} = h/p$. For non-relativistic particles, the (thermal) kinetic energy is of order kT. We can therefore write $(1/2)mv^2 \approx kT$, i.e. $p^2/(2m) \approx kT$, where $p = mv$. Hence $p \approx (2mkT)^{1/2}$, which is of order $(mkT)^{1/2}$ (since $2^{1/2} \approx 1.4 \approx 1$). The de Broglie wavelength of non-relativistic particles is therefore of order $\lambda_{dB} \approx h/(mkT)^{1/2}$.

Question 36   **15 minutes**

(a) Calculate the de Broglie wavelength of (i) a proton and (ii) an electron, in the centre of the Sun. (Use values from Phillips Table 1.2, page 19.)

(b) Which has the larger de Broglie wavelength, and by what factor?

(c) How does this ratio vary from star to star? ∎

Since the de Broglie wavelength of electrons is ≈ 40 times longer than that of nucleons (see Question 36), electrons run out of space and hence reach the quantum limit corresponding to degeneracy sooner than nucleons as the stellar core contracts and its density increases.

Degeneracy can be described in two equivalent ways:

- A condition in which the separation between particles is less than their de Broglie wavelength;
- A condition in which the number of particles per unit volume, n, is higher than n_Q, the quantum concentration. n_Q gives the number of quantum states per unit volume available to particles whose velocities conform to a Maxwell–Boltzmann distribution. Under non-relativistic (NR) conditions, $n_{QNR} = (2\pi mkT/h^2)^{3/2}$ (Phillips 2.22).

Before going further, complete Question 37 to convince yourself that these first two conditions *are* equivalent.

Question 37

Beginning with the second statement of the condition for degeneracy, $n \gg n_Q$, use the definition of the quantum concentration $n_Q = (2\pi mkT/h^2)^{3/2}$ to derive an expression for the mean separation l of the particles in terms of the de Broglie wavelength $\lambda_{dB} = h/p \approx h/(mkT)^{1/2}$. Show that this leads to the first statement for the condition of degeneracy.

(*Hint*: Recall (Phillips page 60) that if the mean separation of particles is l, then the number of particles in a volume $l^3 = 1$. That is, the number of particles per unit volume is $n = 1/l^3$.) ■

You have now shown that there are two expressions for degeneracy that are actually equivalent. That is, they are merely alternative expressions of the same physics. In Question 38 you will derive a third equivalent expression.

Question 38   45 minutes

(a) Rewrite the second description of degeneracy, $n \gg n_Q$, using the definition of the quantum concentration $n_Q = (2\pi mkT/h^2)^{3/2}$, to find a limit for the thermal energy kT. State a third equivalent condition for degeneracy as a limit on the temperature.

(b) Calculate values of the quantity $h^2 n^{2/3}/(2\pi mk)$ for (i) protons and (ii) electrons in the solar centre. Assume the mass fraction of hydrogen $X_H = 0.5$, and the mass fraction of helium $X_{He} = 0.5$. For other values in the solar centre, use Phillips Table 1.2.

Hint 1: In the solar centre, all atoms are fully ionized.

Hint 2: Recall that $n_H = \rho X_H/m_H$.

(c) Consider the results to part (b), and state whether (i) protons and (ii) electrons are degenerate in the centre of the Sun. (Use values as required from Phillips Table 1.2.) ■

You will have found in Question 38 that a third equivalent expression for the condition of degeneracy can be written:

> • A condition in which the temperature of the particles is much less than the value $h^2 n^{2/3}/(2\pi mk)$.

Sometimes this third condition is used to describe a degenerate gas as cold, because its temperature falls below some limit. However, this can be misleading, because electrons may become degenerate at temperatures of millions of kelvin, which is not cold in the common usage of the word.

(The derivation of the quantum properties is detailed by Phillips (Section 2.1), should you wish to follow it, but you are not expected to have read that. You should, however, recognize the physical quantities in the equations above when you see them (as you will in the next section), and know what they represent.)

6.5 Electron degeneracy and helium ignition

The state of the electrons in the core of the star, in particular whether they are degenerate or non-degenerate, plays a major role in determining what happens to a star when helium ignites. For this reason, the current subsection considers degeneracy in the context of stellar cores.

6.5.1 Electron degeneracy

Activity 33

The approach to electron degeneracy

Read Phillips Section 2.2 'Electrons in stars' to the beginning of the subsection 'The degenerate electron gas' (pages 55–56), to learn about the behaviour of electrons in a contracting core.

Keywords: none ■

■ Why do electrons become more important when a star finishes hydrogen burning?

❑ When hydrogen burning ends, interior pressure support tends to diminish so gravity makes the core contract. Hence the particle density increases as $n \propto R^{-3}$. The temperature also increases since $T \propto 1/R$, driving up the quantum concentration as $n_{QNR} \propto T^{3/2} \propto R^{-3/2}$, but this is not fast enough. Eventually the density of particles catches up with the quantum concentration, and hence the matter becomes electron-degenerate. ■

Electrons, along with protons and neutrons, are **fermions**, which means they have spin = ±1/2. The occupation of quantum states by fermions is restricted by the **Pauli exclusion principle**, which says that no more than one identical fermion can occupy a given quantum state. The *only* way to distinguish one fermion from another of the same particle (e.g. to distinguish one electron from another) is its spin, and since this has only two possible values, +1/2 or −1/2, at most two fermions of opposite spin can occupy a given quantum state.

The *average* number of *identical* fermions in a state of energy ε_p is given by

$$f(\varepsilon_p) = \frac{1}{\exp[(\varepsilon_p - \mu')/kT]+1}$$

where μ' is the chemical potential.[6] By the Pauli exclusion principle, $0 \leq f(\varepsilon_p) \leq 1$. If the gas had a temperature of 0 K, the term $[(\varepsilon_p - \mu')/kT]$ would take values $+\infty$ if $\varepsilon_p > \mu'$ or $-\infty$ if $\varepsilon_p < \mu'$, and the term $f(\varepsilon_p)$ would take values 0 and 1 respectively. That is, at 0 K, all quantum states with energy $\varepsilon_p < \mu'$ would be filled, and all quantum states with energy $\varepsilon_p > \mu'$ would be empty. In a cold electron gas, the energy μ' of the most energetic, degenerate electron is called the **Fermi energy**, ε_F, and the momentum of particles with this energy is called the **Fermi momentum**, p_F.

Activity 34	30 minutes

Degenerate electrons

Read Phillips subsection 'The degenerate electron gas' (pages 56–58). You will recognize a certain amount of this from questions in the preceding subsection of the Study Guide.

The density of states, whose derivation we have skipped at Phillips 2.3, is the number of quantum states dN whose momentum lies within a certain range between p and $p + dp$:

$$dN = g_s \frac{V}{h^3} 4\pi p^2 \, dp$$

Phillips finds the total number of degenerate electrons in the gas by adding up (i.e. by integrating over) these occupation numbers for all degenerate momentum values. Since no degenerate electrons have a momentum exceeding the Fermi momentum, it is sufficient to integrate from $p = 0$ to $p = p_F$, which he does in Phillips 2.26 as

$$N = \int_{p=0}^{p=p_F} dN = \int_{p=0}^{p=p_F} g_s \frac{V}{h^3} 4\pi p^2 \, dp$$

Similarly, Phillips 2.28 calculates the internal energy of the gas as the sum of the energies ε_p of each particle:

$$E = \int_{p=0}^{p=p_F} \varepsilon_p \, dN = \int_{p=0}^{p=p_F} \varepsilon_p g_s \frac{V}{h^3} 4\pi p^2 \, dp$$

(The particle energy ε_p appears *inside* the integral because it depends on momentum, which is the variable of integration.)

The first term in the bracket in Phillips 2.29 is the *rest* energy per particle, so the second term is the *kinetic* energy per particle: $3p_F^2/10m$.

The kinetic energy per unit volume = the kinetic energy per particle × the number of particles per unit volume

so   the kinetic energy per unit volume = $3p_F^2 n/10m$

Recall that the total energy of a particle ε_p is given by $\varepsilon_p^2 = (pc)^2 + (mc^2)^2$

---

[6] Note that Phillips uses ε for two different variables: one is the energy of a particle as in Phillips (2.4), the other is the power generation rate (in watts per cubic metre) as in Phillips (4.37). It should always be clear from the context which meaning is intended.

At the bottom of page 57 and on page 58, Phillips refers to the results from Equations 2.14 and 2.15; these are identical to the results from Equations 1.9 and 1.10 that you met in Section 1.2 of this Study Guide that:

- the pressure P_{NR} provided by non-relativistic particles = 2/3 of the kinetic energy per unit volume

- the pressure P_{UR} provided by ultra-relativistic particles = 1/3 of the kinetic energy per unit volume.

Keywords: **Fermi momentum**, **density of states** ■

■ The most general relation between the mass, momentum, and energy of a particle is $\varepsilon_p^2 = (pc)^2 + (mc^2)^2$. What are the simplified relations for the two extreme cases of non-relativistic and ultra-relativistic particles?

❑ For non-relativistic particles, $\varepsilon_p \approx p^2/2m + mc^2$.

For ultra-relativistic particles, $\varepsilon_p \approx pc$. ■

■ What is the key difference between the equations of state for an ideal gas and for degenerate electrons?

❑ The equation of state for an ideal gas depends on the density and temperature, $P = nkT$, but for a degenerate gas it depends only on the density, either as

$$P_{NR} \propto n^{5/3} \quad \text{for non-relativistic gas} \qquad \text{(Phillips 2.31)}$$

$$P_{UR} \propto n^{4/3} \quad \text{for ultra-relativistic gas} \qquad \text{(Phillips 2.34)}$$

This independence of the pressure from the temperature helps give degenerate gas its interesting properties, as you will see in the next reading. ■

■ What is the key difference between the equation of state for a *non*-relativistic electron-degenerate gas compared to an *ultra*-relativistic electron-degenerate gas?

❑ The pressure of an ultra-relativistic electron-degenerate gas has a weaker dependence on density, so as the density increases, the pressure in an ultra-relativistic gas increases less markedly. ■

6.5.2 The helium flash and quiescent helium ignition

Electrons in stars

Reread the last two paragraphs of Phillips page 24 (beginning 'Thermonuclear fusion not only postpones …'), then read the subsections 'Electrons in the sun' and 'Electrons in massive stars' (pages 60–62).

Note the discussion in the middle of page 61 concerning uncertain mass loss. Late in their lives when their radii are large and their luminosities high, stars experience considerable mass loss in a strong stellar wind. This *significantly* reduces the mass of a star and hence affects its evolution, but because the mass-loss process is not very well quantified, there are considerable uncertainties as to exactly what happens to any particular star during this stage. (See the box on mass loss.)

Keywords: **helium flash**, **mass loss**, **planetary nebula**, **supernova** ▪

Recall from Section 4.7 that the minimum mass for the onset of hydrogen burning in the p-p chain is about $0.08 M_\odot$; the cores of lower mass objects do not reach temperatures required to initiate the reaction. Helium burning also has a mass threshold, linked to the higher temperature (10^8 K) required to initiate helium burning. Only stars with $M \gtrsim 0.5 M_\odot$ achieve this. Stars below the $0.5 M_\odot$ mass limit end their lives with inert helium cores.

MASS LOSS

Measurements of mass loss from various stars give rates from $10^{-14} M_\odot \mathrm{yr}^{-1}$ for a quiet main sequence star like the Sun, to $10^{-4} M_\odot \mathrm{yr}^{-1}$ for the most luminous stars known. Clearly the latter could lose a considerable fraction of their mass over a few tens of thousands of years. Although the mass-loss process is not well understood, empirical measurements such as these show that it is strongly dependent on luminosity. One semiempirical formulation of mass loss is the **Reimers law**, which indicates that the mass-loss rate $\dot{M} \equiv \mathrm{d}M/\mathrm{d}t$ varies as $\dot{M} \propto L^{3/2} M^{-1} T_{\mathrm{eff}}^{-2}$. Although the exponent on luminosity is slightly weaker than the exponent of the effective temperature, the luminosity of a star changes by orders of magnitude as it evolves, whereas the surface temperature varies only by a factor of a few, so the luminosity dependence is more important.

As a star evolves to higher luminosity on the giant branch, its rate of mass loss increases significantly. Mass loss from a star can reduce its mass sufficiently that fusion reactions anticipated on the basis of its main-sequence mass alone may no longer be possible. This point will become evident when we consider advanced stages of burning in Section 7.3. Massive stars which have high luminosity even during their main-sequence phase may undergo severe mass loss throughout their lifetime, not only during later stages of evolution.

The decoupling of temperature from pressure in an electron-degenerate gas means that if the temperature for helium ignition is reached in such an environment, it ignites explosively. The energy released by the new burning source increases the temperature, but the pressure in the electron-degenerate core is dominated by the electron pressure, and the pressure of an electron-degenerate gas is independent of temperature (e.g. compare Phillips 2.19 for classical gas with Phillips 2.31 and 2.34 for degenerate gas). Consequently, the hot core does not increase in pressure and drive an expansion that (in a classical gas) would reduce its temperature. So, the pressure does not increase, the temperature rise is not compensated for, and the reaction rate accelerates. This episode, which lasts only seconds, is called the helium flash.

More-massive stars have a lower density for a given temperature, $kT \propto M^{2/3} \rho^{1/3}$, so the temperature for helium ignition will be reached in more-massive stars at lower density. Stars more massive than 2.5–$3 M_\odot$ ignite helium *before* they reach the density required for electron degeneracy. For these stars, in contrast to the lower mass ones like the Sun, helium ignition is controlled rather than explosive, and no helium flash occurs.

■ What is the essential difference between the conditions under which helium ignites in a $1M_\odot$ star and a $5M_\odot$ star? What is the consequence?

❑ A $1M_\odot$ star will be electron-degenerate in its core when T_c reaches ~10^8 K, whereas the core of a $5M_\odot$ star will not be degenerate when this temperature is reached. When nuclear fusion begins in a degenerate gas, where the pressure no longer depends on the temperature, the temperature will increase without triggering an expansion of the core to cool it, so a thermonuclear runaway occurs. This is called the helium flash. ■

6.6 Core helium burning stars

Once helium ignites, stars experience a new period of steady burning. We consider the phase of core helium burning stars in this subsection.

The helium flash of a low-mass star terminates its evolution up the red giant branch, and it begins a new stage of life as a low-mass, core helium burning star. The electron degeneracy is removed at the same time, due to the expansion and heating of the core – recall that a degenerate gas is a 'cold', dense gas – so the new phase is again stable, with pressure and temperature recoupled through the equation of state of an ideal gas. This recoupling leads to an expansion of the core and also of the hydrogen-burning shell further out in the star. The expansion of the hydrogen burning shell reduces its temperature, density, and hence its energy generation. In some mass ranges, hydrogen fusion ceases. The outer hydrogen-rich envelope of the star senses this temperature decrease, so contracts. Since $L = 4\pi R^2 \sigma T_{\text{eff}}^4$, the contraction would lead to an increase in the effective temperature if the luminosity were constant. However, the luminosity of the star is also lower, so the increase in temperature is less pronounced. Changes in luminosity and effective temperature do, of course, shift the star in the H–R diagram. The star's new stable location is partway down and slightly towards the left of the giant branch. Because the new configuration of stable core helium burning and shell hydrogen burning is reasonably long lived, stars remain in this region of the H–R diagram for some time. The location is recognized observationally as a clump of stars in the H–R diagram, due to the slow evolution through this phase of life, and they are called **red giant clump stars** (Figure 38).

Before going on to discuss helium ignition in more massive (non-degenerate) stars, it is important to note that the location of low-mass, core helium burning, shell-hydrogen burning stars depends a great deal on their heavy-element content. (Until now, we have discussed the impact of a growing helium abundance in hydrogen-burning stars, but have ignored the trace ($\leq 2\%$) elements heavier than helium, which astronomers refer to collectively as metals.) Stars with a similar metal composition to the Sun will sit close to the red giant branch as the red giant clump stars. However, stars with *lower* metal content have higher temperatures so their location in the H–R diagram is called the **horizontal branch** (Figure 39).

The position of stars on the horizontal branch also depends on their mass, lower-mass stars being hotter. Stellar evolution models show that horizontal branch stars must have lost a significant fraction ($\approx 25\%$) of their initial mass; stars of low metallicity which had main-sequence masses $M_{\text{ms}} \approx 0.8M_\odot$ apparently lose up to $\approx 0.2M_\odot$ of their envelope soon after helium ignition. Moreover, they must lose *different* amounts from one star to the next, as horizontal-branch stars in a metal-poor cluster (where all stars have the *same* metallicity) span a range of temperatures, the lowest mass stars being hottest. This mass loss process is poorly understood.

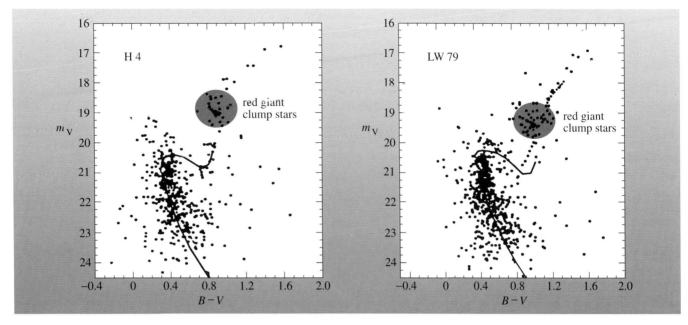

Figure 38 H–R diagram of two star clusters showing a well-populated main sequence and a giant branch with distinct core helium burning red giant clump stars at $m_V \approx 19$ and $B - V \approx 0.8$–1.0.

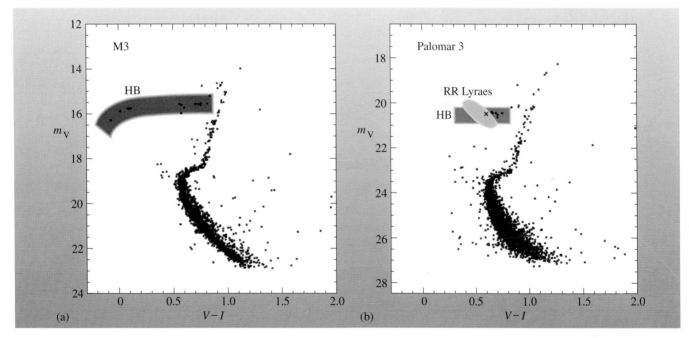

Figure 39 H–R diagrams of the globular clusters (a) M3 and (b) Palomar 3, showing the horizontal branches (HB) at $m_V \approx 15.5$ and 20.5 respectively, which are populated by core helium burning stars with a low metal content. These clusters have ages around 13×10^9 yr, and their metal content is only $\approx 1/30$ of the solar value. Note that whereas the HB of Palomar 3 is quite short, that of M3 has a blue extension to $B - V \approx 0$. The instability strip intersects the HB almost directly above the main-sequence turnoff, giving rise to pulsating stars called RR Lyrae variables. Their approximate location, and typical brightness and colour excursions are indicated for Palomar 3 along with one confirmed RR Lyrae star (**x**). These H–R diagrams are for only a small field within each cluster; many more cluster stars could be observed and added to these diagrams.

Recall from the discussion of $M \approx 2M_\odot$ hydrogen-burning stars leaving the main sequence and going through the δ Scuti phase, that the instability strip for stellar pulsation cuts roughly vertically downwards through the H–R diagram (see Figure 37). The instability strip therefore cuts across the horizontal branch, with the result that a significant fraction of horizontal branch stars pulsate. In globular clusters, the intersection of the instability strip with the horizontal branch is at about the same colour (effective temperature) as the main-sequence turnoff, and causes brightness variations of order $\Delta V \approx \pm 0.5$ mag (as well as colour variations $\Delta V - I \approx \pm 0.10$), for stars over an interval of perhaps 0.2 mag in $V - I$. Pulsating horizontal-branch stars are called **RR Lyrae** stars after the first one discovered. Their periods, ≈ 0.5 days, are longer than the δ Scuti stars, whose luminosity is lower.

RR Lyrae stars are of immense importance in observational astronomy. Because horizontal-branch stars have the same intrinsic luminosity once any light variation is allowed for – they are, after all, *horizontal*-branch stars – they are excellent standard candles for field (i.e. non-cluster) stars. RR Lyrae stars are instantly identifiable from their light curves, which have distinctive periods, amplitudes, and shapes (Figure 40). Once identified, their inferred *intrinsic* luminosities can be compared with their apparent brightness, and their distances computed.

■　Why are RR Lyrae variables used as field standard candles while non-pulsating HB stars are not?

❏　RR Lyrae variables are recognizable from their light curves, whereas other HB stars in the field could be mistaken for nearby main-sequence stars or distant supergiants. ■

Whereas low-mass core helium burning stars occupy the region of clump red giants or the horizontal branch depending on their metal content, higher-mass stars initiate **blue loops** in the H–R diagram once helium burning begins. Because these stars are non-degenerate in their core, helium ignition leads to an expansion of the core and hydrogen burning shell. The temperature at the base of the outer (hydrogen) envelope therefore decreases, and the envelope contracts, decreasing the radius and driving up the effective temperature. That is, the star becomes bluer, the extent of

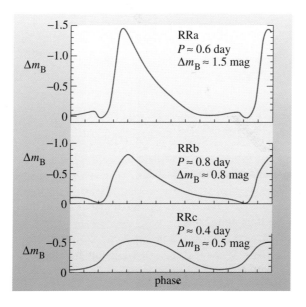

Figure 40 Typical light-curves (in blue light) for three classes of RR Lyrae variable.

the blueward excursion being greater for higher mass stars; see Figure 41. (This is the reverse of the mass distribution along the horizontal branch for low-mass, low-metallicity stars.) The extent of the blue loop also depends on the chemical composition of the star.

Figure 35 shows evolutionary tracks for stars from $1M_\odot$ to $15M_\odot$, from the main sequence, across the Hertzsprung gap, on to the giant branch. Note that amongst low-mass stars, the *less* massive a star is, the *longer* is its red giant branch. This arises because of the need for lower-mass stars to reach higher core densities before the temperatures for helium-ignition can be achieved.

■ Summarize the main similarities and differences between clump red giants, horizontal-branch stars, and RR Lyrae variable stars.

❏ All three classes are burning helium in their cores. Horizontal-branch stars have a lower heavy-element content than clump red giants, and so are hotter. RR Lyraes are a subset of horizontal-branch stars, where the instability strip intersects the horizontal branch. Since horizontal branch stars have a known luminosity, and RR Lyraes are easily recognized, they are valuable standard candles for measuring distances. ■

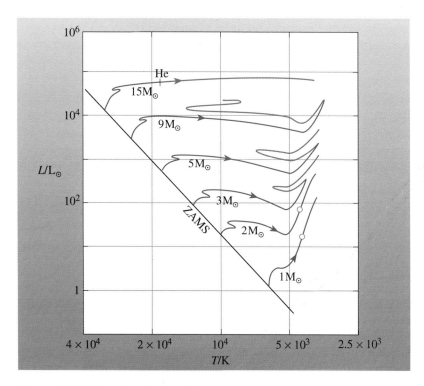

Figure 41 Helium-burning evolutionary tracks, following on from the hydrogen-burning phase shown in Figure 35. In stars with $M \lesssim 2.5M_\odot$, helium is ignited in a degenerate core, and the star moves back down from the top of its red giant track to the red giant clump halfway up the track. In stars with $2.5M_\odot \lesssim M \lesssim 9M_\odot$, the core is not degenerate when helium ignites, and these stars move blueward in the H–R diagram, but evolve redward again once core helium burning is replaced by shell helium burning. This path is called a blue loop. In stars with $M \gtrsim 9M_\odot$, helium ignites when the star is still close to the main sequence and does not interrupt its redward evolution.

6.7 Low- and intermediate-mass stars: helium burning in a shell

In the same way that core hydrogen burning is followed by shell hydrogen burning, so core helium burning is followed by shell helium burning. This second stage of giant-star evolution is explained in this subsection.

Whereas the temperature-dependence of energy generation for the proton-proton chain is $\varepsilon \propto T^4$ and for the CNO cycle goes as $T^{16\,\text{to}\,17}$, for the triple-alpha process the dependence is T^{30}! This makes energy production in the core very centrally concentrated. The helium-burning core soon becomes a helium-burning shell surrounding a carbon and oxygen core (often written CO), outside which the hydrogen-burning shell still burns. The hydrogen-burning shell now burns closer towards the surface, which causes the hydrogen envelope to expand and cool once more. Low-mass stars ($M \lesssim 3.5 M_\odot$) increase in luminosity again as convection (again) becomes important in energy transport, and make a slow return up the giant branch, the return leg being slightly more luminous than for lower mass first-ascent red giants, thus delineating a separate asymptotic giant branch (AGB) (see Figure 42 and Figure 43). Intermediate mass stars ($3.5 \leq M/M_\odot \leq 8$) reverse their blue loops. Broadly speaking, stars move back towards their helium-ignition points in the H–R diagram. The envelope expansion causes the envelope to become more convective, just as it did when the star moved from core hydrogen burning on the main sequence to shell hydrogen burning on the giant branch.

To distinguish the two phases of giant branch evolution, the first being from the main-sequence turnoff to the helium ignition point, and the second being the AGB, the former is sometimes referred to as the **first-ascent giant branch**. In AGB stars with $M \gtrsim 3.5$–$4 M_\odot$ the convection reaches deep enough to effect another dredge-up episode, called the second dredge-up in recognition of its similarity to the event that occurs on the first ascent of the giant branch.

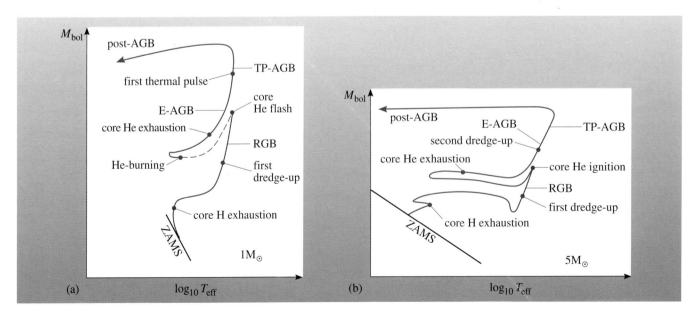

Figure 42 Schematic evolutionary tracks, including the AGB phases, for (a) $1 M_\odot$ and (b) $5 M_\odot$ stars. The extent of the blueward evolution of a star during helium burning depends on its metallicity and the extent of mass loss. The AGB phases are shown divided into the early AGB (E-AGB) and the later thermally pulsing AGB (TP-AGB). The superwind develops as the star reaches the highest luminosities, sending the star into the post-AGB phase.

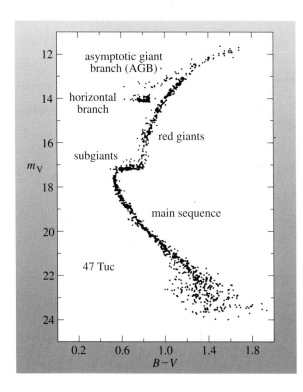

Figure 43 Observational H–R diagram of the old globular cluster 47 Tuc, showing a clear asymptotic giant branch (AGB) occupied by shell-He-burning stars making their way from the horizontal branch toward the top of the giant branch.

Energy generation during the first portion of the AGB – the early-AGB or **E-AGB** – is dominated by the helium-burning shell. (The hydrogen-burning shell may have extinguished temporarily.) Later in this phase, the hydrogen shell dominates, and the fresh production of helium causes the helium-burning shell periodically to burst into life again. Thermal instabilities in the helium shell drive thermal pulses; this later phase is called the thermally pulsing **TP-AGB**. Several tens of pulses, each lasting only ~10^2 years, may occur for a star at intervals of ~10^4 years, and it is during these pulses that conditions appear suitable for s-process nucleosynthesis. This process, which you will study in Section 8.1, is responsible for the production of many of the elements heavier than iron.

As a star becomes very luminous on the AGB, mass loss becomes more and more significant. A **superwind** may develop in which a substantial fraction of the mass is carried off the star. In some cases this corresponds to most of the hydrogen envelope! One consequence of extreme mass loss is the formation of a planetary nebula, which is the topic of Section 7.1. Another effect is that even intermediate-mass stars, which had main-sequence masses $3M_\odot \lesssim M_{ms} \lesssim 8M_\odot$, end up with a mass $M \lesssim 1.4M_\odot$. The significance of this final mass will become clear once we study white dwarfs in Section 7.2 and massive stars in Section 7.3.

■   What underlying process distinguishes an asymptotic-giant-branch star from a first ascent red-giant branch star? Does this distinction hold perfectly in all cases?

❑   Stars on their first ascent of the giant branch burn only hydrogen in a shell, while AGB stars burn helium in a shell as well. For stars *late* in their AGB phase, helium burning periodically diminishes and re-ignites, in thermal pulses. This late phase of evolution is called the thermally pulsing asymptotic giant branch (TP-AGB) phase. ■

6.8 Summary of Section 6

1   The Big Bang produced ^{1}H, ^{2}H, ^{3}He, ^{4}He and ^{7}Li only. Nucleosynthesis of heavier elements was prevented by (i) the Coulomb barriers of elements with higher atomic numbers, (ii) the lack of stable isotopes of mass number 5 and 8, and (iii) the decreasing density of matter as the Universe expanded. The production of all other elements required the formation of stars.

2   The gravitationally contracting helium cores of stars with $M \gtrsim 0.5 M_\odot$ become hot enough to ignite helium burning, which requires $T \approx 1\text{–}2 \times 10^8$ K. As there are no stable isotopes of mass number 5 or 8, helium burning proceeds via a temporary ^{8}Be nucleus. A tiny fraction of the ^{8}Be nuclei fuse with another helium nucleus to form an excited state of ^{12}C, a tiny fraction of which then decays (de-excites) to the ^{12}C ground state. The production rate of ground-state ^{12}C is the equilibrium number density of the excited state divided by the decay lifetime: $dn_{12}/dt = n_{12*}/\tau(^{12}\text{C*} \to ^{12}\text{C})$.

3   The thermodynamic properties of a gas are described by its temperature T, pressure P, and chemical potential μ'. The chemical potential is a measure of the internal energy of the particles; $\mu' = mc^2 - kT\ln(g_s n_{\text{QNR}}/n)$ (for non-relativistic particles). The first term is the mass-energy equivalent $E = mc^2$ of each particle. The second term comprises a thermal energy, the number of polarizations g_s for each particle, the number of gas particles per unit volume, and $n_{\text{QNR}} = (2\pi mkT/h^2)^{3/2}$, the (non-relativistic) quantum concentration which reflects the number of available quantum states.

4   The sum of chemical potentials on one side of an equilibrium reaction equals the sum of chemical potentials on the other side.

5   While hydrogen burning converts 0.66% of proton mass into energy, the triple-alpha process converts only 0.065% of the helium mass, a factor of ten lower. Helium burning therefore liberates *at most a tenth* of the energy that hydrogen burning does. This, and the fact that they are brighter during helium burning, explains why stars' helium-burning lifetimes are less than one-tenth of their main sequence lifetimes.

6   Helium burning also produces oxygen from the fresh ^{12}C via ^{12}C$(\alpha, \gamma)^{16}$O. The nuclear S-factor and hence the rate of this reaction is one of the most important uncertainties in stellar astrophysics.

7   The number of quantum states available to particles is often very large, but nevertheless finite. In the very dense interiors of some astronomical objects, the finite number of available quantum states is insufficient for the huge number of particles squeezed into the confined volume.

8   Degeneracy can be described in three equivalent ways:
   *   when the separation of particles is less than the de Broglie wavelength for their momentum, $\lambda_{\text{dB}} = h/p \approx h/(mkT)^{1/2}$.
   *   when the number of particles per unit volume, n, is higher than n_{Q}, the quantum concentration, which is the number of quantum states available to particles whose velocities conform to a Maxwell–Boltzmann distribution
   *   when the temperature of the particles is much less than the value $h^2 n^{2/3}/(2\pi mk)$. Sometimes a degenerate gas is described as cold, but this can be misleading.

9 Electrons in the Sun are non-relativistic ($kT \ll m_e c^2$) and classical ($n_e \ll n_{QNR}$), but $n_e/n_{QNR} \propto R^{-3/2}$, so as the core contracts, the gas approaches degeneracy.

10 Electrons, along with protons and neutrons, are fermions. The Pauli exclusion principle dictates that no more than one identical fermion can occupy a given quantum state. As spin ($\pm 1/2$) is the only way to distinguish one fermion of a given type from another, at most two can occupy a given quantum state. In a cold electron gas, the energy μ' of the most energetic degenerate electron is called the Fermi energy, ε_F, and its momentum p_F is called the Fermi momentum.

11 Whereas the equation of state for a classical ideal gas depends on the density *and* temperature, e.g. $P = nkT$, for a degenerate gas it depends only on the density: $P_{NR} = K_{NR} n^{5/3}$ and $P_{UR} = K_{UR} n^{4/3}$ where K_{NR} and K_{UR} are constants for non-relativistic and ultra-relativistic conditions. This decoupling of pressure and temperature in degenerate gas disables thermostatic regulation. A classical gas responds to an increased temperature by increasing pressure and hence expanding and cooling slightly. In a degenerate gas a thermonuclear runaway can develop.

12 Stars with $M \lesssim 2.5 M_\odot$ become electron-degenerate in their cores once core hydrogen burning ends, and a hydrogen-burning shell develops. Degenerate electrons then provide the pressure support. When helium-burning ignites, the pressure of degenerate gas does not respond to the increased temperature. A thermonuclear runaway called the helium flash occurs. Most of the released energy goes into expanding and heating the core, which lifts the electron degeneracy, rather than into the luminous power of the star. Pressure and temperature recouple through the equation of state of a classical gas.

13 The helium flash terminates the red giant branch evolution of stars with $M \lesssim 2.5 M_\odot$. The core helium burning low-mass star becomes a red giant clump star or horizontal branch star depending on whether it has a solar or substantially sub-solar metal abundance and the extent of mass loss.

14 For $M \gtrsim 2.5 M_\odot$, the thermal runaway/helium flash is avoided. Helium ignition leads to an expansion of the core and hydrogen-burning shell, the temperature at the base of the envelope decreases, and the envelope contracts, driving up the effective temperature. That is, $M \gtrsim 2.5 M_\odot$ stars initiate blue loops in the H–R diagram.

15 Energy generation for the triple-alpha process varies as T^{30}. A helium-burning shell develops around the new carbon core, beyond which the hydrogen-burning shell burns gradually closer towards the surface, causing the hydrogen envelope to expand and cool. The stars move back towards their helium-ignition points in the H–R diagram as asymptotic giant branch (AGB) stars.

16 On the AGB, low-mass stars ($M \lesssim 3.5 M_\odot$) increase in luminosity as convection again becomes important in energy transport; intermediate mass stars ($3.5 \lesssim M/M_\odot \lesssim 8$) reverse their blue loops and deepening convection causes an increase in luminosity and the second dredge-up. Thermal instabilities in the helium shell drive pulses during the thermally pulsing-AGB (TP-AGB) phase. Several tens of pulses, each lasting only 10^2 years, may occur at intervals of $\approx 10^4$ years, and s-process nucleosynthesis may occur.

7 LATE STAGES OF STELLAR EVOLUTION

We have followed the evolution of stars through their formation and hydrogen- and helium-burning stages. In this section we investigate the ejection of a planetary nebula, the white dwarf remnants, and nucleosynthesis stages late in the evolution of more-massive stars.

7.1 Planetary nebulae

The mass lost from stars at the end of their AGB phase is not immediately visible. In fact, initially the star becomes obscured by the formation of dust grains in the cool ejecta. However, the underlying helium-rich star (with a degenerate carbon and oxygen core) gets smaller and hotter, and a fast, radiation-driven wind develops that induces additional mass loss in a bipolar outflow. Such an object may be described as a *proto*planetary nebula. Two protoplanetary nebulae are shown in the top two images of Figure 44, where the breakout of the fast bipolar wind[7] is visible along with the fainter concentric shells of material previously ejected by the star.

The central star continues to get smaller and hotter, while the nebula expands at typically 30–60 km s^{-1}. Once the central star's surface temperature reaches $T_{\text{eff}} \approx 10\,000$ K, it ionizes the ejected envelope, which is then seen as a planetary nebula.

High-resolution images of the slowly ejected material reveal concentric shells, showing that although the slower ejection is omni-directional, it is not smooth, which is to say the ejection must be episodic. For example, see especially IRAS 17150–3224 in Figure 44, and Figure 45; see also Figure 46.

Figure 44 (*Top row*) Protoplanetary nebulae ($\lesssim 1000$ years old). Concentric shells have been episodically ejected from the AGB star – these are especially obvious in IRAS 17150–3224 – obscuring the central star with newly formed dust. The star is not yet hot enough to ionize the nebula. The fast, radiation driven wind is just beginning to break out. (*Bottom row*) Planetary nebulae (2500–7000 years old). The central star is now visible and sufficiently hot ($T \gtrsim 10\,000$ K) to ionize the nebula. The central star of NGC 6818 has a temperature $T \approx 50\,000$ K. These two nebulae have diameters of ~20 000 AU (300 times the diameter of the Solar System) and 55 000 AU (1000 times the diameter of the Solar System) respectively.

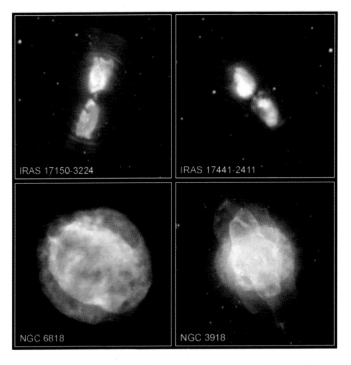

[7] Recall that bipolar outflows are also seen at the other end of the evolutionary lifetime, during protostellar collapse (Section 2.3).

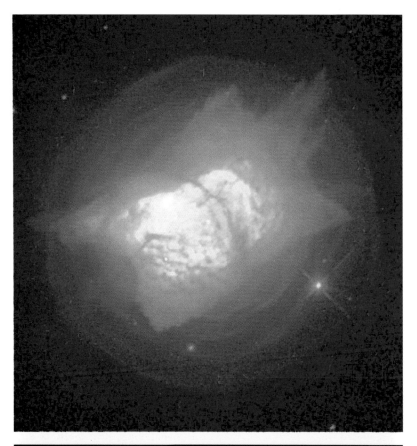

Figure 45 Planetary nebula NGC 7027. The temperature of the central star is $T \approx 90\,000$ K, and the nebula diameter is ~20 000 AU. The outer part of the nebula shows the concentric shells of material episodically ejected from the AGB star. The centre of the image is dominated by the fast ejection of deeper layers of the star.

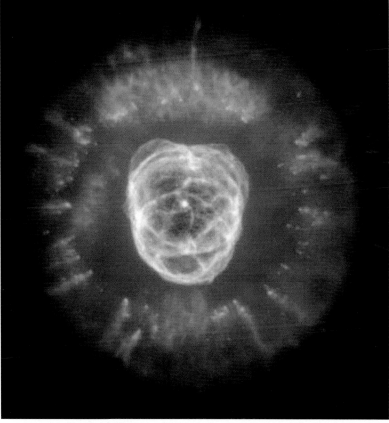

Figure 46 Planetary nebula, NGC 2392 (The Eskimo nebula), ~10 000 years old and with a central star temperature $T \approx 40\,000$ K. The comet-like features around the outer part of the nebula are possibly where fast-moving wind particles are overtaking slower moving matter that was ejected earlier.

The hydrogen-burning shell (if any hydrogen remains) is extinguished when it gets too close to the surface and hence too cool, and the same happens eventually to the helium-burning shell. What is left is a hot C/O core ($X_O \approx 80\%$) surrounded by hot helium, but all nuclear burning has been extinguished, and there is no prospect of thermonuclear reactions being re-ignited. Observations show that although the nebula continues to expand, once the central star reaches $T_{eff} \approx 100\,000$ K it ceases to increase in temperature, drops in luminosity, and begins a long slide to lower luminosity and temperature at almost constant radius (Figure 47). The star has entered the realm of the cooling, white dwarfs, which you will study in the next section.

From the angular extent and distance of a planetary nebula, its physical diameter can be derived. As the expansion velocity of the nebula gas (typically 30–60 km s^{-1}) can be measured by its Doppler shift, the duration of the expansion and hence of the post-AGB phase can be calculated. By extrapolating the observed expansion of the nebula backwards, it is shown that the whole evolution of a planetary nebula lasts only about 20 000 years.

Although a standard picture of planetary nebulae has been presented here, it should be noted that the morphology of these objects is complex, and a topic of ongoing study. In particular, binary-star physics may be an important factor in shaping the evolution and structure of these objects. The final activity of this section encourages you to explore this further.

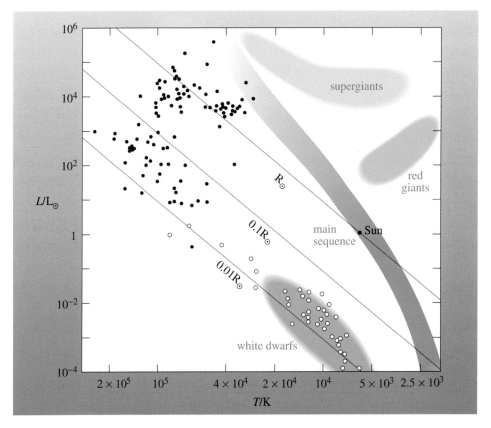

Figure 47 H–R diagram showing the locations of the central stars of planetary nebulae (filled circles) and white dwarfs (open circles). Lines corresponding to stars having radii $R = R_\odot$, $0.1R_\odot$ and $0.01R_\odot$ are shown.

Images of planetary nebulae

Use the Image Archive to find several images of planetary nebulae, and read the captions attached to images. Using information in the captions, attempt to assemble a list of ages, sizes, and/or expansion velocities. (You may have to estimate some of these values from the nebula's diameter and assuming a typical expansion velocity of 50 km s^{-1}.) Note the different appearances of young and old planetary nebulae, where the typical lifetime is 20 000 years.

Keywords: none ■

- Ejection of the stellar envelope becomes significant during the AGB phase. Why isn't the nebula seen until the central star has a surface temperature of 10 000 K?

- The hydrogen in the nebula emits light only once its atoms become ionized and then the electrons recombine with their nuclei. Hydrogen atoms do not become ionized until they are irradiated with ultraviolet photons of sufficiently high energy to remove the electron from the atom, which takes 13.6 eV. The hotter a black body is, the shorter the wavelength and the higher the energy of the photons it radiates. It is not until the surface temperature of the central star reaches 10 000 K that sufficiently high-energy UV photons to ionize the hydrogen are radiated. ■

7.2 White dwarfs

In this subsection you will study Section 6.1 of Phillips, but it is recommended that you begin your study of the topic using this Study Guide. The Study Guide includes some cross-references to equations in Phillips Chapter 6 that you will meet in the subsequent reading activity (Activity 37).

7.2.1 The Chandrasekhar mass

This topic draws on several areas you have already studied, including stellar structure and electron degeneracy. In the first reading, Phillips examines the density at the centre of a degenerate star to determine whether it is relativistic or non-relativistic. In the relativistic limit, he derives an important limiting mass for stars, the Chandrasekhar mass, which divides stable white dwarfs from higher mass objects that cannot be supported by electron degeneracy. The collapse of the latter objects therefore proceeds further than the white dwarfs; we meet them again in Section 8, when we study neutron stars and black holes.

From your study of reaction rates (Example 5), you will be familiar with the general equation (Equation 23) for the number density n_A of some type of particle A in terms of its mass fraction X_A, the particle mass m_A, and the gas density ρ:

$$n_A = \rho X_A / m_A$$

We can write this for electrons just as easily as for nucleons: $n_e = \rho X_e / m_e$.

However, it is more convenient to write

$$X_e \equiv Y_e m_e / m_H \qquad (34)$$

where Y_e is the number of electrons per nucleon.

This leads to the expression

$$n_e = \rho Y_e / m_H \tag{35}$$

■ What is the value of Y_e in (a) pure ionized hydrogen, (b) pure ionized helium?

❑ (a) Hydrogen has one electron and one nucleon (its proton), so $Y_e = 1$.

(b) Helium has two electrons and four nucleons (two protons and two neutrons), so $Y_e = 0.5$ for helium. ■

You can readily convince yourself that $Y_e = 0.5$ for the dominant isotopes of ^{4}He, ^{12}C, and ^{16}O. In fact, $Y_e \approx (1 + X_H)/2$.

For white dwarfs the amount of hydrogen is negligible – it has all been burnt to helium or on to carbon and/or oxygen – so for white dwarfs, $Y_e \approx 0.5$.

For an electron-degenerate gas, you know that the pressure is independent of temperature, and is given by a constant multiplied by some power of the electron density. The constant and the power both depend on whether the degenerate gas is non-relativistic or ultra-relativistic;

- for non-relativistic gas, $P_{NR} = K_{NR} n_e^{5/3}$ while
- for ultra-relativistic gas, $P_{UR} = K_{UR} n_e^{4/3}$

The values of the constants are $K_{NR} = \dfrac{h^2}{5m_e} \left(\dfrac{3}{8\pi}\right)^{2/3}$ and $K_{UR} = \dfrac{hc}{4} \left(\dfrac{3}{8\pi}\right)^{1/3}$.

Using Equation 35, we can write

- for non-relativistic gas, $P_{NR} = K_{NR}(\rho Y_e / m_H)^{5/3}$
- while for ultra-relativistic gas, $P_{UR} = K_{UR}(\rho Y_e / m_H)^{4/3}$

A particular model (by D. D. Clayton) for the internal structure of a star gives the central pressure required to support a star as:

$$P_c \approx (\pi/36)^{1/3} G M^{2/3} \rho_c^{4/3} \qquad \text{(Phillips 5.33)}$$

(The derivation is outside the scope of this course.) By saying that degenerate electrons *provide* the required internal pressure to support the star, i.e. by equating this to the degenerate electron pressure, it is possible to write these equations purely in terms of the mass and central density, which therefore allows us to write one variable in terms of the other.

Question 39   30 minutes

(a) By equating the central pressure in a star to the degenerate pressure of non-relativistic electrons, derive an expression for the central density in terms of its mass M and the number of electrons per nucleon, Y_e. Leave physical constants unevaluated.

(*Hint*: Use the expression for the central pressure from Clayton's stellar model.)

(b) Write your answer to (a) in terms of M/M_*, where M_* is a (large) unit of mass whose value is given by[8]

$$M_* = \left(\frac{Gm_{\mathrm{H}}^2}{\hbar c}\right)^{-3/2} m_{\mathrm{H}}$$

Hint: To express the result in terms of M/M_*, multiply your answer to (a) by

$$\left(\left(\frac{Gm_{\mathrm{H}}^2}{\hbar c}\right)^{-3/2} m_{\mathrm{H}} \bigg/ M_*\right)^2$$

i.e. by 1, and then cancel whichever terms you can.

(c) Using the relation between electron number density n_{e} and gas density ρ_{c} in the centre of the star, express the central electron density as a function of stellar mass.

(d) Evaluate M_* in solar mass units.

(e) Rewrite your answer for part (c) using the value from (d). ■

Question 39 shows that in the non-relativistic case, the degenerate electron density in the centre of a star may be written

$$n_{\mathrm{e}} = \frac{250}{81}\left(\frac{m_{\mathrm{e}}c}{h}\right)^3 \frac{1}{Y_{\mathrm{e}}^4}\left(\frac{M/M_{\odot}}{1.85}\right)^2 \qquad \text{(Phillips 6.1 with 6.4)}$$

Phillips asks whether this material really is non-relativistic. The **Fermi kinetic energy** E_{FK} of degenerate electrons is given by $E_{\mathrm{FK}} \approx p_{\mathrm{F}}^2/2m$ (in the purely non-relativistic case) where p_{F} is the Fermi momentum given by $(3n_{\mathrm{e}}/8\pi)^{1/3}h$ (Phillips 2.27). Therefore, the Fermi kinetic energy of the degenerate, non-relativistic electrons in the centre of a white dwarf is

$$E_{\mathrm{FK}} \approx \left[\left(\frac{3}{8\pi}n_{\mathrm{e}}\right)^{1/3}h\right]^2 \frac{1}{2m}$$

$$\approx \left[\frac{3}{8\pi}\frac{250}{81}\left(\frac{m_{\mathrm{e}}c}{h}\right)^3 \frac{1}{Y_{\mathrm{e}}^4}\left(\frac{M/M_{\odot}}{1.85}\right)^2\right]^{2/3}\frac{h^2}{2m_{\mathrm{e}}}$$

$$\approx \frac{1}{2}\left[\frac{750}{648\pi}\frac{1}{Y_{\mathrm{e}}^4}\left(\frac{M/M_{\odot}}{1.85}\right)^2\right]^{2/3} m_{\mathrm{e}}c^2$$

For white dwarfs, $Y_{\mathrm{e}} \approx 0.5$. Evaluating the expression for a low-mass white dwarf with $M = 0.4M_{\odot}$, the Fermi kinetic energy is $E_{\mathrm{FK}} = 0.21m_{\mathrm{e}}c^2$. (Phillips gives $0.19m_{\mathrm{e}}c^2$, where the slightly lower coefficient results from using the special-relativistic relation between kinetic energy E_{KE} and momentum p: $E_{\mathrm{K}} + mc^2 = [(pc)^2 + (mc^2)^2]^{1/2}$.) This is already 21% of the rest energy, which makes it doubtful that the non-relativistic treatment is reliable for a white dwarf with $M \gtrsim 0.4M_{\odot}$. In more massive white dwarfs the Fermi kinetic energy is higher (since $E_{\mathrm{FK}} \propto M^{4/3}$)

[8] Phillips introduces M_* as 'the fundamental stellar mass'. It would be possible to derive these equations without referring to M_*, as many other textbooks do, but we retain it to maintain comparability with Phillips' equations. There is nothing mysterious about the number; it is just a constant with a conveniently large value for stellar analysis.

and the non-relativistic treatment will be progressively worse. If we consider a white dwarf with $M = 1.3M_\odot$, even the purely non-relativistic treatment indicates $E_{FK} \approx m_e c^2$, indicating that the ultra-relativistic treatment is required.

Question 40   **15 minutes**

(a) By equating the central pressure in a star to the degenerate pressure of ultra-relativistic electrons, derive an expression for the mass of a star supported by ultra-relativistic electrons, in terms of the other physical quantities.

(*Hint*: This is similar to Question 39, but for ultra-relativistic electrons.)

(b) Evaluate the mass, assuming $Y_e = 0.5$, in SI units and solar masses. ■

The discussion following Question 39 showed that as the mass of a white dwarf is increased, the matter becomes more relativistic.

> The mass for the star when the ultra-relativistic limit is reached should be viewed as the maximum stellar mass which can be supported by degenerate electron pressure. This extremely important limiting mass is called the **Chandrasekhar mass**.

We improve the numerical value derived in Question 40 below.

If the mass is increased further, the pressure *needed* to support the star, given by $P_c \approx (\pi/36)^{1/3} GM^{2/3} \rho_c^{4/3}$ (Phillips 5.33) also increases, but the ultra-relativistic degenerate electrons will not be able to increase their pressure to support it. Something has to give … . That something is the material supporting the star. There *is* a stable configuration of material at higher mass, but it is not degenerate electrons. Rather, the electrons and protons of higher mass objects are forced to combine as neutrons, and the stable object above the maximum white dwarf mass is called a neutron star. We study such objects in Section 8.3.

Question 41

Question 39 and Question 40 assumed the central pressure needed to support a star of mass M was given by Clayton's model, $P_c \approx (\pi/36)^{1/3} GM^{2/3} \rho_c^{4/3}$ (Phillips 5.33). A more realistic calculation gives a slightly lower pressure, about 87% of this (see Phillips Figure 5.2 (page 156)). Revise Question 40 using this lower pressure, and improve your estimate for the maximum mass of a white dwarf. ■

The most realistic computations estimate the Chandrasekhar mass as $1.4M_\odot$. We examine later what happens to a star whose remnant exceeds the Chandrasekhar mass.

Activity 37   **40 minutes**

The Chandrasekhar mass

Read Phillips, Chapter 6, up to the beginning of the subsection 'Mass and radius' (page 171–177). *Skip* the material from Equation 6.10 to the bottom of page 175.

Note the behaviour of the central density as a function of white dwarf mass, shown in Fig. 6.1 (page 176), and in particular that it becomes infinite as a star approaches the Chandrasekhar mass whereupon the electrons become ultra-relativistic.

Polytropic models (page 176) are a class of models in which the pressure at some radius is proportional to the density at that radius to some power, $P(r) \propto \rho(r)^{\gamma}$. Use of a polytropic model with $\gamma = 4/3$ would produce a slightly lower numerical value than the $(\pi/36)^{1/3}$ of Clayton's model, and hence implies a slightly larger value for the Chandrasekhar mass.

Keywords: **polytrope/polytropic model** ▨

■ Fig. 6.1 of Phillips shows that 0.1–0.8M_{Ch} white dwarfs have central densities of order 10^8–10^{10} kg m^{-3}. Convert these values into kg cm^{-3}, and think of some everyday objects with this volume (1 cm^3) and objects with this mass.

❑ 1 cm = 10^{-2} m, so 1 cm^3 = 10^{-6} m^3. Therefore the densities are 100–10 000 kg cm^{-3}. One cubic centimetre is about the size of a sugar cube or a finger tip. Objects with masses of 100 kg include adult people (typically 50–100 kg), and objects with masses 10 000 kg include lorries/trucks. So, the density 100 kg cm^{-3} would be like a sugar cube with the same mass as a large adult, and the density 10 000 kg cm^{-3} would be like a sugar cube with the same mass as a truck. ■

7.2.2 The white-dwarf mass–radius relation

The mean density of a star is $\langle \rho \rangle$ = mass/volume = $M/\frac{4}{3}\pi R^3$. It can be related to the central density if the density profile of the star is known, and in this context Phillips notes (as you will see in Activity 38) that for a star described by a polytropic model with $P \propto \rho^{5/3}$, the mean density is one-sixth of the central density: $\langle \rho \rangle = \rho_c/6$. It is therefore possible to write a relation between the radius, mass, and central density of a star. Where the central density is dictated by non-relativistic degenerate electrons, for which

$$\rho_c = \frac{3.1}{Y_e^5}\left(\frac{M/M_\odot}{1.85}\right)^2 \frac{m_H}{(h/m_e c)^3}$$ (Phillips 6.4)

we can eliminate the density, and find an expression for the radius of the object as a function of mass.

(a) Rearrange the definition of the mean density $\langle \rho \rangle = M/\frac{4}{3}\pi R^3$ to get an expression for the radius in terms of the mass and mean density.

(b) Use the result for a polytropic model with $P \propto \rho^{5/3}$, that $\langle \rho \rangle = \rho_c/6$, to re-express the radius in terms of mass and *central* density.

(c) Substitute in the expression for the central density of non-relativistic degenerate electrons, to derive an expression for the radius of a white dwarf as a function of mass. Give your final answer in units normalized to the solar mass and solar radius.

(d) Re-express the final result in solar masses and *Earth* radii. ■

The result of Question 42 is remarkable for two reasons:

$$R_{WD} = \frac{R_\odot}{74}\left(\frac{M}{M_\odot}\right)^{-1/3}$$

First, it shows that the radius of a white dwarf with the same mass as the Sun is almost 100 times smaller. White dwarfs are indeed very compact, comparable in radius to the Earth!

Second, note the mass-dependence of the white-dwarf radius: $R_{WD} \propto M^{-1/3}$. Compare this to the result for main-sequence stars which you derived in Question 25. There you found that for main-sequence stars burning hydrogen by the p-p chain, $R_{MS} \propto M^{2/5}$, while for CNO-cycling stars the relation was $R_{MS} \propto M^{4/5}$. Note the important result that the *sign* of the exponent is different for white dwarfs!

> While more-massive main-sequence stars have *larger* radii, more-massive white dwarfs have *smaller* radii!

Recall from Section 1 that it was possible to draw lines of constant radius on the H–R diagram. These are lines sloping from top-left to lower-right. As a white dwarf has a constant mass as it radiates away its energy, it is clear that it will gradually slide down one of these constant radius lines. (See Figure 47.) In the previous section you saw that the central stars of planetary nebulae were to be found at high luminosities and high temperatures, in the top-left of the H–R diagram. The next stage of evolution of these stars is therefore a gradual decent along a line of constant radius in the H–R diagram, which we study over the next few subsections.

Activity 38	20 minutes

White dwarfs

Read Phillips, Section 6.1, subsection 'Mass and radius', to the end of page 179 (pages 177–179) ignoring the material on the gravitational redshift (page 180). Much of this material will already be familiar to you, as we have derived some of the results above.

Keywords: none ■

■ Substitute $R_\odot$ from the mass–radius relation of white dwarfs into the luminosity–radius–effective temperature relation $L = 4\pi R^2 \sigma T_{eff}^4$ to indicate how bright a $1 M_\odot$, solar-temperature white dwarf is.

❑ $L_{WD} = 4\pi R_{WD}^2 \sigma T_{eff,WD}^4 \approx 4\pi \left(\dfrac{R_\odot}{74}\right)^2 \left(\dfrac{M_{WD}}{M_\odot}\right)^{-1/3} \sigma T_{eff,WD}^4$

For $M_{WD} = 1 M_\odot$ and $T_{eff,WD} = T_{eff,\odot}$ this becomes

$$L_{WD} \approx 4\pi \left(\frac{R_\odot}{74}\right)^2 \sigma T_{eff,\odot}^4$$

Since $L_\odot \approx 4\pi R_\odot^2 \sigma T_{eff,\odot}^4$, we can write $L_{WD} \approx \left(\dfrac{1}{74}\right)^2 L_\odot$

i.e. a $1 M_\odot$, solar-temperature white dwarf is approximately 5500 times fainter than the Sun. ■

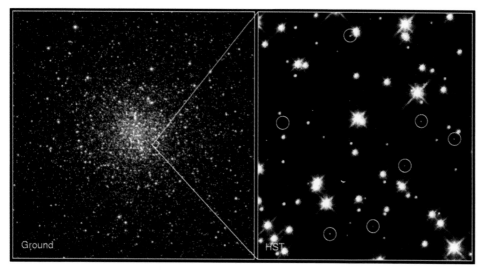

Figure 48 (*Left*) The old globular cluster M4, which is $\approx 13 \times 10^9$ yr old and contains more than 100 000 stars, was the target of a Hubble Space Telescope search for white dwarf stars. Ancient red giant stars are predominant in this view from a ground-based telescope. The field is 47 light-years across. The box (right of centre) shows the small area that the Hubble Space Telescope probed. (*Right*) This image from the Hubble Space Telescope shows a small portion of the cluster only 0.63 light-years across, and reveals seven white dwarf stars (inside circles) among the cluster's much brighter population of yellow Sun-like stars and cooler red dwarf stars. The cluster is expected to contain about 40 000 white dwarfs in total. The Hubble results will allow astronomers to refine theoretical predictions of the rate at which white dwarfs cool. This is an important prerequisite for making reliable estimates for the age of the Universe and of our Milky Way galaxy, based on white dwarf temperatures.

Figure 48 shows how faint the white dwarfs in the globular cluster M4 are compared to the main-sequence and red-giant stars.

Activity 39   **30 minutes**

Simplified theory versus detailed models

Phillips expression for the mass–radius relation of white dwarfs,

$$R_{WD} \approx \frac{R_\odot}{74} \left(\frac{M}{M_\odot} \right)^{-1/3}$$

(Phillips 6.23)

differs from the Nauenberg formula given in Block 1:

$$R_{WD} = 7.83 \times 10^6 \times \left(\left(\frac{1.44}{M_1} \right)^{2/3} - \left(\frac{M_1}{1.44} \right)^{2/3} \right)^{1/2}$$

Use the spreadsheet to plot these two functions together, to compare them on one graph.

If you still have the spreadsheet file in which you plotted the Nauenberg formula in Block 1, simply add an extra column containing the Phillips formula. You will then need to either regenerate the chart, this time plotting two curves, or else edit the existing one to include the second data series. If you have not kept the original file, you will need to generate it again. ■

155

■ Compare the two plots you have just produced in Activity 39. Why do you think they differ?

❑ The two curves are most alike, both in the values for the radius and the way it decreases with increasing mass, for $M \lesssim 0.5M_\odot$, but diverge for higher masses. Recall that Phillips' derivation was based on the assumption that the electrons are non-relativistic, which we showed is incorrect as M approaches $1.3M_\odot$. Furthermore, a star is unsupportable at the Chandrasekhar mass, $1.4M_\odot$, and approaches infinite density (zero radius). The Nauenberg formula gives a more accurate picture of the *radius* of white dwarfs, but it is a fitting formula designed to give you the right result without any explanation of why. The Phillips formula, while unable to correctly describe white dwarfs near the Chandrasekhar mass, does encapsulate real *physical ideas* which are valid for low-mass stars. There is a place in science for both! ■

7.2.3 Fading (and cooling) of white dwarfs

As there are no nuclear energy sources active in a white dwarf, its luminosity is due solely to the slow leakage of thermal energy into space, as radiation. That is, $L = -dE/dt$, where the minus sign indicates that the luminosity is positive when the star is losing energy (dE/dt is negative). This equation can be developed into an expression for the time dependence of the luminosity, which shows that $L \propto t^{-7/5}$. (The proof is beyond the scope of this course.) It takes $\sim 10^9$ yr for white dwarfs to fade to $L \sim 10^{-3}L_\odot$. As white dwarfs fade, they also cool.

■ Consider the time evolution of the white dwarf luminosity, $L \propto t^{-7/5}$. What does this indicate about their rate of evolution in the H–R diagram?

❑ White dwarfs decrease in brightness rapidly at the start, but more slowly later on. Therefore they pile up towards the bottom of the H–R diagram. By seeing how bright the faintest white dwarfs are, it is possible to infer the age of the stellar population to which they belong. ■

■ Why do we say that the luminosity of white dwarfs is provided by thermal leakage rather than slow gravitational contraction?

❑ White dwarfs are degenerate, so their temperature and pressure are decoupled As they cool, the pressure is unchanged so the radius is unchanged. This is why they cool and fade in the H–R diagram along a line of constant radius. If the radius is constant, there is *no* release of gravitational potential energy. ■

7.3 Carbon, neon, oxygen and silicon burning in massive ($M \gtrsim 8M_\odot$) stars

In Section 6, we examined helium burning, which converts helium into carbon and/or oxygen. The degree of oxygen production depends on the $^{12}C(\alpha, \gamma)^{16}O$ reaction which is more significant at higher temperatures, i.e. in more massive stars. We followed low- and intermediate-mass helium-burning stars through the planetary nebula phase, and in this section have examined their final evolution to become white dwarfs. However, we have yet to deal with massive stars whose energy generation does not finish with helium burning. More advanced stages of nucleosynthesis in massive objects will be discussed in this subsection.

Advanced burning

Read Phillips Section 4.4 'Advanced burning' (page 136–139) to learn about the fusion reactions (besides hydrogen burning and helium burning) that occur in $M_{ms} \gtrsim 8M_\odot$ stars.

Keywords: **carbon burning, neon burning, oxygen burning, silicon burning, silicon melting, photodisintegration reaction, nuclear binding energy** ■

The temperatures for the onset of various stages of nuclear burning cannot be regarded as absolute, because reaction rates increase gradually with temperature and also depend on the density of the material in which fusion occurs. A summary of typical values is given below:

carbon burning	$5–9 \times 10^8$ K
neon burning	$1–1.7 \times 10^9$ K
oxygen burning	$2–2.3 \times 10^9$ K
silicon burning	$3–4 \times 10^9$ K

■ What is the first reaction in silicon burning, and why does it happen?

❑ The first reaction is a photodissociation of ^{28}Si, being ^{28}Si$(\gamma, \alpha)^{24}$Mg (Phillips 4.75). It happens because the gravitationally contracting silicon core becomes so hot that the thermal blackbody photons have γ-ray energies. ■

■ Once some silicon is photodissociated, what is the main type of reaction that follows? What simple ratio exists between the number of protons and the number of neutrons in the nuclei produced? (Note that silicon has an atomic number $Z = 14$.)

❑ The liberated α-particles begin to combine with remaining ^{28}Si nuclei in a series of (α, γ) reactions one after another, giving the reaction chain

$$^{28}_{14}\text{Si}(\alpha,\gamma)^{32}_{16}\text{S}(\alpha,\gamma)^{36}_{18}\text{Ar}(\alpha,\gamma)^{40}_{20}\text{Ca}(\alpha,\gamma)^{44}_{22}\text{Ti}(\alpha,\gamma)^{48}_{24}\text{Cr}(\alpha,\gamma)^{52}_{26}\text{Fe}(\alpha,\gamma)^{56}_{28}\text{Ni}$$

Since ^{28}Si has the same number of protons ($Z = 14$) and neutrons ($N = A - Z = 28 - 14 = 14$), and α-particles have the same number of neutrons as protons ($Z = 2$ and $N = A - Z = 4 - 2 = 2$), then so do the major products of the silicon-burning (α, γ) reactions. ■

From the reading and Phillips' Table 4.2, note the increasing ignition temperatures and decreasing timescales for burning of carbon, neon, oxygen and silicon. In particular, neon and oxygen burning last only a few years or months, in great contrast to the long time spent undergoing hydrogen burning.

By the time stars of main-sequence mass $M_{ms} = 8M_\odot$ approach carbon ignition late in their life, mass loss has stripped them of $\approx 80\%$ of their mass, with only $\approx 1.4M_\odot$ remaining. The similarity of this mass to the Chandrasekhar mass is no mere coincidence. Recall from Section 7.2.1 and Activity 39 that electron-degenerate white dwarfs approach infinite density at this mass. Only stellar cores that continue to collapse attain the temperatures necessary to ignite carbon. Intermediate mass stars, with $3M_\odot \lesssim M_{ms} \lesssim 8M_\odot$ lose so much mass as giants that only $M < 1.4M_\odot$ remains to form the white dwarf. These CO cores are supported against further collapse by degenerate electrons, and hence do not attain the temperatures required to initiate carbon burning. They leave **CO white dwarfs** as remnants. (These white dwarfs may later become supernovae if they can acquire additional matter from a close companion star.)

There is a narrow range of massive stars, $8M_\odot \lesssim M_{ms} \lesssim 11M_\odot$, whose remaining cores are massive enough to collapse and ignite carbon, but which ultimately fall below the Chandrasekhar mass due to continued mass loss. When carbon burning terminates they will be supported by degenerate electrons again and will contract no further, leaving oxygen–neon–magnesium **ONeMg white dwarfs**.

Stars initially having $M_{ms} \gtrsim 11M_\odot$ retain enough mass during mass loss that their cores continue to exceed the Chandrasekhar mass, and at the end of each burning phase their cores contract and heat up more. These stars complete all advanced burning phases including silicon burning.

■   What distinguishes helium white dwarfs, CO white dwarfs, and ONeMg white dwarfs?

❑   A helium white dwarf is the end point of the evolution of a very low-mass star ($M_{ms} \lesssim 0.5M_\odot$) in which helium burning (by the helium flash) has not occurred. A CO white dwarf is the end point of low and intermediate-mass stars ($0.5M_\odot \lesssim M_{ms} \lesssim 8M_\odot$) in which helium burning occurred, producing carbon and oxygen in the core. ONeMg white dwarfs result from the lightest high-mass stars ($8M_\odot \lesssim M_{ms} \lesssim 11M_\odot$) in which carbon burning has occurred, producing Ne and Mg, but which have not burnt neon or oxygen. ■

The final stage of burning, silicon burning, lasts only a day! It begins with the photodisintegration (by thermal photons) of some fraction of the ^{28}Si produced previously by oxygen burning. The α-particles (^{4}He nuclei) released in these disintegrations can then combine with remaining ^{28}Si nuclei. As Phillips notes, this happens in conditions close to thermodynamic equilibrium, so the differences in binding energy determine the equilibrium ratios of the nuclei involved in the reactions. The equilibrium reactions are governed by a **Boltzmann factor** with the relative nuclear abundances given by $n_A n_\alpha / n_{(A+\alpha)} \propto \exp(-Q/kT)$ where Q is the energy released in the α-capture. Where Q is positive (i.e. energy is in fact released) the exponential is <1, and hence favours formation of the heavier ($A + \alpha$) nucleus. Where Q is negative (i.e. energy is *absorbed* in the capture) the exponential is >1 and favours the separate A and α-particles to the ($A + \alpha$) nucleus. As the binding energy per nucleon peaks around $A = 56$ (see Figure 49), Q is positive for captures at $A < 56$ and negative for captures at $A > 56$. The equilibrium therefore drives the nuclei towards $A = 56$. Essentially, the nuclear abundances are rearranged, always favouring the production of more stable nuclei, and this accounts for the high abundance of nuclei near $A = 56$ – the iron peak. The process produces primarily $^{56}_{28}$Ni, which subsequently β$^+$-decays (inverse beta-decays) to $^{56}_{27}$Co, which in turn undergoes β$^+$-decay to $^{56}_{26}$Fe. Because the process is governed by thermodynamic equilibrium, the nuclei are said to be formed in a process of **nuclear statistical**

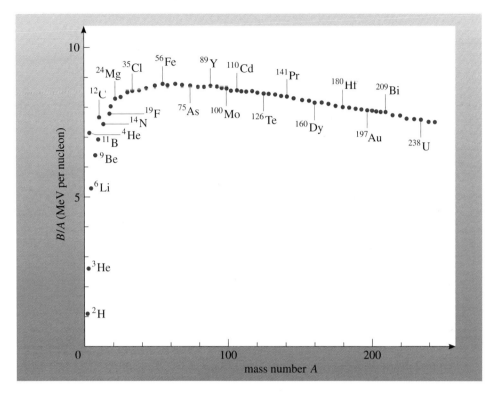

Figure 49 Nuclear binding energy per nucleon. Note that for $A \gtrsim 15$, this changes only slowly with atomic mass, but nevertheless has a peak around $A = 56$. This accounts for the build-up of elements near iron – the iron peak – during silicon burning.

equilibrium or **NSE**; unofficially, I like to think of it as natural selection for elements. This process produces elements from Si (the starting point) at atomic number $Z = 14$ up to the so-called **iron-peak nuclei** in the group between $Z = 22$ and 30: titanium (Ti), vanadium (V), chromium (Cr), manganese (Mn), iron (Fe), cobalt (Co), nickel (Ni), copper (Cu), and zinc (Zn).

By the end of the various burning phases, e.g. carbon burning, neon burning, oxygen burning, and silicon burning, the star has built up a series of shells of different composition (see Figure 50). The outermost shell is unprocessed hydrogen and helium, while the next shell contains helium from hydrogen burning. Progressively deeper shells are composed of carbon and oxygen from helium burning, neon, sodium and magnesium from carbon burning, oxygen and magnesium from neon burning, silicon from oxygen burning, and elements from silicon to the iron-peak elements from silicon burning in NSE. The stratification indicates that the core attained higher peak temperatures than layers further out, and the fact that at higher temperatures, fusion of nuclei with higher atomic numbers is possible. This layering is sometimes referred to as an **onion-skin structure**.

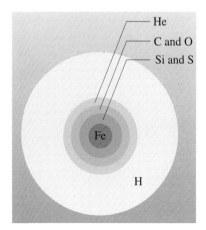

Figure 50 Schematic diagram (not to scale) of onion-skin structure of a massive star ($M \geq 10 M_\odot$) that has synthesized elements up to the iron peak in its core.

■ The next fusion process after carbon burning in massive stars is neon burning, which produces oxygen and magnesium, followed by oxygen burning to produce silicon. Why aren't silicon white dwarfs produced?

❑ Stars which are massive enough to burn neon and then oxygen exceed the Chandrasekhar mass, so they are too massive to leave white dwarf remnants. ■

7.4 Summary of Section 7

1   As AGB stars become very luminous, a superwind removes most of the hydrogen envelope. A *proto*planetary nebula develops as the mass-losing star becomes obscured by dust. The underlying helium-rich star gets smaller and hotter, developing a fast, radiation-driven wind that causes mass loss in a bipolar outflow.

2   Once the central star's surface temperature reaches $T_{eff} \approx 10\,000$ K, it ionizes the ejected envelope, which is then seen as a planetary nebula expanding at 30–60 km s^{-1}. The star's hydrogen burning and helium-burning shells (if any hydrogen remains) are extinguished when they get too close to the surface and hence too cool, leaving a hot, degenerate C/O core surrounded by hot helium, but with all nuclear burning extinguished. Once the central star reaches $T_{eff} \approx 100\,000$ K, it begins to fade and cool at almost constant radius as a white dwarf. The whole evolution of a planetary nebula lasts only about $20\,000$ years.

3   The number density n_A of some type of particle A can be written in terms of its mass fraction X_A, mass m_A and the gas density ρ, as $n_A = \rho X_A / m_A$. Hence $n_e = \rho Y_e / m_H$, where Y_e is the number of electrons per nucleon defined by $X_e \equiv Y_e m_e / m_H$. For hydrogen, $Y_e = 1$, whereas for helium, carbon and oxygen (and hence for white dwarfs), $Y_e = 0.5$. More generally, $Y_e \approx (1 + X_H)/2$.

4   By saying that degenerate electrons provide the pressure support of a star, it is possible to express the Fermi kinetic energy, E_{FK}, in terms of the mass.

  For *non-relativistic* degenerate electrons, $E_{FK} \propto M^{4/3}$, so degenerate electrons become more relativistic in more-massive white dwarfs.

  For *ultra-relativistic* degenerate electrons, the central density becomes infinite as the mass increases to the Chandrasekhar mass, $\approx 1.4 M_\odot$, the maximum value which can be supported by degenerate electron pressure.

5   By ascribing the central density of a star to non-relativistic degenerate electrons, a relation between the radius and mass of a white dwarf can be derived:

$$R_{WD} \approx (R_\odot/74)(M/M_\odot)^{-1/3}$$

almost 100 times smaller than the Sun and comparable to the radius of the Earth. While more-massive main-sequence stars have *larger* radii, more-massive white dwarfs have *smaller* radii! As the radius depends only on the mass, a white dwarf cools and fades along a line of constant radius in the H–R diagram.

6   Combining the mass-radius relation $R_{WD} \approx (R_\odot/74)(M/M_\odot)^{-1/3}$ with the luminosity–radius–effective temperature relation $L = 4\pi R^2 \sigma T_{eff}^4$ indicates that a white dwarf with the same mass and effective temperature as the Sun would be ≈ 5500 times fainter.

7   White dwarfs can tap neither nuclear nor gravitational energy sources, so are reservoirs of thermal energy which is lost at a rate $L = -dE/dt$. The time-dependence of the temperature and luminosity indicate that white dwarfs cool very slowly, reaching $L \sim 10^{-3} L_\odot$ after $\sim 10^9$ yr.

8   High-mass stars ($M_{ms} \gtrsim 8M_\odot$) become hot (and dense) enough in their cores to fuse carbon and heavier nuclei. The sequence of nucleosynthesis is:

carbon burning (at $5\text{–}9 \times 10^8$ K) on timescale ~ 600 yr:

^{12}C(^{12}C, α)^{20}Ne, ^{12}C(^{12}C, p)^{23}Na and ^{12}C(^{12}C, n)^{23}Mg

neon burning (at $1\text{–}1.7 \times 10^9$ K) on timescale ~ 1 yr:

^{20}Ne(γ, α)^{16}O and ^{20}Ne(α, γ)^{24}Mg

oxygen burning (at $2\text{–}2.3 \times 10^9$ K) on timescale ~ 6 months:

^{16}O(^{16}O, α)^{28}Si

silicon burning (at $3\text{–}4 \times 10^9$ K) on timescale ~ 1 day:

^{28}Si(γ, α)^{24}Mg

elements between silicon and the iron group in an equilibrium (NSE) between photodissociation and α-, p- and n-capture reactions.

9   The silicon burning equilibrium reactions are governed by a Boltzmann factor. When energy is *released* it favours formation of the heavier ($A + \alpha$) nucleus. Where energy is *absorbed* it favours separate A and α-particles. The binding energy per nucleon peaks around $A = 56$. The equilibrium therefore drives the nuclei towards $A = 56$, which accounts for the high abundance of nuclei near the iron peak.

10   By the end of silicon burning, the star has built up a series of shells of different composition.

8 NEUTRONS, SUPERNOVAE AND REMNANTS

This section completes our description of the nucleosynthesis of the elements and then presents the closing chapter in the life of massive stars. It considers the supernovae of massive stars and their compact remnants: neutron stars and (briefly) black holes.

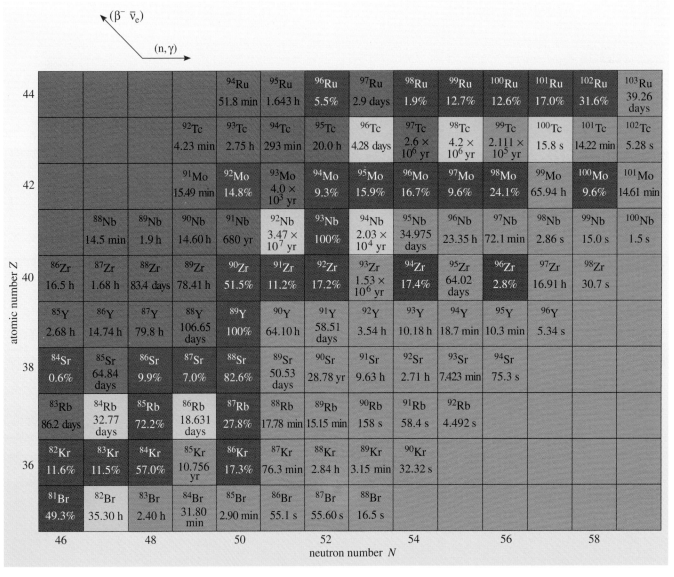

Figure 51 A small region of the chart of nuclides. Neutron number N increases from left to right, and atomic number Z increases from bottom to top. Stable nuclei are coloured grey. Isotopes are labelled according to their atomic mass number A, half-life (for unstable nuclei), and the percentage of the element accounted for by the isotope in the Solar System (for stable isotopes). For example, ^{88}Sr is a stable isotope with $N = 50$, $Z = 38$, $A = 88$, and accounts for 82.6% of Solar System strontium. ^{99}Tc is an unstable isotope with $N = 56$, $Z = 43$, $A = 99$, has a half-life of 2.111×10^5 yr, and decays by β^--decay.

The reactions pathways of (n, γ) and β^--decay $(\beta^- \, \bar{\nu}_e)$ are indicated. The coloured squares represent the major decay modes for the unstable nuclei. Blue represents β^--decay, dark pink is electron capture, and light pink is either β^--decay or electron capture.

8.1 Neutron-capture nucleosynthesis

Our discussion of fusion reactions concentrated on charged nuclei, but the heaviest elements cannot be produced that way. First, they would have to overcome huge Coulomb barriers which tend to keep positively charged nuclei apart. Second, silicon burning occurs in thermodynamic equilibrium, producing primarily nuclei with the highest binding energy per nucleon, i.e. around the iron peak. This produces elements up to $Z \approx 30$ (zinc), but with ≈ 100 elements in existence, many cannot be produced this way; some other process(es) must exist.

There is a series of reactions which avoids the Coulomb barrier completely, called **neutron-capture reactions**, where a single neutron is captured by a nucleus. Because the neutron is charge-neutral, there is no Coulomb barrier at all. This makes neutron capture a particularly important mechanism for the production of nuclei with high atomic number, especially as the Gamow energy that characterizes the Coulomb barrier increases as Z^2. Neutron-capture reactions are in fact the main mechanism for the nucleosynthesis of elements heavier than the iron peak. Neutron capture can also be important for some lighter elements.

8.1.1 The chart of nuclides

Nucleosynthesis pathways are often best visualized in the **chart of nuclides**. This plots each isotope separately, with atomic number, Z, on the vertical axis and neutron number, N, on the horizontal axis. It shows unstable as well as stable isotopes. A portion of the chart of nuclides is shown in Figure 51 (opposite), where colour distinguishes stable and unstable isotopes. Each increment along the vertical axis corresponds to a new element, e.g. hydrogen at $Z = 1$, helium at $Z = 2$, lithium at $Z = 3$, while each increment along the horizontal axis corresponds to a more neutron-rich isotope. Lines of constant atomic mass number, A, where $A = Z + N$, lie at 45° between upper-left and lower-right. Stable nuclei occupy a zone stretching from low N and Z to high N and Z, called the **valley of stability**. The valley is clearly seen in an alternative 3D view of the chart, Figure 52, where the binding energy per nucleon is added as the vertical axis. Many heavy elements have several stable isotopes spanning up to ≈ 10 units in N.

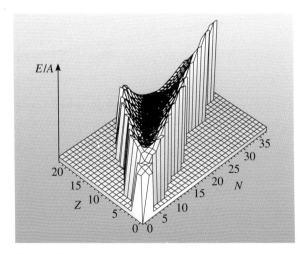

Figure 52 A three-dimensional view of the binding energy per nucleon as a function of atomic number Z and neutron number N, for elements up to calcium. The valley of stability is clearly illustrated.

8.1.2 Neutron capture and β^--decay

The capture of a free neutron by a nucleus, followed by the emission of a γ-ray, leads to a neutron-rich isotope of that same element. That is, although the neutron number N and the atomic mass A both increase by one, the atomic number Z, which is the number of protons in the nucleus, is unchanged. The symbol for an element X with these particle numbers is written $^A_Z X_N$, so the neutron capture reaction could be written

$$^A_Z X_N + \text{n} \rightarrow {}^{A+1}_Z X_{N+1} + \gamma$$

or equivalently

$$^A_Z X_N (\text{n}, \gamma)^{A+1}_Z X_{N+1}$$

Viewed in the chart of nuclides, it's just a jump to the right.

Neutron-rich isotopes are generally unstable. Even if they are not unstable after the addition of just *one* neutron, they will be after the capture of *several* more. The radioactive decay mode of neutron-rich unstable nuclei is by β^--decay. This results in the conversion of one of the neutrons in the nucleus into a proton, with the ejection of a β^--particle (an electron). This process does not change the atomic mass number A, as the number of nucleons is unchanged, but it does increase the atomic number (proton count) by one, and thus produces a new element one step further along in the Periodic Table.

Thus, a single neutron capture on to a nucleus $^A_Z X_N$ leads initially to a neutron-rich isotope $^{A+1}_Z X_{N+1}$, and if this is unstable it β^--decays to give a new element $^{A+1}_{Z+1}(X+1)_N$, by the reaction

$$^{A+1}_Z X_{N+1} \rightarrow {}^{A+1}_{Z+1}(X+1)_N + \text{e}^- + \bar{\nu}_e$$

A β^--decay, which converts a neutron into a proton, decreases N while increasing Z by one unit. In the chart of nuclides, the nucleus moves diagonally to the upper-left at $45°$, one step along a line of constant atomic mass number A.

◼ If ^{87}Sr captured a neutron, what would be the next stable isotope produced?

❑ The neutron capture would convert ^{87}Sr into ^{88}Sr. According to Figure 51, this is stable. ◼

◼ If ^{88}Sr captured a neutron, what would be the next stable isotope produced?

❑ The neutron capture would convert ^{88}Sr into ^{89}Sr, which according to Figure 51 is unstable to β^--decay. The ^{89}Sr would therefore β^--decay with a half-life of 50.53 days to ^{89}Y, which according to Figure 51 is stable. ◼

8.1.3 Closed neutron shells/magic neutron numbers

Switching for a moment from nuclear physics to atomic physics, you may be aware that certain electronic configurations are very stable, and elements with these configurations are inert. Such elements are called the **noble gases**, e.g. He, Ne, Ar and are said to have full *electron* shells at $Z = 2$, 10, 18, etc. Returning now to nuclear physics, an analogous behaviour corresponding to full *neutron* shells (**closed neutron shells**) is found for certain values of the neutron number N, including $N = 50$, 82 and 126. These values are called **neutron magic numbers**. The closed-shell nuclei have very low **neutron-capture cross-sections**, which means that nuclei reaching these isotopes have a very low probability of capturing another neutron and hence a high probability of remaining in that state. Nuclei which *form* with magic neutron numbers also tend to be more stable than those with slightly higher neutron numbers, so should a nucleus with a full neutron shell at $N = N_m$ capture another neutron, the new nucleus at $N = N_m + 1$ generally β^--decays very rapidly, to produce an element with a higher atomic number Z, but again with neutron number N_m. As a result of this, nuclei with closed neutron shells are amongst the most abundant elements above the iron peak, and distinct peaks in the abundances of heavy elements can be ascribed to this aspect of nuclear physics. We will return to this point later in this section.

■   Consider the closed-shell neutron numbers given in the previous paragraph. Identify which stable nuclei in Figure 51 are closed-neutron-shell nuclei.

❑   Nuclides with neutron number $N = 50$ are closed-shell nuclei. The stable ones are ^{86}Kr, ^{87}Rb, ^{88}Sr, ^{89}Y, ^{90}Zr and ^{92}Mo. ■

8.1.4 The competition between neutron capture and β^--decay

Once a nucleus has captured a neutron, what happens next? Does it β^--decay or does it capture another neutron first? The timescale for β^--decay depends on the isotope in question and is governed by the nuclear physics. The timescale for neutron capture, on the other hand, depends also on the environment, and in particular on the probability that a collision with a neutron occurs. From your earlier reading, you saw that the fusion rate for nuclei is given by $R_{AB} = n_A n_B \langle \sigma v_r \rangle$ (Phillips 4.19). For neutron capture, the nuclear physics enters via the cross-section, σ, while the environment influences the rate via the number density of free neutrons, n_n.

Consider the initial state of the solar material, which is composed typically of 70% hydrogen, 28% helium, and 2% heavier element (by mass). What is the fraction of free neutrons? Zero; all neutrons are locked up in helium and heavier elements. Furthermore, *free* neutrons are unstable and spontaneously decay ($n \rightarrow p + e^- + \bar{\nu}_e$) with a half-life of only ≈ 10 minutes. Consequently, neutron-capture reactions can only be activated once other nuclear reactions liberate neutrons. Clearly, the density of free neutrons can vary greatly depending on the particular environment. That is, the neutron-capture rate, and hence the competition between neutron capture and β^--decay, depends on the stellar environment more than the nuclear physics. It has been common to consider one of two cases which represent the extremes of the possibilities: one in which the neutron-capture rate is much slower than the β^--decay rates, so the β^--decay dominates, and one in which the neutron-capture rate is much faster than the β^--decay rate, so that neutron captures dominate.

Low neutron number densities: the s-process

The slow neutron-capture process, or **s-process**, occurs when neutron-capture number densities are sufficiently low that the neutron-capture rate is well below the β^--decay rate. Any unstable nucleus formed β^--decays to a stable nucleus of higher atomic number before another neutron capture occurs. That stable nucleus is then able to neutron capture too, but once an unstable isotope is formed, β^--decay occurs prior to another neutron capture. In this way, the s-process involves the temporary production of unstable nuclei no more than one neutron capture event from the valley of stability. The trajectory taken by a nucleus undergoing the s-process in the chart of nuclides is called the **s-process pathway**. Most of the connected stable nuclei in Figure 53 are at least partially produced by this process. They are produced primarily in TP-AGB stars between the hydrogen-burning and helium-burning shells, and during core helium burning in more massive stars ($M \gtrsim 10 M_\odot$).

Although the s-process pathway remains close to the valley of stability, it is not quite a *single* route. It has a small number of **branching points** where the β^--decay timescales for some unstable nuclei (e.g. ^{79}Se) depend on whether they are in their ground state or an excited state. Such branching points lead to a splitting of the s-process pathway into two routes that rejoin after typically a few nuclei.

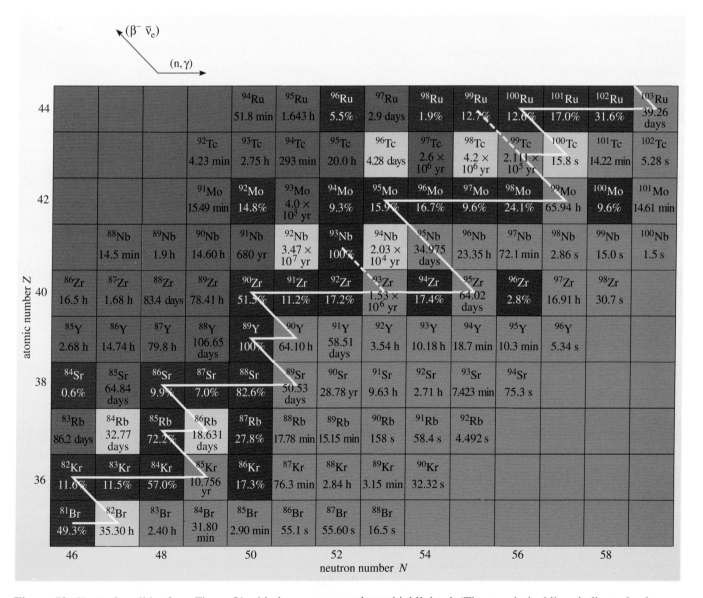

Figure 53 Chart of nuclides from Figure 51 with the s-process pathway highlighted. (The two dashed lines indicate the decays of the long-lived s-process isotopes ^{93}Zr and ^{99}Tc *after* the s-process terminates.)

High neutron number densities: the r-process

The rapid neutron-capture process, or **r-process**, is when neutron number densities are sufficiently high that the neutron-capture rate is well above the β^--decay rate. Multiple successive neutron captures occur, temporarily producing very neutron-rich unstable isotopes. Whereas the s-process pathway remains close to the valley of stability, the r-process proceeds far to the right (neutron-rich) side of the valley. Only after the neutron source terminates and the neutron number density falls are the unstable nuclei able to β^--decay back to the valley of stability. The most likely sites for a rapid flux of neutrons is in supernova explosions or possibly in rare but highly effective collisions between pairs of neutron stars.

8.1.5 The different products of s- and r-process nucleosynthesis

Most neutron-capture elements can be produced by both the s-process and the r-process. However, because the s- and r-processes take different pathways through the chart of nuclides, there are some differences in the isotopes which can be produced.

Isolated neutron-rich isotopes of the r-process

There are some stable isotopes on the neutron-rich side of the valley of stability that are separated from lower neutron-number stable isotopes of the same elements by an *unstable* isotope. The s-process is unable to jump the gap, because by definition of the s-process the β^--decay rate of the intermediate unstable isotope is greater than the neutron-capture rate. Such isolated neutron-rich isotopes can only be produced by the r-process. The examples in Figure 51 are ^{86}Kr, ^{87}Rb, ^{96}Zr, and ^{100}Mo. (You could be forgiven for thinking that ^{94}Zr is also an isolated pure-r-process nucleus, but the beta-decay half-life of ^{93}Zr is so long – 1.5×10^6 yr – that it forms a bridge for the s-process to reach ^{94}Zr too.)

Shielded isotopes of the s-process

As noted previously, the β^--decay path is along a 45° line in the chart of nuclides, from lower-right to upper-left. In the r-process, β^--decays begin from very neutron-rich unstable nuclei. Once the β^--decay reaches a *stable* nucleus with atomic number Z and neutron number N, no further β^--decay of that nucleus occur. Any nuclei on the s-process path which are shielded thus from r-process β^--decays must originate purely from the s-process and *not also* the r-process. The examples in Figure 51 are ^{86}Sr (which is shielded from the r-process by ^{86}Kr), ^{87}Sr (which is shielded by ^{87}Rb), ^{94}Mo (shielded by ^{94}Zr), ^{96}Mo (shielded by ^{96}Zr), and ^{100}Ru (shielded by ^{100}Mo).

Abundance peaks due to closed neutron shells

As noted above, nuclei having closed neutron shells ($N = 50, 82, 126$) are more stable than more neutron-rich species and have lower neutron-capture cross-sections. As the s-process pathway is close to the valley of stability, the s-process produces many stable nuclei with those neutron numbers. This produces peaks in the abundances of the s-process nuclei around $N = 50, 82$ and 126, which correspond to $A \approx 90, 138$ and 208; see Figure 54. The r-process, on the other hand, follows a path far to the neutron-rich side of the valley of stability. Nuclei with closed neutron shells are still produced abundantly, but in the r-process these are unstable and β-decay at constant atomic mass number A. For a given closed-shell neutron number N, the unstable r-process nuclei have much lower atomic number Z and atomic mass number A than s-process nuclei. Consequently, the abundance peaks of the r-process are found at lower A than the peaks of the s-process. The r-process peaks at $N = 50$, 82 and 126 correspond to $A \approx 85$, 130 and 195 (see Figure 54).

As the s-process remains close to the valley of stability, only a small *range* of atomic numbers Z is associated with any particular closed neutron shell. The r-process, on the other hand, brings nuclei spanning a larger range of atomic numbers to a particular closed shell N-value. The result is that the closed neutron shell abundance peaks for the r-process are not only at lower A than for the s-process, but are also *wider* than the s-process peaks.

The p-process exceptions

Several stable nuclei in Figure 53 lie on the neutron-poor (= proton-rich) side of the valley of stability where they are shielded from the r-process but do not lie on the s-process path either. The five nuclei are ^{84}Sr, ^{92}Mo, ^{94}Mo, ^{96}Ru and ^{98}Ru. ^{94}Mo is off the s-process path because the β⁻-decay half-lives of ^{93}Zr and ^{94}Nb are so long compared to typical neutron capture intervals that those isotopes appear stable to the s-process. These five are called **p-process** nuclei, where the 'p' signifies a proton-rich nucleus compared to the valley of stability. p-process isotopes are very rare (see Figure 54), but the fact that they exist at all indicates that the s- and r-processes are not the only mechanisms for the production of heavy nuclei. You *might* think that the name 'p-process' *implies* proton-capture, but in fact as many as three different processes have been considered for the synthesis of these trace p-isotopes; the details are beyond the scope of this course.

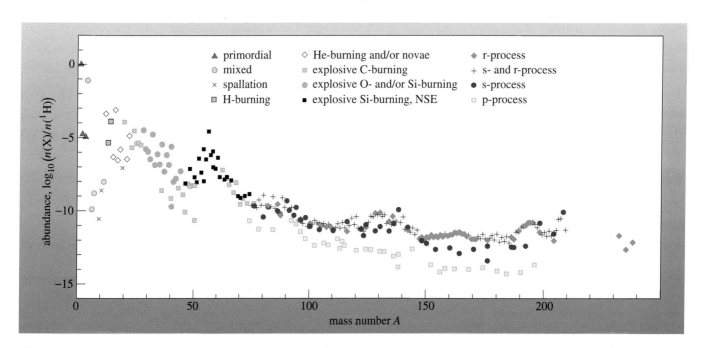

Figure 54 Abundances (logarithmic relative to hydrogen) for stable isotopes. These are grouped according to their main nucleosynthetic origin. Of particular interest in this section are the neutron-capture elements above the iron peak, i.e. with $A \gtrsim 75$. These are grouped into primarily r-process, primarily s-process, mixed s- and r-process, and the p-process. The s-process gives rise to abundance peaks at $A \approx 90$, 138 and 208, whereas the r-process leads to broader, more rounded peaks at $A \approx 85$, 130 and 195.

■ Spend a moment considering these p-process nuclei in Figure 53. Which nuclei shield them from the r-process?

❑ ^{84}Sr is shielded from the r-process by ^{84}Kr, ^{92}Mo is shielded by ^{92}Zr, ^{94}Mo is shielded by ^{94}Zr, ^{96}Ru is shielded by ^{96}Zr (*not* by ^{96}Mo), and ^{98}Ru is shielded by ^{98}Mo. ■

■ Neutron-capture reactions are responsible for the production of most nuclei heavier than zinc. Why don't 'normal' fusion reactions involving nuclei, protons, and/or α-particles produce these?

❑ There are two main reasons. First, the Coulomb barriers of nuclei are too large to permit charged-particle fusion of elements more massive than zinc. Second, the binding energy per nucleon reaches a maximum near ^{56}Fe, so production of heavier nuclei requires that energy be extracted from the environment rather than contributed to the environment, and they would be very rare in an equilibrium process like silicon burning. ■

Question 43

Produce a table summarizing the nucleosynthesis stages you have studied. Include the major reactions and their products, the stellar masses responsible, ignition temperatures, and timescales. Where appropriate, use information from Phillips Tables 1.3 (page 26) and 4.2 (page 139). ■

8.2 Supernovae

In Section 7 we found that a star whose final mass is below the Chandrasekhar mass is supported against collapse by the pressure of degenerate electrons. It ends its days as a white dwarf which slowly cools and fades. In Section 8.2 we see what happens to a star whose final mass *exceeds* this limit and in Section 8.3 and 8.4 we discover what remnant it may leave behind.

Activity 41   30 minutes

The onset of core collapse

Read Phillips, Section 6.2, 'Collapse of a stellar core', to the end of the subsection 'Electron capture' (pages 180–184).

Keywords: **core collapse supernova**, **neutronization** ■

■ The initiation of exothermic (energy-liberating) fusion reactions provides pressure *support* for stars during their long-lasting burning phases. What process, in general terms, can undermine this and lead to the *collapse* of the core?

❑ The initiation of *endothermic* (energy-absorbing) reactions draws kinetic energy out of the material and hence eliminates the pressure support. ■

■ What are the two main processes that trigger the collapse of a stellar core, and how much energy is associated with each? Is that energy released or absorbed?

Many writers discussing supernovae use cgs units, in which the unit of energy is the erg. One erg is only 10^{-7} J, so the typical SN ejecta kinetic energy of 10^{44} J is often expressed as 10^{51} erg.

❏ Photodisintegration of iron by thermal γ-rays, which exist because of the high temperature, can absorb $\approx 1.4 \times 10^{45}$ J, and electron captures by protons bound in nuclei (neutronization), which happen because of the high density, can absorb $\approx 1.6 \times 10^{45}$ J. A total of $\approx 3 \times 10^{45}$ J can be absorbed from the thermal reservoir. ■

Question 44

If each nucleus of iron can absorb 124.4 MeV of energy by photodisintegration in the process $\gamma + {}^{56}_{26}\text{Fe} \rightarrow 13\,{}^{4}_{2}\text{He} + 4\text{n}$, calculate the energy absorbed per kilogram.

(*Hint*: The equation is not given in the text; you must reason it through!) ■

Consider Phillips' comment at the end of the subsection on nuclear photodisintegration. Over its lifetime, the star has been supported against collapse by the thermal energy derived from converting hydrogen to iron, via intermediate species. Some of this energy is radiated away by the surface of the star over its long lifetime. Then, at the end of its life, it seeks to reverse that entire process by converting the iron in the core back into hydrogen. Things are not looking good for the star, which is destined to collapse from a lack of pressure support. If this wasn't bad enough, neutrinos are also being liberated by **neutronization**. Neutronization is the conversion of protons (in nuclei) to neutrons by electron capture, which is possible if the gas is sufficiently dense for degenerate electrons to have an energy above the 1.3 MeV mass-energy excess of neutrons compared to protons ($m_{\text{p}}c^2 = 938.3$ MeV, while $m_{\text{n}}c^2 = 939.6$ MeV). (Actually, the energy excess required for electron capture by *bound*, *nuclear* protons (rather than *free* protons) is usually somewhat higher and depends on the nucleus, but is nevertheless usually a few MeV.) The neutrinos liberated in this process are capable of carrying off a similar amount of energy to that absorbed by photodisintegration. Things really, really, do not look good for the future of the star!

Activity 42   45 minutes

The aftermath of core collapse

Read Phillips, Section 6.2, subsection 'The aftermath' (pages 185–189).

Keywords: **type I supernova**, **type II supernova**, **neutron star**, **black hole** ■

The supernova SN1987A mentioned in Phillips is shown in Figure 55.

■ How are supernovae usually detected? What are the main ways in which liberated energy is carried away from a supernova? Quantify them.

❏ Supernovae are usually detected by the sudden brightening of a previously invisible star. However, photons provide the *least* effective means of removing the energy, only ~10^{42} J over the first year. The expansion of the ejected material at velocities of tens of thousands of km s^{-1} carries 100 times as much as kinetic energy, ~10^{44} J. However, the binding energy of the neutron star is ~10^{47} J, so much more energy must be removed than the photons and kinetic energy carry. The majority is carried away by neutrinos. ■

The reading from Phillips concentrates on **core-collapse supernovae** (type II), but be aware that there is a second major type of supernova (type Ia) involving the accretion of matter on to a white dwarf. If the accretion is sufficient to raise the mass of the white dwarf above the Chandrasekhar mass, then a thermonuclear reaction will be set off that unbinds the entire star. The main distinctions between these two main types of supernovae are as follows:

Supernovae type Ia (SN Ia)	Supernovae type II (SN II)
hydrogen *not* visible in spectrum	hydrogen visible in spectrum
associated with old stars	associated with young stars
standard light curve; used as distance indicator	less predictable light curve
probably leaves no compact remnant, only a fireball	leaves neutron star or black hole remnant
due to accretion on to white dwarf, which then exceeds Chandrasekhar mass ($1.4 M_\odot$)	due to core collapse of massive star ($M_{ms} \gtrsim 8\text{–}10 M_\odot$)

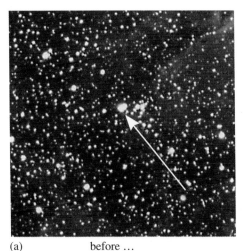

(a)   before …

(b)   during …

(c)   after …

Figure 55 Before, during, and after (10 years on) images of the best studied supernova, SN1987A. This was the first supernova whose progenitor (parent star) was identifiable from archival photographs, and the first supernova from which neutrinos were detected. Although it occurred in a neighbouring galaxy, the Large Magellanic Cloud, it was visible to the unaided eye at maximum brightness. Because of its proximity, circumstellar material ejected before the supernova explosion can now be seen (c) as a bright equatorial ring surrounding the SN. Two larger rings, possibly associated with bipolar mass outflow, are also seen. Around 1999, the slowly expanding equatorial ring was struck by the fastest ejecta from the supernova explosion, causing the ring to vary in brightness. Also around 1999, the envelope of the expanding supernova became large enough to resolve. (a) and (b) are to the same scale; (c) is a 1.5× enlargement showing only the central region. The close pair of stars in the bottom-right corner of (c) are just resolved in (a) above the tail of the arrow.

■ Why might core-collapse supernovae (SN II) be associated with young stars, while SN Ia are associated with old stars?

❑ SN II involve the core-collapse of massive stars with $M_{ms} \gtrsim 8\text{–}10M_{\odot}$, whose main-sequence lifetimes are typically $t_{ms} \approx 10(M/M_{\odot})^{-2.5} \times 10^9$ yr $\lesssim 30 \times 10^6$ yr (see Section 5.1). SN Ia, on the other hand, are associated with lower-mass stars that become white dwarfs, probably with initial masses $M_{ms} \lesssim 2M_{\odot}$, and therefore having main-sequence lifetimes $t_{ms} \approx 10(M/M_{\odot})^{-2.5} \times 10^9$ yr $\gtrsim 2 \times 10^9$ yr. ■

Question 45

(a) State the equation for the gravitational potential energy (E_{GR}) released in the collapse of a stellar core of mass M, from an initial radius R_1 to a final radius R_2, where $R_1 \gg R_2$.

(b) A typical value for the initial radius is 1000 km and for the final radius is 10 km. Rewrite your result from (a) using solar mass units and R in units of 10 km.

(c) Quantify and rank (from the least to the greatest) the following energy loss mechanisms in a core-collapse supernova, and indicate how much of the gravitational energy released they appear to dissipate:

(i)   kinetic energy of the expanding ejecta;

(ii) electromagnetic radiation, i.e. the light curve, which is powered after the first month or so by the decay of radioactive nuclei $^{56}Ni \rightarrow ^{56}Co \rightarrow ^{56}Fe$;

(iii) neutrinos emitted from the surface of the newly formed neutron star. ■

■ The supernova remnant Cassiopeia A (see Figure 56) had for a long time shown no evidence for a compact stellar remnant, but new images taken in X-rays seem to reveal one. If this is correct, was Cassiopeia A a type Ia or type II supernova?

❑ Type II. Type Ia completely disrupt the stars, leaving a brilliant 'fireball' but no compact remnant. ■

Phillips notes (page 186) that the mechanism by which the outer layers of a core-collapse supernova are ejected is uncertain. It is clear that there is the *energy* to do it, but the means by which that energy and momentum is *imparted* to the outer layers is unclear. When the collapsing envelope of the star reaches the collapsed neutron core which resists further compression, a rebounding shock-wave is set up that helps reverse the infall of the envelope. This begins to convert the collapse into an explosion, but current models fall short of completing the process. Current research in this area is investigating the possibility that interactions between neutrinos and the stellar envelope above the newly formed neutron star deposit some of the neutrino energy into the envelope. (Usually we think of neutrinos as not interacting strongly with matter, but the flux of neutrinos is so large above the newly formed neutron star, and the matter so dense, that sufficient interactions may nevertheless take place.) This rapid heating of the stellar matter by the intense neutrino flux may then drive the expansion that ejects the envelope into space. This same event is also widely regarded as the probable site of r-process neutron-capture reactions responsible for synthesizing many of the elements above the iron peak.

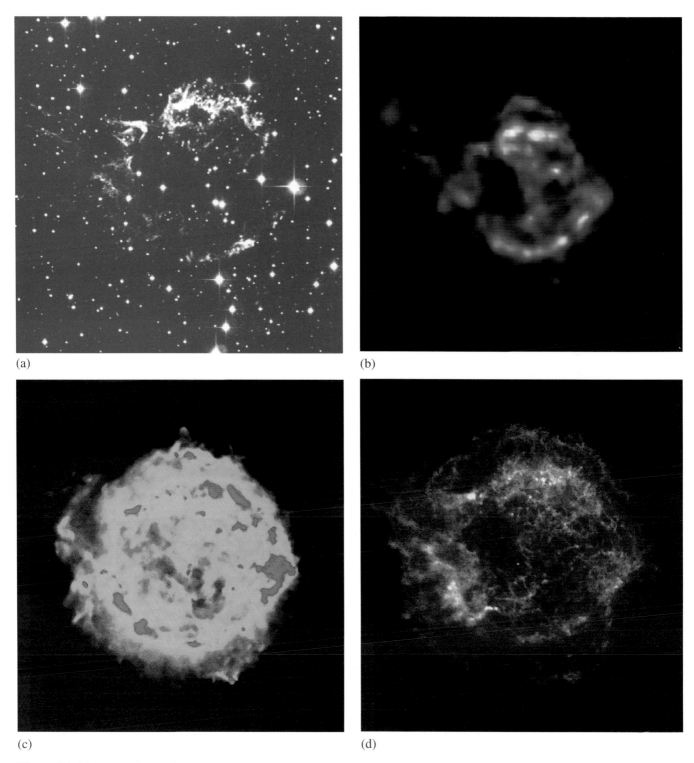

(a)   (b)

(c)   (d)

Figure 56 The appearance of a supernova remnant depends greatly on the waveband observed. Cassiopeia A, the remnant of a ~300 year old supernova in the Galaxy, is inconspicuous at optical wavelengths (a), where many stars in the field radiate with similar brightness, but in infrared (b), radio (c), and X-ray (d) wavelengths it is the only source visible. The X-ray image, which is the most recent, shows a probable stellar remnant for the first time, and also shows that the gaseous remnant consists of two shocks, an inner one caused by the collision between the supernova ejecta and the circumstellar shell, which is heated to ~10 million K, and an outer shock caused possibly by a sonic boom running ahead of the expanding ejecta.

Supernova remnants

Use the Image Archive to identify other remnants of supernova explosions, and read the associated captions. Contrast the explosive appearance of these events with the more ordered appearance of planetary nebulae. (You may wish to browse again the images of planetary nebulae as well.) Note also the inconspicuous nature of the compact stellar remnants of supernovae, and consider the difficulty in detecting them at all, compared to the central stars (white dwarfs) of planetary nebulae.

Keywords: none ■

8.3 Neutron stars

Core-collapse supernovae leave behind one of two **remnants**: either a **neutron star** or a **black hole**. These two classes of object will now be examined in turn.

8.3.1 Composition and radius

Neutron-star composition and radius

Read Phillips Section 6.3 'Neutron stars', to the end of the subsection 'Gravitational binding energy of neutron stars' (pages 189–194).

Keywords: **neutron drip** ■

In the subsection 'Matter inside neutron stars', Phillips establishes that neutrons are of order 200 times more abundant than protons and electrons in the resulting material. We see, then, that neutron stars are aptly named, and why they are not, for example, called nucleon stars.

■ Normally, free neutrons are unstable and decay with a half-life of 10 minutes via β^--decay, $n \rightarrow p + e^- + \bar{\nu}_e$. However, the neutrons that make up a neutron star do not decay. Why not?

❑ Although the *entry* channel for the reaction exists – n, free neutrons – the *exit* channel $p + e^- + \bar{\nu}_e$ is blocked by the Pauli exclusion principle. That is, in the highly degenerate material in the neutron star, there are no permitted states which an electron or proton could occupy. This prevents the reaction from proceeding. ■

Phillips provides several warnings about oversimplifying the assumptions about conditions in a neutron star. Newtonian gravity should be replaced by Einstein's general-relativistic treatment, because for a neutron star of mass M and radius R_{NS}, a neutron's gravitational potential energy, GMm_n/R_{NS}, is comparable to its rest-mass energy, $m_n c^2$. Phillips (Equation 6.62) gives the ratio as

$$\frac{GMm_n}{R_{NS}} \bigg/ m_n c^2 = \frac{GM}{Rc^2} \approx 0.2 \left(\frac{M}{1.85 M_\odot} \right)^{4/3}$$

which is not much less than unity. The momenta of neutrons also approach the relativistic limits, requiring special relativity. Nevertheless, the non-relativistic approximation can lead to useful insights into the size of the star, and an understanding of the dominant physics. In particular, it is interesting to compare calculations of the radius of a white dwarf, supported by degenerate electrons, and a neutron star, supported by degenerate neutrons. The following question takes you through such a calculation. (You may find it helpful to revise your study of white dwarfs as you complete this exercise.)

Question 46   30 minutes

Set up two columns on a sheet of paper, one for a white dwarf and one for a neutron star. Then in each column:

(a) Write the equation for the pressure of non-relativistic degenerate material as a function of particle *number*-density.

(b) Rewrite the equation to give the pressure in terms of the *mass* density for degenerate matter at the centre of the star.

(*Hint*: In a neutron star, neutrons are ~200 times more abundant than protons or electrons, so treat the neutron star as composed solely of neutrons.)

(c) Rearrange the expression for the central pressure of a Clayton stellar model

$$P_c \approx (\pi/36)^{1/3} G M^{2/3} \rho_c^{4/3} \qquad\qquad \text{(Phillips 5.33)}$$

to give an expression for the central density. (This equation is the same for both objects.)

(d) As the central pressure required to support the object is provided by the degenerate particles, use your result from (b) to substitute for the central pressure in (c), and obtain a new expression for the central density in terms of the other variables. (Actually, instead of finding an expression for ρ_c, it will be more convenient to find an expression for $\rho_c^{-1/3}$.)

(*Hint*: As the density appears explicitly in the pressure term, you have to rearrange the equation to get all of the density terms on the left-hand side. You may find it easier first to obtain an expression for $\rho_c^{-1/4}$, then take the (4/3)-power to find an expression for $\rho_c^{-1/3}$.)

(e) Rearrange the definition of the mean density $\langle \rho \rangle = M/((4/3)\pi R^3)$ to get an expression for the radius in terms of the mass and mean density, and then use the result that a polytropic star with $P \propto \rho^{5/3}$ has a central density six times the mean density, to re-express the radius in terms of mass and *central* density. (This is the same for white dwarfs and neutron stars.)

(f) Substitute into this equation your result from (d) to find an expression for the radius of the stars. ∎

The final result for Question 46 shows that

$$R_{\text{WD}} = \left(\frac{9}{2\pi}\right)^{1/3} \frac{324^{1/3}}{4\pi G} \left(\frac{h^2}{5m_e}\right) \left(\frac{Y_e}{m_H}\right)^{5/3} M^{-1/3}$$

and $$R_{\text{NS}} = \left(\frac{9}{2\pi}\right)^{1/3} \frac{324^{1/3}}{4\pi G} \left(\frac{h^2}{5m_n}\right) \left(\frac{1}{m_n}\right)^{5/3} M^{-1/3}$$

Taking the ratio of the second to the first, noting that $m_H \approx m_n$, gives

$$\frac{R_{NS}}{R_{WD}} = \left(\frac{m_e}{m_n}\right) \times \left(\frac{1}{Y_e^{5/3}}\right) \approx 1/580$$

There are two differences which affect the two types of star, one minor and one major.

- *Minor factor*: Y_e appears in the white dwarf radius but not in the neutron star radius. Recall that Y_e is the number of degenerate particles (electrons) per nucleon in a white dwarf. This is relevant in the white dwarf because the degenerate particles do not dominate the composition of the material. Typically $Y_e \approx 0.5$, so this affects the mass ratio by only a factor of ≈ 3.
- *Major factor*: The radius of a degenerate star is scaled according to the mass of the particle whose degenerate pressure supports the star. (The mass of the particle also determines its de Broglie wavelength, so you could also say that the de Broglie wavelength determines the radius.) As the pressure in a neutron star is provided by neutrons that are almost 2000 times more massive than the electron, neutron stars are almost a factor of 2000 smaller in radius. In Question 42, you showed that the radius of a white dwarf is

$$R_{WD} = 1.5 R_{Earth}(M/M_\odot)^{-1/3}$$

From the above ratio, we can therefore write

$$R_{NS} = R_{WD}\left(\frac{m_e}{m_n}\right) \times \left(\frac{1}{Y_e^{5/3}}\right)$$

$$= 1.5\left(\frac{m_e}{m_n}\right) \times \left(\frac{1}{Y_e^{5/3}}\right) R_{Earth}\left(\frac{M}{M_\odot}\right)^{-1/3}$$

$$= 0.0026 \, R_{Earth}\left(\frac{M}{M_\odot}\right)^{-1/3}$$

That is, whereas white dwarfs are comparable in size to the Earth, neutron stars have radii of only $\approx$ 5–10 km!

8.3.2 Energy, evolution and maximum mass

Activity 45   **1 hour**

Neutron-star energy, evolution and mass

Read the remaining two subsections of Phillips Section 6.3, beginning from 'Rotating neutron stars and pulsars' (page 194–201). *Skip* from the end of the third paragraph on page 199 to the beginning of the last paragraph of page 200.

Note that Phillips again uses the constant $M_* = 1.85 M_\odot$. Don't be distracted by this; think of it merely as a mass unit that you can easily convert into solar masses.

Keywords: **pulsars**, **Crab pulsar**, **magnetic dipole radiation**, **general relativity**, **hyperon**, **pion** ▪

By equating the gravitational and centrifugal accelerations, Phillips shows that the minimum period for a rotating body is $\tau_{min} = 2\pi(R^3/GM)^{1/2}$ (Phillips 6.64). As the mean density of a sphere is $\langle \rho \rangle = M/(4/3)\pi R^3$, we can write $R^3/M = 3/4\pi\langle \rho \rangle$ and thus can rewrite Phillips 6.64 as $\tau_{min} = (3\pi/G\langle \rho \rangle)^{1/2}$. That is,

$$\langle \rho \rangle \geq 3\pi/G\tau_{obs}^2 \quad \text{(see Figure 57)} \tag{35}$$

The period of the Crab pulsar (Figure 58), 33 ms, indicates it has a *mean* density in excess of $1.3 \times 10^{14} \, \text{kg m}^{-3}$, well above even the *central* densities of white dwarfs (see Phillips Fig. 6.1). This quickly confirms that pulsars are neutron stars with matter at nuclear densities.

■ Why is it more difficult to specify the upper mass limit for neutron stars than for white dwarfs?

❑ Interactions between neutrons are significant. They repel one another at close separations $<1.4 \times 10^{-15}$ m, which makes them less compressible, but also their energies are so high that they produce hyperons and pions which reduce the pressure and makes them more compressible. The net effect is to allow more massive neutron stars.

The gravitational fields are so strong that Einstein's theory of gravity, general relativity, must be used instead of Newton's theory of gravity, and under general relativity, the gravity also depends on pressure. Whereas in a normal star internal pressure resists gravity, under general relativity it *strengthens* the gravity, which reduces the maximum stable mass. ■

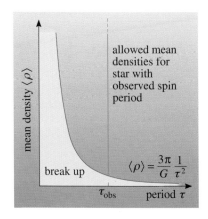

Figure 57 Schematic of mean density, $\langle \rho \rangle$, against period, τ. The region with $\tau < \tau_{min} = (3\pi/G\langle \rho \rangle)^{1/2}$ is forbidden, as this would cause break-up of the star. For an observed period τ_{obs}, permitted values of the mean density are $\langle \rho \rangle \geq 3\pi/G\tau_{obs}^2$.

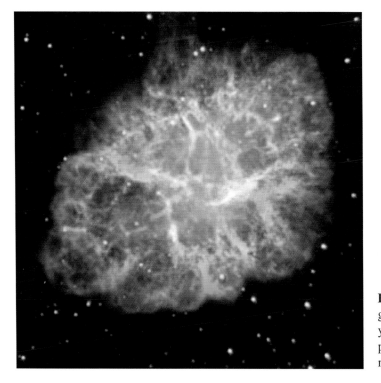

Figure 58 An optical image of the Crab nebula, the gaseous remnant of a supernova in 1054 (i.e. ≈ 1000 years ago). At the heart of the gaseous remnant lies a pulsar with a 33 ms period, being the neutron-star remnant of the collapsed core of the massive progenitor.

8.4 Black holes

So far we have studied two stellar remnants: white dwarfs and neutron stars. One other stellar remnant remains to be discussed: black holes. Black holes have many unusual properties, but in this final topic on the life and death of stars, we will consider them only briefly, as an end point of stellar evolution for sufficiently massive stars.

Activity 46   **20 minutes**

Black holes

To round off your study of the final states of stellar evolution, read Phillips Section 6.4, 'Black holes' (pages 201–204).

Keywords: **space-time**, **Schwarzschild radius**, **gravitational redshift** ■

■ The maximum mass of a neutron star is $1.0–3.0 M_\odot$; all heavier remnants become black holes. We also know that a star with $M_{ms} \approx 8 M_\odot$ burns carbon but leaves a ONeMg *white dwarf* remnant, not a black hole. How do such stars avoid becoming black holes?

❑ Don't forget mass loss! Stars lose a large fraction of their mass during their giant phases, so although a star must *begin* life with a *main-sequence mass* in excess of $8 M_\odot$ if it is to ignite carbon, it is much less massive by the time it actually does so. ■

8.5 Summary of Section 8

1 The nucleosynthesis of elements above the iron peak faces two problems: very high Coulomb barriers and a decreasing binding energy per nucleon. Neutron capture avoids the Coulomb barrier and is the main mechanism for the nucleosynthesis of elements heavier than the iron-peak group.

2 The chart of nuclides records atomic number, Z, on the vertical axis and neutron number, N, on the horizontal axis. Lines of constant atomic mass number, A, lie at 45° between upper-left and lower-right. Stable nuclei occupy a zone stretching from low N and Z to high N and Z, called the valley of stability.

3 A neutron capture leads to a neutron-rich isotope of an element;

$$^A_Z X_N (n, \gamma)^{A+1}_Z X_{N+1}$$

Unstable neutron-rich isotopes β^--decay. This increases the atomic number by one while decreasing the neutron number N, and thus produces a new element

$$^{A+1}_Z X_{N+1} \rightarrow ^{A+1}_{Z+1}(X+1)_N + e^- + \bar{v}_e$$

β^--decay moves diagonally to the upper-left at 45°, along a line of constant atomic mass number A, in the chart of nuclides.

4 Nuclei with closed neutron shells (magic numbers $N = 50, 82$ and 126) are more stable than those with slightly higher neutron numbers and have low neutron-capture cross-sections, so they are more abundant.

5   The β^--decay timescale depends solely on the isotope, whereas the neutron-
     capture timescale also depends on the environment (the number-density of free
     neutrons). Two extremes are the s- (slow) process in which the neutron-capture
     rate is much lower than the β^--decay rates, so the β^--decay dominates, and the
     r- (rapid) process in which the neutron-capture rate is much faster than the
     β^--decay rate, so that neutron captures dominate. The s-process pathway thus
     remains close to the valley of stability. The r-process temporarily produces very
     neutron-rich unstable isotopes far to the right (neutron-rich) side of the valley of
     stability. Only after the neutron number-density falls are the unstable nuclei able
     to β^--decay back to the valley of stability.

6   Some slightly neutron-rich stable isotopes are separated from the rest of the
     valley of stability by short-lived unstable nuclei. The s-process cannot jump the
     gap and they can only be produced by the r-process.

7   Any nucleus on the s-process path which is shielded from r-process β^--decays
     by another stable nucleus must originate purely from the s-process.

8   Some very rare neutron-poor (proton-rich) isotopes cannot be made by the s- or
     r-processes; they are p-process nuclei.

9   The abundance peaks of the r-process are found at lower A than the peaks of the
     s-process. The r-process peaks for $N = 50$, 82 and 126 appear at $A \approx 85$, 130 and
     195, while the s-process peaks are at $A \approx 90$, 138 and 208. The closed neutron
     shell abundance peaks for the r-process are also *wider* than the s-process peaks.

10   Stars with $M_{\mathrm{ms}} \gtrsim 11 M_\odot$ achieve silicon burning, which forms an iron core
     supported by degenerate electrons that become ultra-relativistic. When the
     Chandrasekhar limit ($\approx 1.4 M_\odot$) is reached, the electrons can no longer support
     the star. Nuclear photodisintegration by thermal photons and electron capture by
     nuclear protons (neutronization) absorb energy so efficiently they send the core
     into free-fall.

11   Photodisintegration of iron into hydrogen proceeds as

     $\gamma + {}^{56}_{26}\mathrm{Fe} \rightarrow 13\,{}^{4}_{2}\mathrm{He} + 4\mathrm{n}$, and $\gamma + {}^{4}_{2}\mathrm{He} \rightarrow 2\mathrm{p} + 2\mathrm{n}$, which could

     photodissociate about three-quarters of the iron core, and absorb $\approx 1.4 \times 10^{45}$ J.
     This is comparable to the energy previously liberated via nuclear burning over
     the star's lifetime!

     Neutronization is the conversion of nuclear protons into neutrons via electron
     capture: $\mathrm{e}^- + \mathrm{p} \rightarrow \mathrm{n} + \nu_\mathrm{e}$. The electron capture $\mathrm{e}^- + {}^{56}\mathrm{Fe} \rightarrow {}^{56}\mathrm{Mn} + \nu_\mathrm{e}$ occurs
     once the Fermi kinetic energy E_{FK} of the electrons exceeds 3.7 MeV, which
     occurs once the electron density n_e is high enough. The neutrinos carry away the
     energy. Up to $\approx 1.6 \times 10^{45}$ J could be lost this way.

12   The collapse of a stellar core is halted when the density reaches that of nuclear
     matter. The compression and rebounding of the nuclear matter sends a shock
     wave through the rest of the star that partially, if not fully, reverses the stellar
     collapse, leading to the ejection of the outer layers as a supernova. (Heating by
     neutrinos may also be required to eject the envelope.) The typical luminous
     energy is $\sim 10^{42}$ J, and the kinetic energy of the ejecta is $\sim 10^{44}$ J. The
     gravitational binding energy is an order of magnitude more than the energy (i)
     required to photodissociate the iron core or (ii) that is lost by neutronization,
     and (iii) two orders of magnitude more than the kinetic energy of the ejecta.
     Thus most of the liberated energy is probably lost in an intense neutrino burst
     from the surface of the new, hot neutron star, such as that measured for
     SN1987A.

13 The main distinctions between these two main types of supernovae are as follows:

Supernovae type Ia (SN Ia)	Supernovae type II (SN II)
hydrogen *not* visible in spectrum	hydrogen visible in spectrum
associated with old stars	associated with young stars
standard light curve; used as distance indicator	less predictable light curve
probably leaves no compact remnant, only a fireball	leaves neutron star or black hole remnant
due to accretion on to white dwarf, which then exceeds Chandrasekhar mass (1.4M$_\odot$)	due to core collapse of massive star ($M_{ms} \gtrsim 8$–10M$_\odot$)

14 Neutronization converts nuclear protons into neutrons. When the density reaches 4×10^{14} kg m^{-3}, neutrons drip from the nuclei, giving rise to free neutrons, nuclei, and electrons. Once the density exceeds the density of normal nuclear matter, 2.3×10^{17} kg m^{-3}, nuclei merge into a dense gas of electrons, protons and neutrons.

15 Free neutrons normally decay with a half-life of 10 minutes via $n \rightarrow p + e^- + \bar{\nu}_e$, but neutron stars survive because their normal decay is blocked by the Pauli exclusion principle, because the energy states which the resulting proton and electron would occupy are full. Neutrons greatly outnumber protons: $n_n \sim 200 n_p$.

16 The radii of white dwarfs and neutron stars are set *primarily* by the mass of the degenerate particle providing pressure support. Since the neutron mass is 1840 times the electron mass, the radius of a neutron star is much smaller than a white dwarf of comparable mass. The radii of neutron stars are ≈ 580 times smaller, or ≈ 5–10 km.

17 In neutron stars, Newtonian gravity gives way to general relativity.

18 Equating gravitational and centrifugal accelerations, $GM/R^2 = (2\pi)^2 R/\tau^2$, shows that the minimum mean density of a rotating object is $\langle \rho \rangle \geq 3\pi/G\tau^2$, where τ is its rotation period. The Crab pulsar, with a period of 33 ms, therefore has a *mean* density in excess of 1.3×10^{14} kg m^{-3}. This confirms that pulsars are neutron stars with nuclear densities.

19 By ascribing the observed spin-down rate $d\omega/dt$ to an energy loss via magnetic dipole radiation (caused by the spin axis and magnetic axis being misaligned), it is possible to estimate the magnetic field strength of the Crab pulsar as $\sim 10^8$ T, which is huge but may be consistent with a field trapped and concentrated during collapse to $R_{NS} \approx 10$ km.

20 A maximum mass exists for neutron stars, analogous to that for white dwarfs, corresponding to the neutrons becoming ultra-relativistic. Unfortunately it is more difficult to calculate the neutron star value because of neutron interactions (which make the maximum mass higher) and the need to use general relativity (which is strengthened at high energy density and pressure, and makes the maximum mass smaller).

21 Objects exceeding the mass of a neutron star collapse to a black hole, a hole in space-time with a Schwarzschild radius $R_S = 2GM/c^2$. This is the distance at which the gravitational redshift becomes infinite. Black hole candidates are recognized from the high masses inferred from observations of companion stars and from the high-energy phenomena (e.g. X-ray emission) from material heated as it flows towards a black hole.

9 CONSOLIDATION

This final section of the block does not introduce *new* material, but rather provides additional perspectives on topics you have met already. This will help you revise what you have learnt and identify what you should revisit. In contrast to the earlier sections, where numerous questions and answers are provided, in this consolidation section several *self-study suggestions* are given to help you question your own understanding and identify what you should study in more detail. As these activities are more open ended, and the answers are to be found elsewhere in this Study Guide or in Phillips, no additional answers are given here.

Use the next two subsections to prompt your own questions on the issues covered in this block: ask yourself whether you have understood the previous readings on these topics, and take the opportunity to revise and summarize their main points. Similarly, note what you regard to be the key equations and write *in words* the physics they encapsulate. Finally, if topics come up in the following subsections that you remember studying only vaguely, use that as a hint to revise those sections in greater detail, perhaps revisiting the questions asked in this Study Guide and/or those at the end of each chapter of Phillips.

9.1 Simulating stellar evolution

Activity 47   **1 hour**

Visualizing stellar evolution

This interactive multimedia tutorial provides a visualization of some of the stellar evolution processes that you have studied in this block. From *The Energetic Universe* MM guide on your computer, start the package 'Visualizing stellar evolution', and follow the instructions that appear on the screen. There are questions in the package which you should answer.

Keywords: none ■

> *Self-study suggestion:* When you have completed the multimedia activity, reread the section summaries in this Study Guide for Sections 4–8, then summarize in your own words each of the evolutionary stages you saw in the simulations. Your notes should cover not only what you saw but the physics driving it. Pick out the key equations that describe the physics, write those down, and describe in words the meanings of the terms and the equations overall.

9.2 A research view on stellar evolution and nucleosynthesis

This subsection involves a non-mathematical reading that should help you develop a more complete, overall picture of various aspects of stellar evolution and nucleosynthesis that you have studied. The reading, prepared by the Joint Institute for Nuclear Astrophysics, Michigan State University and the University of Notre Dame, summarizes a meeting on 'Opportunities in Nuclear Astrophysics' held in June 1999. The goal of the meeting was 'to define and summarize the state of the field of nuclear astrophysics and the opportunities for the future of the field'. Even though this document was written as an outline of future directions for front-line research, you will now be very familiar with many of the topics, and so should be able to follow large sections of the report. Hopefully this will help you put the topics you have studied into a coherent, modern perspective.

A research view on stellar evolution and nucleosynthesis

Connect to *The Energetic Universe* home page, and access the list of Web-based activities (under Course resources). Select Block 2, Activity 48 and follow the instructions on screen to download the white paper 'Opportunities in Nuclear Astrophysics'. As the paper is very long, I suggest you read only parts of it. It is 4 + 62 pages in length, but you may not wish to read beyond the end of page 40; my recommendations follow below. Bear in mind that the paper was written from a research perspective for astronomers and nuclear physicists, so do not be surprised if some of the nuclear physics terminology is foreign to you. For the purpose of your study, concentrate on the astronomy.

Read the following sections:

Overview:	Part I (first and last subsections only)
	Part III (subsection *Stellar evolution*)
Nucleosynthesis:	Part IV, VI, and IX.
Supernovae:	The first page of Part VII and the first page of Part X.
Neutrinos:	Part XI (first two pages).

Keywords: none ■

Self-study suggestion: Remember, this reading is not examinable, but it may be a good reminder of what you have covered in Sections 1–8 of the block. As you read the paper, note down any key terms that you recognize, and write a brief glossary entry for each one. Compare what you have written with the entries in Collins or the S381 *Glossary*.

9.3 Is this the end or just the beginning?

Planetary nebulae leading to white dwarfs, and supernovae leading to neutron stars and black holes might be thought of as the final link in the chain of the formation, life and death of stars. You might consider the process to end with the compact remnants, but the process does *not* end. Rather, mass-loss via stellar winds, planetary nebulae and supernovae is a vital link in a *cycle* of activity that explains the chemical evolution of entire galaxies and the Universe.

As you learnt in Sections 1 and 2, stars form in gravitationally contracting gas clouds. They ignite hydrogen in their cores if their masses exceed $\approx 0.08 M_\odot$, and produce helium and possibly nitrogen (via the CNO cycle) (Sections 3, 4, and 5). If their masses exceed $\approx 0.5 M_\odot$, later they ignite helium to produce carbon and oxygen (Section 6), and if their main-sequence masses exceed $\approx 10 M_\odot$ they produce elements up to the iron peak (Section 7). Carbon and nitrogen synthesized in low- and intermediate-mass stars ($M \leq 2M_{\odot}$ and $2M_{\odot} \leq M \leq 8M_{\odot}$ respectively) are returned to the interstellar medium via mass-loss late in the life of AGB stars (where s-process nuclei are also made) and planetary nebulae (Section 6). Most heavier elements are produced in supernova or their precursor stars. SN II eject the products of nucleosynthesis that range from helium in the outer layers of the star, down to iron-peak elements on the edge of the iron core, and even elements beyond the iron peak that are produced by the r-process during the explosion (Section 7 and 8). SN Ia, whilst being lower mass objects not possessing an iron core *prior* to the explosion, are prolific producers of iron *during* the explosion.

The nucleosynthesis products *ejected* during (though not necessarily *produced* during) supernova explosions enrich the interstellar medium, and accompanying shock waves from the explosion are believed to compress interstellar clouds and trigger the next episode of star formation. Stars that form from gas enriched by these events have a higher metal content than previous generations of stars. Their stellar structure also differs, which in turn affects the ways they evolve. By observing the different chemical compositions, ages, and space motions of the stars that make up galaxies, astronomers can piece together the history of entire galaxies; that is the research field called galactic chemical evolution.

Self-study suggestion: Reread the section summaries in this Study Guide for Sections 1–3, then summarize in your own words each of the processes. Your notes should cover not only what happens but the physics driving it. Pick out the key equations that describe the physics, write those down, and describe in words the meanings of the terms and the equations overall.

9.4 Final summaries

| Activity 49 | 1 hour total |

Chapter summaries

If you have not already done so, read the chapter summaries in Phillips for Chapters 1–6. You have not studied all chapters completely, so you may wish first to survey which sections you *have* studied. Where appropriate, use this as a prompt to write your own brief summaries of material covered in Phillips or the Study Guide.

Keywords: none ■

ACHIEVEMENTS

Now that you have completed this block, you should be able to:

A1   Explain the meaning of the newly defined (emboldened) terms introduced in this block, and understand these when they are used in scientific articles not specifically written for students.

A2   Carry out interactive multimedia tutorials.

A3   Develop numerical models using spreadsheet calculation and graphics tools.

A4   Manipulate numbers, symbols, powers and equations that describe processes in the life and death of stars.

A5   Work with logarithmic and exponential functions and with vector quantities.

A6   Carry out calculations and express answers in scientific notation to an appropriate number of significant figures.

A7   Understand what is signified by derivatives and integrals, and what is implied by partial differentiation and by the grad of a scalar field.

A8   Differentiate and integrate functions having applications to the life and death of stars.

A9   Understand and apply the ideal gas law where it affects the life and death of stars.

A10   Explain the information conveyed by a Hertzsprung–Russell diagram, and how the observational and theoretical H–R diagrams differ.

A11   Understand the relationship between the luminosity, effective temperature, and radius of a star, and how this relates to the H–R diagram.

A12   Describe the groupings of stars in the H–R diagram, their energy sources and their lifetimes, and how these depend on stellar mass.

A13   Describe the events in the life cycle of a star, how it ends up in particular regions of the H–R diagram, and the probable end point of its evolution.

A14   Explain what is meant by hydrostatic equilibrium, both in words and mathematically, and its relevance to stellar evolution.

A15   Describe the virial theorem, both in words and mathematically, and how it can be used to understand the evolution of stars.

A16   Understand the difference between the virial theorem for non-relativistic and ultra-relativistic particles, and the implications this has for the pressure-support and stability of stars.

A17   Understand the definition and usefulness of the adiabatic index γ.

A18   Understand what sets the lower limit on the mass of a star, and what that limit is.

A19   Recognize the different forms of the Jeans criterion for the collapse of a gas cloud.

A20   Understand what causes cloud fragmentation.

A21   Appreciate the difference between the free-fall and Kelvin–Helmholtz timescales in star formation, how long each one is, and when each one applies.

A22   Describe how a collapsing star moves in the temperature–density plane, and what marks the different stages and the turning points.

A23   Estimate typical radii for a collapsing cloud and protostar at various stages of evolution from a cloud of cold molecular hydrogen.

A24   Know the observational appearances of protostars and pre-main-sequence objects.

A25   Describe the location of the Hayashi boundary and explain its origin.

A26   Describe the evolutionary tracks in the H–R diagram of new stars approaching the main sequence.

A27   Know the temperature required for hydrogen ignition in a main-sequence object and the main reactions.

A28   Understand the relationship between the luminosity of a star, its lifetime, and its energy generation mechanism, and which determines which.

A29   Estimate the mean density, the mean (volume-averaged) pressure, and the typical internal temperature of a main-sequence star of given mass.

A30   Identify the potential sources of pressure support in stars, know how their equations of state differ, and understand the implications for the stability of stars.

A31   Know the typical sizes of nuclei, appreciate the difference between geometric cross-sections and collision cross-sections, and know how the collision cross-section of a target nucleus relates to the mean free path of a projectile.

A32   Explain the use of wave functions $\psi(x, t)$ to describe particles, and the significance of the squared amplitude $|\psi|^2$.

A33   Explain barrier penetration/quantum tunnelling and its importance in stars.

A34   Understand how the Gamow energy characterizes the Coulomb repulsion of nuclei.

A35   Recognize the terms that make up the reaction cross-section for nuclear fusion, and explain how the competing energy-dependence of the terms gives it a Gaussian form.

A36   Interpret the logarithmic derivative $v \equiv \dfrac{\mathrm{d} \ln R_{AB}}{\mathrm{d} \ln T}$ as the temperature dependence of nuclear burning, and calculate how it varies for different fusion reactions.

A37   Explain the conversion of hydrogen to helium in the proton-proton chain and the CNO cycle, state the main bottlenecks in these reactions, and describe any observable consequences of these reactions.

A38   Calculate the energy liberated into stellar cores on the basis of the mass defect.

A39   Understand the consequences of reactions attaining equilibrium, and calculate the equilibrium ratios of the isotopes from their chemical potentials.

A40   Explain the relationship between the observed mass–luminosity relation of main-sequence stars and their lifetimes as a function of mass, and describe how this affects the appearance and interpretation of the H–R diagram.

A41   Understand how the mean molecular weight of a gas depends on both the chemical composition and its state of dissociation and ionization.

A42   Understand what is meant by a Kramers opacity.

A43   Understand what causes a star to change from a core-burning to a shell-burning object, and what this does to its appearance in the H–R diagram.

A44   Explain the conditions under which convection becomes important, and discuss its implications for the luminosity of a star and the consequences of dredge-ups.

A45   Appreciate the different nucleosynthetic origins of various groups of elements, and why different sites are able or unable to produce certain isotopes.

A46   Understand what is meant by degeneracy, show that it can be described in several equivalent ways, and describe how the equation of state of degenerate gas differs from that for an ideal gas. Know what stars are affected by degeneracy, and how and why it depends on stellar mass.

A47   Describe the conditions required for helium burning and how helium ignition depends on the state of degeneracy. Explain the reactions involved in helium burning and their products, where such stars are found in the H–R diagram, and why their helium-burning lifetime is so much shorter than their hydrogen burning phase.

A48   Describe the development of a planetary nebula beginning from mass-loss by an AGB star, and the evolution of the central star along with timescales.

A49   Appreciate the distinction between non-relativistic and ultra-relativistic degenerate electrons and the implications for the stability of a stellar remnant.

A50   Understand the relationship between the mass and radius of a white dwarf, and its evolution in the H–R diagram.

A51   Describe the conditions required for nuclear fusion beyond helium burning, the stars in which this occurs, and the temperatures, timescales, and products of these reactions.

A52   Explain why the most advanced stages of burning lead to a peak of elements around iron.

A53   Discuss the difficulties for synthesizing elements heavier than the iron peak, how they are produced, and the probable sites of these reactions.

A54   Describe how the various isotopes of heavy elements may originate in different processes, and the observable consequences for the isotopes and their abundances.

A55   Explain what processes occur when a massive star's iron core exceeds the Chandrasekhar limit, how energy is redistributed, and what the observable consequences may be.

A56   Appreciate the distinctions between the two main types of supernovae.

A57   Discuss the relationship between the evolution of stars, nucleosynthesis of the elements, and ultimately the chemical evolution of galaxies.

A58   Explain why neutron stars are called *neutron* stars, and how neutrons survive rather than decay.

A59   Compare the physics of white dwarfs and neutron stars to explain the differences in their radii and their maximum masses.

A60   Explain how we can be sure that pulsars are neutrons stars, and why the magnetic dipole model is favoured.

A61   Describe the basic properties of black holes.

ANSWERS TO QUESTIONS

Question 1

The free-fall time is given by $\tau_{FF} = \left(\dfrac{3\pi}{32G} \dfrac{1}{\rho} \right)^{1/2}$

To calculate this, we need the density of the gas, ρ. The density of a uniform sphere having the same mass and radius as the Sun is given by $\rho = \text{mass/volume} = M_\odot / \frac{4}{3}\pi R_\odot^3$. Substituting this into the free-fall time, we find

$$\tau_{FF} = \left(\frac{3\pi}{32G} \frac{\frac{4}{3}\pi R_\odot^3}{M_\odot} \right)^{1/2} = \left(\frac{4\pi^2}{32G} \frac{R_\odot^3}{M_\odot} \right)^{1/2} = \pi \left(\frac{1}{8G} \frac{R_\odot^3}{M_\odot} \right)^{1/2}$$

$$= \pi \left(\frac{1}{8 \times 6.673 \times 10^{-11}\,\text{N}\,\text{m}^2\,\text{kg}^{-2}} \frac{(6.96 \times 10^8\,\text{m})^3}{1.99 \times 10^{30}\,\text{kg}} \right)^{1/2}$$

$$= 1.77 \times 10^3 \left(\frac{\text{m}}{\text{N}\,\text{kg}^{-1}} \right)^{1/2} = 1.77 \times 10^3 \left(\frac{\text{m}}{\text{kg}\,\text{m}\,\text{s}^{-2}\,\text{kg}^{-1}} \right)^{1/2} = 1.77 \times 10^3\,\text{s}$$

Question 2

The Jeans mass is $M_J = \dfrac{3kT}{2G\overline{m}} R$ (Phillips page 14). Rearranging this gives

$$R = M_J \frac{2G\overline{m}}{3kT} = M_\odot \frac{2G2u}{3kT}$$

since the average mass of a H_2 molecule is $\overline{m} \approx 2u$ (where u is the atomic mass unit). Substituting in values gives

$$R = 1.99 \times 10^{30}\,\text{kg} \frac{2 \times 6.673 \times 10^{-11}\,\text{N}\,\text{m}^2\,\text{kg}^{-2} \times 2 \times 1.661 \times 10^{-27}\,\text{kg}}{3 \times 1.381 \times 10^{-23}\,\text{J}\,\text{K}^{-1} \times 20\,\text{K}}$$

$$= 1.07 \times 10^{15} \frac{\text{N}\,\text{m}^2}{\text{J}} = 1.07 \times 10^{15} \frac{\text{N}\,\text{m}^2}{\text{N}\,\text{m}} = 1.07 \times 10^{15}\,\text{m}$$

Since $1\,\text{pc} = 3.086 \times 10^{16}\,\text{m}$, $1\,\text{AU} = 1.496 \times 10^{11}\,\text{m}$, and $R_\odot = 6.96 \times 10^8\,\text{m}$, we can also express this distance as

$R = 1.07 \times 10^{15}\,\text{m}/3.086 \times 10^{16}\,\text{m}\,\text{pc}^{-1} = 0.0347\,\text{pc}\ (\approx 0.03\,\text{pc})$, or

$R = 1.07 \times 10^{15}\,\text{m}/1.496 \times 10^{11}\,\text{m}\,\text{AU}^{-1} = 7.15 \times 10^3\,\text{AU}\ (\approx 7000\,\text{AU})$, or

$R = 1.07 \times 10^{15}\,\text{m}/6.96 \times 10^8\,\text{m}\,\text{R}_\odot^{-1} = 1.54 \times 10^6\,\text{R}_\odot\ (\approx 1.5\ \text{million}\ \text{R}_\odot)$

Question 3

The density is $\rho = \rho_J = \dfrac{3}{4\pi M^2} \left(\dfrac{3kT}{2G\overline{m}} \right)^3$, so the free-fall time is

$$\tau_{FF} = \left(\frac{3\pi}{32G} \frac{1}{\rho} \right)^{1/2} = \left(\frac{3\pi}{32G} \frac{4\pi M^2}{3} \left(\frac{2G\overline{m}}{3kT} \right)^3 \right)^{1/2} = \left((\pi G)^2 M^2 \left(\frac{\overline{m}}{3kT} \right)^3 \right)^{1/2}$$

The mass of a molecule of H_2 is $\overline{m} \approx 2u$, so

$$\tau_{FF} = \left((\pi G)^2 M_\odot^2 \left(\frac{2u}{3kT} \right)^3 \right)^{1/2} = \pi G M_\odot \left(\frac{2u}{3kT} \right)^{3/2}$$

$$= \pi \times 6.673 \times 10^{-11} \, \text{N m}^2 \, \text{kg}^{-2} \times 1.99 \times 10^{30} \, \text{kg}$$

$$\times \left(\frac{2 \times 1.661 \times 10^{-27} \, \text{kg}}{3 \times 1.381 \times 10^{-23} \, \text{J K}^{-1} \times 20 \, \text{K}} \right)^{3/2}$$

$$= 3.35 \times 10^{12} \, \text{s} \approx 1.1 \times 10^5 \, \text{yr}$$

Question 4

The Jeans mass is $M_J = \dfrac{3kT}{2G\overline{m}} R$, but the quantities we have are the particle masses (via their identifications) and number densities, and the temperature of the gas, so this equation needs more work done on it.

A cloud collapses if its mass M exceeds the value of the Jeans mass

$$M > \frac{3kT}{2G\overline{m}} R \equiv M_J$$

Since the cloud density $\rho = \text{mass/volume} = M / \frac{4}{3} \pi R^3$, we can write $R = (M / \frac{4}{3} \pi \rho)^{1/3}$ and use this to eliminate R from the Jeans mass, giving

$$M > \frac{3kT}{2G\overline{m}} \left(\frac{M}{\frac{4}{3} \pi \rho} \right)^{1/3}$$

The mass per unit volume ρ is just the number of particles per unit volume n multiplied by the mass of each particle $\overline{m}$, $\rho = n\overline{m}$, so we can rearrange this and write

$$M > \frac{3kT}{2G\overline{m}} \left(\frac{M}{\frac{4}{3} \pi n\overline{m}} \right)^{1/3}, \quad \text{so} \quad MM^{-1/3} > \frac{3kT}{2G\overline{m}} \left(\frac{3}{4\pi n\overline{m}} \right)^{1/3}$$

Raising each side to the (3/2)-power gives $M > \left(\dfrac{3kT}{2G\overline{m}} \right)^{3/2} \left(\dfrac{3}{4\pi n\overline{m}} \right)^{1/2}$.

Since the cloud collapses if its mass M exceeds the value on the right-hand side, we can identify this as an alternative expression of the Jeans mass

i.e. $M_J = \left(\dfrac{3kT}{2G\overline{m}} \right)^{3/2} \left(\dfrac{3}{4\pi n\overline{m}} \right)^{1/2}$

Note that since all of the Jean's criteria are developed from a single condition, $E_{TOT} < 0$, they can be used interchangeably, and an alternative starting point would

have been the Jeans density $\rho_J = \dfrac{3}{4\pi M^2} \left(\dfrac{3kT}{2G\overline{m}} \right)^3$, which can be rearranged directly

to give $M = \sqrt{\dfrac{3}{4\pi \rho_J} \left(\dfrac{3kT}{2G\overline{m}} \right)^3}$, into which we substitute $\rho = n\overline{m}$!

We can now evaluate the Jeans masses.

(a) Using $\overline{m} \approx 1u$ (i.e. 1 amu) for neutral atomic hydrogen,

$$M_{\rm J} = \left(\frac{3kT}{2G\overline{m}}\right)^{3/2}\left(\frac{3}{4\pi n\overline{m}}\right)^{1/2}$$

$$= \left(\frac{3\times 1.381\times 10^{-23}\,{\rm J\,K^{-1}}\times 100\,{\rm K}}{2\times 6.673\times 10^{-11}\,{\rm N\,m^2\,kg^{-2}}\times 1.661\times 10^{-27}\,{\rm kg}}\right)^{3/2}$$

$$\times\left(\frac{3}{4\pi\times 10^6\,{\rm m^{-3}}\times 1.661\times 10^{-27}\,{\rm kg}}\right)^{1/2}$$

$$= 3.06\times 10^{34}\left(\frac{\rm J}{\rm N\,m^2\,kg}\right)^{3/2}\left(\frac{\rm m^3}{\rm kg}\right)^{1/2}$$

$$= 3.06\times 10^{34}({\rm kg^{3/2}\,m^{-3/2}})({\rm m^{3/2}\,kg^{-1/2}}) = 3.06\times 10^{34}\,{\rm kg}$$

Since $1{\rm M}_\odot = 1.99\times 10^{30}\,{\rm kg}$, $M_{\rm J} = 3.06\times 10^{34}\,{\rm kg}/1.99\times 10^{30}\,{\rm kg\,M_\odot^{-1}}$
$= 1.54\times 10^4\,{\rm M}_\odot$

(b) Using $\overline{m} \approx 2u$ (i.e. 2 amu) for molecular hydrogen,

$$M_{\rm J} = \left(\frac{3kT}{2G\overline{m}}\right)^{3/2}\left(\frac{3}{4\pi n\overline{m}}\right)^{1/2}$$

$$= \left(\frac{3\times 1.381\times 10^{-23}\,{\rm J\,K^{-1}}\times 10\,{\rm K}}{2\times 6.673\times 10^{-11}\,{\rm N\,m^2\,kg^{-2}}\times 2\times 1.661\times 10^{-27}\,{\rm kg}}\right)^{3/2}$$

$$\times\left(\frac{3}{4\pi\times 10^9\,{\rm m^{-3}}\times 2\times 1.661\times 10^{-27}\,{\rm kg}}\right)^{1/2}$$

$$= 7.66\times 10^{30}\,{\rm kg}$$

Since $1{\rm M}_\odot = 1.99\times 10^{30}\,{\rm kg}$, $M_{\rm J} = 7.66\times 10^{30}\,{\rm kg}/1.99\times 10^{30}\,{\rm kg\,M_\odot^{-1}} = 3.85{\rm M}_\odot$.

Question 5

(a) Beginning with the Jeans mass (written in terms of density and temperature)

$$M_{\rm J} = \sqrt{\frac{3}{4\pi\rho}\left(\frac{3kT}{2G\overline{m}}\right)^3}$$

we seek an expression for the temperature T. Begin by re-writing the square-root as a (1/2)-power, giving

$$M_{\rm J} = \left(\frac{3}{4\pi\rho}\right)^{1/2}\left(\frac{3kT}{2G\overline{m}}\right)^{3/2}$$

and then multiply both sides by

$$\left(\frac{4\pi\rho}{3}\right)^{1/2}\left(\frac{2G\overline{m}}{3k}\right)^{3/2}\quad\text{to get}\quad\left(\frac{4\pi\rho}{3}\right)^{1/2}\left(\frac{2G\overline{m}}{3k}\right)^{3/2}M_{\rm J} = T^{3/2}$$

Raising each side to the (2/3)-power, and re-ordering the terms gives

$$T = \frac{2G\overline{m}}{3k}\left(\frac{4\pi}{3}\right)^{1/3}M_{\rm J}^{2/3}\rho^{1/3}$$

(b) Since $\log_{10} AB = \log_{10} A + \log_{10} B$, and $\log_{10} A^k = k \log_{10} A$, we get

$$\log_{10} T = \log_{10}\left(\frac{2G\overline{m}}{3k}\left(\frac{4\pi}{3}\right)^{1/3}\right) + \frac{2}{3}\log_{10} M_J + \frac{1}{3}\log_{10}\rho$$

where all quantities are in SI units. The first term on the right-hand side of the equation is merely a constant, whereas the second and third depend on mass and density. Drawn in the log temperature versus log density plane, the curve of T against ρ for a *given* protostellar mass M is a straight line of slope 1/3. The Jeans line for a protostellar mass 10 times higher (or lower) is also a straight line of slope 1/3, but offset vertically from the first by +2/3 (or −2/3) logarithmic units.

Question 6

(a) We have two expressions for pressure, $P \propto \rho^{\gamma}$ for an adiabatic process, and $P = \rho kT/\overline{m}$ for an ideal gas.

Substituting for P in the first gives $\rho kT/\overline{m} \propto \rho^{\gamma}$.

Dividing both sides by $\rho k/\overline{m}$ gives $T \propto (\overline{m}/k)\rho^{\gamma-1}$, but $\overline{m}$ and k are both constants, so we can write $T \propto \rho^{\gamma-1}$.

(b) Since $T \propto \rho^{\gamma-1}$, we can also write $T = \text{const} \times \rho^{\gamma-1}$ where 'const' is a constant. Taking logarithms of both sides of the equation gives
$\log_{10} T = \log_{10}(\text{const}) + (\gamma - 1)\log_{10}\rho$.
Therefore the adiabats are straight lines of slope $\gamma - 1$.

(c) $\gamma = \dfrac{1 + (s/2)}{(s/2)}$, so for $s = 3$, $\gamma = 5/3$, and the slope $\gamma - 1$ of the adiabat of an ideal gas with three degrees of freedom is $5/3 - 3/3 = 2/3$.

(d) s takes values 3 to ∞, so γ takes values 5/3 to 1, and the slope is in the range 2/3 to 0.

(e) If $\gamma = 4/3$, then the adiabat has slope $\gamma - 1 = 1/3$.

Question 7

Convert to SI units first. One electronvolt is the product of the charge on an electron, 1.602×10^{-19} C with 1 V (1 J C^{-1}), or 1.602×10^{-19} J. The energy 13.6 eV is therefore $13.6 \times 1.602 \times 10^{-19}$ J $= 2.18 \times 10^{-18}$ J.

You now need to express this energy as a kT-equivalent, and hence find the corresponding value of the temperature. The Boltzmann constant $k = 1.381 \times 10^{-23}$ J K^{-1}, so the characteristic temperature is $T = 2.18 \times 10^{-18}$ J$/1.381 \times 10^{-23}$ J K$^{-1} \approx 158\,000$ K.

Question 8

The Jeans length is

$$R_J = \frac{2G\overline{m}}{3kT}M_J$$

$$= \frac{2 \times 6.673 \times 10^{-11}\,\text{N m}^2\,\text{kg}^{-2} \times 2 \times 1.661 \times 10^{-27}\,\text{kg}}{3 \times 1.381 \times 10^{-23}\,\text{J K}^{-1} \times 20\,\text{K}} \times 1.99 \times 10^{30}\,\text{kg}$$

$$= 1.06 \times 10^{15}\,\frac{\text{N m}^2}{\text{J}} = 1.06 \times 10^{15}\,\frac{\text{N m}^2}{\text{N m}} = 1.06 \times 10^{15}\,\text{m}$$

Question 9

(a) $\tau_{KH,\odot} = GM_\odot^2/R_\odot L_\odot$

$$= \frac{6.673 \times 10^{-11}\,\text{N}\,\text{m}^2\,\text{kg}^{-2} \times (1.99 \times 10^{30}\,\text{kg})^2}{6.96 \times 10^8\,\text{m} \times 3.83 \times 10^{26}\,\text{J}\,\text{s}^{-1}}$$

$$= 9.90 \times 10^{14}\,\frac{\text{N}\,\text{m}^2\,\text{kg}^{-2}\,\text{kg}^2}{\text{m}\,\text{J}\,\text{s}^{-1}} = 9.90 \times 10^{14}\,\frac{\text{N}\,\text{m}^2}{\text{m}\,\text{N}\,\text{m}\,\text{s}^{-1}}$$

$$= 9.90 \times 10^{14}\,\text{s} \approx 10^{15}\,\text{s}$$

(b) Since 1 year $= 31.56 \times 10^6\,\text{s}$,

$$\tau_{KH,\odot} = 9.90 \times 10^{14}\,\text{s}/31.56 \times 10^6\,\text{s}\,\text{yr}^{-1}$$

$$= 3.14 \times 10^7\,\text{yr, or} \approx 3 \times 10^7\,\text{yr}$$

Question 10

Schrödinger's (time-independent) equation in three dimensions

$$\left[-\frac{\hbar^2 \nabla^2}{2m_r} + V(r) \right] \psi(r) = E\psi(r)$$

becomes $\dfrac{\partial^2}{\partial x^2}\psi(x) = \dfrac{2m_r}{\hbar^2}(V(x) - E)\psi(x)$ in one dimension.

(a) This wave function gives

$$\frac{\partial^2}{\partial x^2}\left(\left(\frac{2}{L}\right)^{1/2} \sin\left(\frac{2\pi x}{L}\right) \right) = \frac{2m_r}{\hbar^2}(V - E)\left(\left(\frac{2}{L}\right)^{1/2} \sin\left(\frac{2\pi x}{L}\right) \right)$$

Take the constants outside

$$\left(\frac{2}{L}\right)^{1/2} \frac{\partial}{\partial x}\left(\frac{\partial}{\partial x}\left(\sin\left(\frac{2\pi x}{L}\right) \right) \right) = \frac{2m_r}{\hbar^2}(V - E)\left(\frac{2}{L}\right)^{1/2} \sin\left(\frac{2\pi x}{L}\right)$$

Cancel the $(2/L)^{1/2}$ terms, and take the first derivative

$$\frac{\partial}{\partial x}\left(\frac{2\pi}{L}\cos\left(\frac{2\pi x}{L}\right) \right) = \frac{2m_r}{\hbar^2}(V - E)\sin\left(\frac{2\pi x}{L}\right)$$

take the constants outside

$$\frac{2\pi}{L}\frac{\partial}{\partial x}\left(\cos\left(\frac{2\pi x}{L}\right) \right) = \frac{2m_r}{\hbar^2}(V - E)\sin\left(\frac{2\pi x}{L}\right)$$

and take the next derivative

$$-\frac{2\pi}{L}\left(\frac{2\pi}{L}\sin\left(\frac{2\pi x}{L}\right) \right) = \frac{2m_r}{\hbar^2}(V - E)\sin\left(\frac{2\pi x}{L}\right)$$

Cancel the sine terms

$$-\left(\frac{2\pi}{L}\right)^2 = \frac{2m_r}{\hbar^2}(V - E)$$

Rearrange the rest

$$-\frac{\hbar^2}{2m_r}\left(\frac{2\pi}{L}\right)^2 = V - E$$

to give an expression for E

$$E_2 = V + 2^2 \frac{\pi^2 \hbar^2}{2m_r L^2}$$

(b) Following the same steps as in (a), this wave function gives

$$\frac{\partial^2}{\partial x^2}\left(\left(\frac{2}{L}\right)^{1/2} \cos\left(\frac{3\pi x}{L}\right)\right) = \frac{2m_r}{\hbar^2}(V - E)\left(\left(\frac{2}{L}\right)^{1/2} \cos\left(\frac{3\pi x}{L}\right)\right)$$

$$\left(\frac{2}{L}\right)^{1/2} \frac{\partial}{\partial x}\left(\frac{\partial}{\partial x}\left(\cos\left(\frac{3\pi x}{L}\right)\right)\right) = \frac{2m_r}{\hbar^2}(V - E)\left(\frac{2}{L}\right)^{1/2} \cos\left(\frac{3\pi x}{L}\right)$$

$$\frac{\partial}{\partial x}\left(-\frac{3\pi}{L}\sin\left(\frac{3\pi x}{L}\right)\right) = \frac{2m_r}{\hbar^2}(V - E)\cos\left(\frac{3\pi x}{L}\right)$$

$$-\frac{3\pi}{L}\frac{\partial}{\partial x}\left(\sin\left(\frac{3\pi x}{L}\right)\right) = \frac{2m_r}{\hbar^2}(V - E)\cos\left(\frac{3\pi x}{L}\right)$$

$$-\frac{3\pi}{L}\left(\frac{3\pi}{L}\cos\left(\frac{3\pi x}{L}\right)\right) = \frac{2m_r}{\hbar^2}(V - E)\cos\left(\frac{3\pi x}{L}\right)$$

$$-\left(\frac{3\pi}{L}\right)^2 = \frac{2m_r}{\hbar^2}(V - E)$$

$$-\frac{\hbar^2}{2m_r}\left(\frac{3\pi}{L}\right)^2 = V - E$$

$$E_3 = V + 3^2 \frac{\pi^2 \hbar^2}{2m_r L^2}$$

(c) Following the same steps as in (a), this wave function gives

$$\frac{\partial^2}{\partial x^2}\left(\left(\frac{2}{L}\right)^{1/2} \sin\left(\frac{4\pi x}{L}\right)\right) = \frac{2m_r}{\hbar^2}(V - E)\left(\left(\frac{2}{L}\right)^{1/2} \sin\left(\frac{4\pi x}{L}\right)\right)$$

$$\left(\frac{2}{L}\right)^{1/2} \frac{\partial}{\partial x}\left(\frac{\partial}{\partial x}\left(\sin\left(\frac{4\pi x}{L}\right)\right)\right) = \frac{2m_r}{\hbar^2}(V - E)\left(\frac{2}{L}\right)^{1/2} \sin\left(\frac{4\pi x}{L}\right)$$

$$\frac{\partial}{\partial x}\left(\frac{4\pi}{L}\cos\left(\frac{4\pi x}{L}\right)\right) = \frac{2m_r}{\hbar^2}(V - E)\sin\left(\frac{4\pi x}{L}\right)$$

$$\frac{4\pi}{L}\frac{\partial}{\partial x}\left(\cos\left(\frac{4\pi x}{L}\right)\right) = \frac{2m_r}{\hbar^2}(V - E)\sin\left(\frac{4\pi x}{L}\right)$$

$$-\frac{4\pi}{L}\left(\frac{4\pi}{L}\sin\left(\frac{4\pi x}{L}\right)\right) = \frac{2m_r}{\hbar^2}(V - E)\sin\left(\frac{4\pi x}{L}\right)$$

$$-\left(\frac{4\pi}{L}\right)^2 = \frac{2m_r}{\hbar^2}(V - E)$$

$$-\frac{\hbar^2}{2m_r}\left(\frac{4\pi}{L}\right)^2 = V - E$$

$$E_4 = V + 4^2 \frac{\pi^2 \hbar^2}{2m_r L^2}$$

Question 11

The Schrödinger (time-independent) equation in one dimension is

$$\left[-\frac{\hbar^2}{2m_r} \frac{\partial^2}{\partial x^2} + V(x) \right] \psi(x) = E\psi(x)$$

which can also be written

$$\frac{\partial^2}{\partial x^2} \psi(x) = \frac{2m_r}{\hbar^2} (V(x) - E)\psi(x)$$

or $\qquad \dfrac{\partial^2}{\partial x^2} \psi(x) = \chi^2 \psi(x) \quad$ where $\quad \chi^2 = \dfrac{2m_r}{\hbar^2} (V(x) - E)$

To verify that the wave function $\psi(x) = \exp(\chi x)$ is a solution for a constant potential (i.e. when V and hence χ do not depend on x), substitute this into the left-hand side of the Schrödinger equation:

$$\frac{\partial^2}{\partial x^2} \psi(x) = \frac{\partial^2}{\partial x^2} \exp(\chi x)$$

Expand the double derivative

$$\frac{\partial^2}{\partial x^2} \psi(x) = \frac{\partial}{\partial x} \frac{\partial}{\partial x} \exp(\chi x)$$

Evaluate the first derivative

$$\frac{\partial^2}{\partial x^2} \psi(x) = \frac{\partial}{\partial x} \chi \exp(\chi x)$$

and then the second, but note that $\exp(\chi x) = \psi(x)$

$$\frac{\partial^2}{\partial x^2} \psi(x) = \chi^2 \exp(\chi x) = \chi^2 \psi(x)$$

which equals the right-hand side of Schrödinger equation, as required. Note that if the barrier potential had not been constant, then χ would depend on x, and the differentiation would not be so straightforward.

Question 12

The Gamow energy is $E_G = 2m_r c^2 (\pi \alpha Z_A Z_B)^2$, where m_r is the reduced mass of the two-body system, given by $m_r = m_A m_B / (m_A + m_B)$.

(a) Begin by calculating the reduced mass:

$$m_r = \frac{m_p m_p}{m_p + m_p} = \frac{m_p^2}{2m_p} = \frac{m_p}{2} = \frac{1.673 \times 10^{-27} \text{ kg}}{2}$$

$$= 8.365 \times 10^{-28} \text{ kg}$$

Then $\quad E_G = 2m_r c^2 (\pi \alpha Z_p Z_p)^2$

$$= 2 \times 8.365 \times 10^{-28} \text{ kg} \times (2.998 \times 10^8 \text{ m s}^{-1})^2 (\pi \times \tfrac{1}{137.0} \times 1 \times 1)^2$$

$$= 7.907 \times 10^{-14} \text{ kg m}^2 \text{ s}^{-2}$$

$$= 7.907 \times 10^{-14} \text{ J}$$

Since $1 \text{ J} = 1.602 \times 10^{-19} \text{ eV}$, $E_G = 7.907 \times 10^{-14} \text{ J}/1.602 \times 10^{-19} \text{ J eV}^{-1} = 493.6 \text{ keV}$.

(b) $m_r = \dfrac{m_p m_d}{m_p + m_d} \approx \dfrac{m_p \times 2m_p}{m_p + 2m_p} = \dfrac{2m_p^2}{3m_p} = \dfrac{2m_p}{3}$

$ = \dfrac{2 \times 1.673 \times 10^{-27}\,\text{kg}}{3} = 1.115 \times 10^{-27}\,\text{kg}$

Then $E_G = 2m_r c^2 (\pi \alpha Z_p Z_p)^2$

$ = 2 \times 8.365 \times 10^{-28}\,\text{kg} \times (2.998 \times 10^8\,\text{m s}^{-1})^2 (\pi \times \tfrac{1}{137.0} \times 1 \times 1)^2$

$ = 7.907 \times 10^{-14}\,\text{kg m}^2\,\text{s}^{-2}$

$ = 7.907 \times 10^{-14}\,\text{J}$

Since $1\,\text{J} = 1.602 \times 10^{-19}\,\text{eV}$, $E_G = 1.054 \times 10^{-13}\,\text{J} / 1.602 \times 10^{-19}\,\text{J eV}^{-1} = 657.9\,\text{keV}$.

The charge is the same as in (a), but the reduced mass m_r is greater by a factor of 4/3 because of the extra neutron.

(c) $m_r = \dfrac{m_3 m_3}{m_3 + m_3} = \dfrac{m_3^2}{2m_3} = \dfrac{m_3}{2} = \dfrac{3m_p}{2}$

$ = \dfrac{3 \times 1.673 \times 10^{-27}\,\text{kg}}{2} = 2.510 \times 10^{-27}\,\text{kg}$

Then

$ E_G = 2m_r c^2 (\pi \alpha Z_{3He} Z_{3He})^2$

$ = 2 \times 2.510 \times 10^{-27}\,\text{kg} \times (2.998 \times 10^8\,\text{m s}^{-1})^2 (\pi \times \tfrac{1}{137.0} \times 2 \times 2)^2$

$ = 3.796 \times 10^{-12}\,\text{J}$

Since $1\,\text{J} = 1.602 \times 10^{-19}\,\text{eV}$, $E_G = 3.796 \times 10^{-12}\,\text{J} / 1.602 \times 10^{-19}\,\text{J eV}^{-1} = 23.70\,\text{MeV}$.

Question 13

(a) If $T_c = 15.6 \times 10^6\,\text{K}$, then $kT_c = 1.381 \times 10^{-23}\,\text{J K}^{-1} \times 15.6 \times 10^6\,\text{K}$
$= 2.15 \times 10^{-16}\,\text{J}$.

Since $1\,\text{J} = 1.602 \times 10^{-19}\,\text{eV}$, $kT_c = 2.15 \times 10^{-16}\,\text{J} / 1.602 \times 10^{-19}\,\text{J eV}^{-1} = 1.34\,\text{keV}$.

(b) The penetration probabilities are

$$P_{pen} \approx \exp\left[-\left(\frac{E_G}{E}\right)^{1/2}\right] \approx \exp\left[-\left(\frac{E_G}{kT}\right)^{1/2}\right]$$

(i) proton–proton

$$P_{pen} \approx \exp\left[-\left(\frac{493.6\,\text{keV}}{1.34\,\text{keV}}\right)^{1/2}\right] = 4.6 \times 10^{-9}$$

(ii) proton–deuteron

$$P_{pen} \approx \exp\left[-\left(\frac{657.9\,\text{keV}}{1.34\,\text{keV}}\right)^{1/2}\right] = 2.4 \times 10^{-10}$$

(iii) $^3\text{He}-^3\text{He}$

$$P_{\text{pen}} \approx \exp\left[-\left(\frac{23\,700\,\text{keV}}{1.34\,\text{keV}}\right)^{1/2}\right] = 1.7 \times 10^{-58}\,!$$

Note that the answers have been given to only 2 significant figures, rather than the 3 s.f. available, because the approximation that the energy is given by $E \approx kT_c$ degrades the accuracy further.

Question 14

Assume that $S(E)$ is such a weak function of energy that it can be treated as a constant, so the integrand can be written

$$f = S \exp\left[-\left(\frac{E_G}{E}\right)^{1/2} - \frac{E}{kT}\right]$$

Differentiating gives

$$\frac{df}{dE} = S \frac{d}{dE} \exp\left[-\left(\frac{E_G}{E}\right)^{1/2} - \frac{E}{kT}\right]$$

but using Hint 2 gives

$$\frac{df}{dE} = S \exp\left[-\left(\frac{E_G}{E}\right)^{1/2} - \frac{E}{kT}\right]\frac{d}{dE}\left[-\left(\frac{E_G}{E}\right)^{1/2} - \frac{E}{kT}\right]$$

$$= S \exp\left[-\left(\frac{E_G}{E}\right)^{1/2} - \frac{E}{kT}\right]\left[-E_G^{1/2}\left(-\frac{1}{2}E^{-3/2}\right) - \frac{1}{kT}\right]$$

$$= S \exp\left[-\left(\frac{E_G}{E}\right)^{1/2}\right]\exp\left(-\frac{E}{kT}\right)\left[\frac{E_G^{1/2}}{2}(E^{-3/2}) - \frac{1}{kT}\right]$$

The integrand $f(E)$ is either a minimum or maximum when $df/dE = 0$, which is when one of the following terms is zero:

(i) $S = 0$; this is a trivial, uninteresting case.

(ii) $\exp[-(E_G/E)^{1/2}] = 0$; this occurs when E is very small.

(iii) $\exp[-E/(kT)] = 0$; this occurs when E is very large.

(iv) $\left[\frac{E_G^{1/2}}{2}(E^{-3/2}) - \frac{1}{kT}\right] = 0$

We rearrange this to get an expression for E

$$\frac{E_G^{1/2}}{2}(E^{-3/2}) = \frac{1}{kT}$$

$$E^{-3/2} = \frac{2}{kT}E_G^{-1/2}$$

then take the $(-2/3)$-power of all terms

$$E = \left(\frac{kT}{2}\right)^{2/3} E_G^{1/3} = \left(\left(\frac{kT}{2}\right)^2 E_G\right)^{1/3}$$

That is, $df/dE = 0$ when $E = [E_G(\frac{1}{2}kT)^2]^{1/3}$. This is the interesting case, and

the energy $E_0 = [E_G(\frac{1}{2}kT)^2]^{1/3}$ is called the Gamow peak.

(Do not confuse this with the Gamow energy E_G.)

Question 15

(a) $R_{AB} = 6.48 \times 10^{-24} \dfrac{n_A n_B}{A_r Z_A Z_B} S(E_0) \left(\dfrac{E_G}{4kT}\right)^{2/3} \exp\left[-3\left(\dfrac{E_G}{4kT}\right)^{1/3}\right] \text{m}^{-3}\,\text{s}^{-1}$

Following Hint 1, define $a = 6.48 \times 10^{-24} \dfrac{n_A n_B}{A_r Z_A Z_B} S(E_0)$, so

$$R_{AB} = a\left(\dfrac{E_G}{4kT}\right)^{2/3} \exp\left[-3\left(\dfrac{E_G}{4kT}\right)^{1/3}\right] \text{m}^{-3}\,\text{s}^{-1}$$

and in preparation for using Hint 2, write

$$u = a\left(\dfrac{E_G}{4kT}\right)^{2/3} \text{ and } v = \exp\left[-3\left(\dfrac{E_G}{4kT}\right)^{1/3}\right]$$

so $R_{AB} = uv$ and then $\dfrac{dR_{AB}}{dT} = u\dfrac{dv}{dT} + v\dfrac{du}{dT}$

For the sake of clarity, calculate these two parts separately.

Step 1: Calculate dv/dT

$$\dfrac{dv}{dT} = \dfrac{d}{dT}\exp\left[-3\left(\dfrac{E_G}{4kT}\right)^{1/3}\right]$$

but using Hint 3

$$\dfrac{d\exp(y)}{dx} = \dfrac{d\exp(y)}{dy}\dfrac{dy}{dx} = \exp(y)\dfrac{dy}{dx}$$

$$\dfrac{dv}{dT} = \exp\left[-3\left(\dfrac{E_G}{4kT}\right)^{1/3}\right]\dfrac{d}{dT}\left[-3\left(\dfrac{E_G}{4kT}\right)^{1/3}\right]$$

Note that the first exponential is just v again. Taking constants out of the differentiation gives

$$\dfrac{dv}{dT} = v\left[-3\left(\dfrac{E_G}{4k}\right)^{1/3}\right]\dfrac{d}{dT}T^{-1/3}$$

Differentiate using $\dfrac{d}{dx}x^k = kx^{k-1}$

$$\dfrac{dv}{dT} = v\left[-3\left(\dfrac{E_G}{4k}\right)^{1/3}\right]\left(-\dfrac{1}{3}\right)T^{-4/3} = v\left[\left(\dfrac{E_G}{4kT}\right)^{1/3}\right]\dfrac{1}{T}$$

Step 2: Calculate du/dT

$$\dfrac{du}{dT} = \dfrac{d}{dT}a\left(\dfrac{E_G}{4kT}\right)^{2/3}$$

taking the constants out of the differentiation gives

$$\frac{du}{dT} = a\left(\frac{E_G}{4k}\right)^{2/3}\frac{d}{dT}T^{-2/3} = a\left(\frac{E_G}{4k}\right)^{2/3}\left(-\frac{2}{3}\right)T^{-5/3}$$

$$= a\left(\frac{E_G}{4kT}\right)^{2/3}\left(-\frac{2}{3}\right)\frac{1}{T}$$

but the first term on the right-hand side of the equation is just u again, so

$$\frac{du}{dT} = u\left(-\frac{2}{3}\right)\frac{1}{T}$$

Step 3: Calculate $\dfrac{dR_{AB}}{dT} = u\dfrac{dv}{dT} + v\dfrac{du}{dT}$

Substitute the results from Steps 1 and 2

$$\frac{dR_{AB}}{dT} = uv\left[\left(\frac{E_G}{4kT}\right)^{1/3}\right]\frac{1}{T} + vu\left(-\frac{2}{3}\right)\frac{1}{T}$$

take out the common factor uv/T

$$\frac{dR_{AB}}{dT} = \frac{uv}{T}\left[\left(\frac{E_G}{4kT}\right)^{1/3} - \frac{2}{3}\right]$$

and note that uv is simply R_{AB}

$$\frac{dR_{AB}}{dT} = \frac{R_{AB}}{T}\left[\left(\frac{E_G}{4kT}\right)^{1/3} - \frac{2}{3}\right]$$

of which Phillips (Equation 4.29) is a simplification.

(b) The equation from (a) can be rearranged as

$$\frac{dR_{AB}}{R_{AB}} = \frac{dT}{T}\left[\left(\frac{E_G}{4kT}\right)^{1/3} - \frac{2}{3}\right]$$

but $dx/x = d\ln x$, so

$$d\ln R_{AB} = d\ln T\left[\left(\frac{E_G}{4kT}\right)^{1/3} - \frac{2}{3}\right]$$

i.e. $$\frac{d\ln R_{AB}}{d\ln T} = \left[\left(\frac{E_G}{4kT}\right)^{1/3} - \frac{2}{3}\right]$$

Question 16

$R_{AB} \propto T^{\left[(E_G/4kT)^{1/3} - \frac{2}{3}\right]}$, so you need to evaluate the value

$$v = \left(\frac{E_G}{4kT}\right)^{1/3} - \frac{2}{3}$$

for each reaction. Recall that

$$E_G = (\pi\alpha Z_A Z_B)^2 2m_r c^2, \quad \text{so} \quad v = \left(\frac{2m_r c^2(\pi\alpha Z_A Z_B)^2}{4kT}\right)^{1/3} - \frac{2}{3}$$

(a) For p + p, begin by calculating the reduced mass:

$$m_r = \frac{m_p m_p}{m_p + m_p} = \frac{m_p^2}{2m_p} = \frac{m_p}{2}$$

$$= \frac{1.673 \times 10^{-27}\ \text{kg}}{2} = 8.365 \times 10^{-28}\ \text{kg}$$

Then, using $T_{\odot,\text{centre}} = 15.6 \times 10^6$ K we obtain

$$\nu = \left(\frac{2m_r c^2 (\pi \alpha Z_p Z_p)^2}{4kT} \right)^{1/3} - \frac{2}{3}$$

$$= \left(\frac{2 \times 8.365 \times 10^{-28}\ \text{kg} \times (2.998 \times 10^8\ \text{m s}^{-1})^2 (\pi \times \frac{1}{137.0} \times 1 \times 1)^2}{4 \times 1.381 \times 10^{-23}\ \text{J K}^{-1} \times 15.6 \times 10^6\ \text{K}} \right)^{1/3} - \frac{2}{3}$$

$$= \left(91.8\ \frac{\text{kg m}^2\ \text{s}^{-2}}{\text{J}} \right)^{1/3} - \frac{2}{3} = \left(91.8\ \frac{\text{J}}{\text{J}} \right)^{1/3} - \frac{2}{3}$$

$$= 3.84$$

i.e. $R_{pp} \propto T^{3.8}$.

(b) For p + ^{14}N begin by calculating the reduced mass (where the reduced mass of ^{14}N is given as m_{14})

$$m_r = \frac{m_p m_{14}}{m_p + m_{14}} = \frac{1u \times 14u}{1u + 14u} = \frac{14u^2}{15u} = \frac{14}{15}u$$

$$= \left(\frac{14}{15} \right) \times 1.661 \times 10^{-27}\ \text{kg} = 1.550 \times 10^{-27}\ \text{kg}$$

Then

$$\nu = \left(\frac{2m_r c^2 (\pi \alpha Z_p Z_p)^2}{4kT} \right)^{1/3} - \frac{2}{3}$$

$$= \left(\frac{2 \times 1.550 \times 10^{-27}\ \text{kg} \times (2.998 \times 10^8\ \text{m s}^{-1})^2 (\pi \times \frac{1}{137.0} \times 1 \times 7)^2}{4 \times 1.381 \times 10^{-23}\ \text{J K}^{-1} \times 15.6 \times 10^6\ \text{K}} \right)^{1/3} - \frac{2}{3}$$

$$= 19.6$$

i.e. $R_{p14N} \propto T^{19.6}$.

Question 17

The first step of the p-p chain is $p + p \rightarrow d + e^+ + \nu_e$

The fusion rate (Equation 4.27), with the number-density term appropriate for *identical* particles, is

$$R_{pp} = 6.48 \times 10^{-24}\ \frac{n_p^2}{2}\ \frac{1}{A_r Z_p Z_p}\ \frac{S(E_0)}{[\text{keV barns}]} \left(\frac{E_G}{4kT} \right)^{2/3} \exp\left[-3\left(\frac{E_G}{4kT} \right)^{1/3} \right] \text{m}^{-3}\ \text{s}^{-1}$$

Step 1: Compute the energy factor $E_G/4kT$

$$\frac{E_G}{4kT} = \frac{(\pi \alpha Z_p Z_p)^2 2m_r c^2}{4kT} = \frac{(\pi \alpha Z_p Z_p)^2 2 \dfrac{m_p m_p}{m_p + m_p} c^2}{4kT}$$

$$= \frac{(\pi \alpha Z_p Z_p)^2 2 \dfrac{m_p^2}{2m_p} c^2}{4kT} = \frac{(\pi \alpha Z_p Z_p)^2 m_p c^2}{4kT}$$

$$= \frac{(\pi \times \frac{1}{137.0} \times 1 \times 1)^2 \times 1.673 \times 10^{-27} \text{ kg} \times (2.998 \times 10^8 \text{ m s}^{-1})^2}{4 \times 1.381 \times 10^{-23} \text{ J K}^{-1} \times 15.6 \times 10^6 \text{ K}}$$

$$= 91.8 \frac{\text{kg m}^2 \text{ s}^{-2}}{\text{J}}$$

$$= 91.8$$

Step 2: Compute the fusion rate

The proton density in the solar centre is given by $n_p = \rho_{\odot,\text{centre}} X / m_p$, where X is the mass fraction of hydrogen.

The reduced atomic mass (in atomic mass units) is

$$A_r = m_r / [1\,\text{amu}] = \frac{m_p m_p}{m_p + m_p} \bigg/ u = \frac{m_p}{2u}$$

so we can write

$$R_{pp} = 6.48 \times 10^{-24} \frac{n_p^2}{2\,[\text{m}^{-6}]} \frac{1}{A_r Z_p Z_p} \frac{S(E_0)}{[\text{keV barns}]} \left(\frac{E_G}{4kT}\right)^{2/3} \exp\left[-3\left(\frac{E_G}{4kT}\right)^{1/3}\right] \text{m}^{-3} \text{ s}^{-1}$$

$$= 6.48 \times 10^{-24} \frac{(\rho_c X / m_p)^2}{2\,[\text{m}^{-6}]} \frac{2u}{m_p} \frac{1}{Z_p Z_p} \frac{S(E_0)}{[\text{keV barns}]} \left(\frac{E_G}{4kT}\right)^{2/3}$$

$$\times \exp\left[-3\left(\frac{E_G}{4kT}\right)^{1/3}\right] \text{m}^{-3} \text{ s}^{-1}$$

$$= 6.48 \times 10^{-24} \frac{(\rho_c X)^2}{m_p^3\,[\text{m}^{-6}]} \frac{u}{Z_p Z_p} \frac{S(E_0)}{[\text{keV barns}]} \left(\frac{E_G}{4kT}\right)^{2/3} \exp\left[-3\left(\frac{E_G}{4kT}\right)^{1/3}\right] \text{m}^{-3} \text{ s}^{-1}$$

$$= 6.48 \times 10^{-24} \frac{(1.48 \times 10^5 \text{ kg m}^{-3} \times 0.5)^2}{(1.673 \times 10^{-27} \text{ kg})^3\,[\text{m}^{-6}]} \frac{1.661 \times 10^{-27} \text{ kg}}{1 \times 1} \frac{3.8 \times 10^{-22} \text{ keV barns}}{[\text{keV barns}]}$$

$$\times (91.8)^{2/3} \exp[-3(91.8)^{1/3}] \text{m}^{-3} \text{ s}^{-1}$$

$$= 1.3 \times 10^{14} \text{ m}^{-3} \text{ s}^{-1}$$

That is, there are 130 trillion fusion reactions per cubic metre per second!

Step 3: Compute the proton lifetime

The fusion rate R_{pp} in $m^{-3}\,s^{-1}$ can also be expressed as the number density of protons, n_p, in m^{-3} divided by the lifetime of a proton pair before they fuse, τ_{pp}, in seconds: $R_{pp} = n_p/\tau_{pp}$, so the lifetime $\tau_{pp} = n_p/R_{pp}$ (see Phillips 4.18 and 4.19). Noting again that $n_p = \rho_c X/m_p$ gives

$$\tau_{pp} = \rho_c X/m_p R_{pp}$$
$$= 1.48 \times 10^5 \,\text{kg m}^{-3} \times 0.5/(1.673 \times 10^{-27}\,\text{kg} \times 1.3 \times 10^{14}\,\text{m}^{-3}\,\text{s}^{-1})$$
$$= 3.4 \times 10^{17}\,\text{s} \approx 11 \times 10^9 \text{ years}$$

This is the lifetime of *two* protons, so the average proton lifetime $\tau_p = \tau_{pp}/2 = 5.5 \times 10^9$ years, more than 5 billion years.

Question 18

(a) First calculate the energy ratio:

$$\frac{E_G}{4kT} = (\pi\alpha Z_p Z_{13C})^2 2\frac{m_p m_{13C}}{m_p + m_{13C}}\frac{c^2}{4kT}$$
$$= (\pi \times \tfrac{1}{137.0} \times 1 \times 6)^2 \times 2 \times \frac{1u \times 13u}{1u + 13u}\frac{(2.998 \times 10^8\,\text{m s}^{-1})^2}{4 \times 1.381 \times 10^{-23}\,\text{J K}^{-1} \times 15.6 \times 10^6\,\text{K}}$$
$$= 3.667 \times 10^{30} u\frac{(\text{m s}^{-1})^2}{\text{J}}$$
$$= 3.667 \times 10^{30} \times 1.661 \times 10^{-27}\,\text{kg}\frac{\text{m}^2\,\text{s}^{-2}}{\text{kg m}^2\,\text{s}^{-2}}$$
$$= 6091$$

Next compute the fusion rate per unit mass fraction:

$$\frac{R_{p13C}}{X_{13C}} = 6.48 \times 10^{-24}\frac{(A_p + A_{13C})\rho_{cen}^2 X_p}{(A_p A_{13C}u)^2 Z_p Z_{13C}}\frac{S(E_0)}{[\text{keV barns}]}\left(\frac{E_G}{4kT}\right)^{2/3}$$
$$\times \exp\left[-3\left(\frac{E_G}{4kT}\right)^{1/3}\right]\text{m}^{-3}\,\text{s}^{-1}$$
$$= 6.48 \times 10^{-24}\frac{(1+13) \times (1.48 \times 10^5\,\text{kg m}^{-3})^2 \times 0.5}{(1 \times 13 \times 1.661 \times 10^{-27}\,\text{kg})^2 \times 1 \times 6} \times \frac{5.5\,\text{keV barns}}{[\text{keV barns}]}$$
$$\times (6091)^{2/3} \exp\left[-3(6091)^{1/3}\right]\text{m}^{-3}\,\text{s}^{-1}$$
$$= 1.0 \times 10^{18}\,\text{m}^{-3}\,\text{s}^{-1}$$

(b) First calculate the energy ratio:

$$\frac{E_G}{4kT} = (\pi\alpha Z_p Z_{14N})^2 2\frac{m_p m_{14N}}{m_p + m_{14N}}\frac{c^2}{4kT}$$
$$= (\pi \times \tfrac{1}{137.0} \times 1 \times 7)^2 \times 2 \times \frac{1u \times 14u}{1u + 14u}\frac{(2.998 \times 10^8\,\text{m s}^{-1})^2}{4 \times 1.381 \times 10^{-23}\,\text{J K}^{-1} \times 15.6 \times 10^6\,\text{K}}$$
$$= 5.017 \times 10^{30} u\frac{(\text{m s}^{-1})^2}{\text{J}}$$
$$= 5.017 \times 10^{30} \times 1.661 \times 10^{-27}\,\text{kg}\frac{\text{m}^2\,\text{s}^{-2}}{\text{kg m}^2\,\text{s}^{-2}}$$
$$= 8333$$

Next compute the fusion rate per unit mass fraction:

$$\frac{R_{p14N}}{X_{14N}} = 6.48 \times 10^{-24} \frac{(A_p + A_{14N})\rho_{cen}^2 X_p}{(A_p A_{14N} u)^2 Z_p Z_{14N}} \frac{S(E_0)}{[keV\ barns]} \left(\frac{E_G}{4kT}\right)^{2/3}$$

$$\times \exp\left[-3\left(\frac{E_G}{4kT}\right)^{1/3}\right] m^{-3}\ s^{-1}$$

$$= 6.48 \times 10^{-24} \frac{(1+14) \times (1.48 \times 10^5\ kg\ m^{-3})^2 \times 0.5}{(1 \times 14 \times 1.661 \times 10^{-27}\ kg)^2 \times 1 \times 7} \times \frac{3.3\ keV\ barns}{[keV\ barns]}$$

$$\times (8333)^{2/3} \exp\left[-3(8333)^{1/3}\right] m^{-3}\ s^{-1}$$

$$= 1.5 \times 10^{15}\ m^{-3}\ s^{-1}$$

(c) First calculate the energy ratio:

$$\frac{E_G}{4kT} = (\pi \alpha Z_p Z_{15N})^2 2 \frac{m_p m_{15N}}{m_p + m_{15N}} \frac{c^2}{4kT}$$

$$= (\pi \times \tfrac{1}{137.0} \times 1 \times 7)^2 \times 2 \times \frac{1u \times 15u}{1u + 15u} \frac{(2.998 \times 10^8\ m\ s^{-1})^2}{4 \times 1.381 \times 10^{-23}\ J\ K^{-1} \times 15.6 \times 10^6\ K}$$

$$= 5.039 \times 10^{30} u \frac{(m\ s^{-1})^2}{J}$$

$$= 5.039 \times 10^{30} \times 1.661 \times 10^{-27}\ kg \frac{m^2\ s^{-2}}{kg\ m^2\ s^{-2}}$$

$$= 8370$$

Next compute the fusion rate per unit mass fraction:

$$\frac{R_{p15N}}{X_{15N}} = 6.48 \times 10^{-24} \frac{(A_p + A_{15N})\rho_{cen}^2 X_p}{(A_p A_{15N} u)^2 Z_p Z_{15N}} \frac{S(E_0)}{[keV\ barns]} \left(\frac{E_G}{4kT}\right)^{2/3}$$

$$\times \exp\left[-3\left(\frac{E_G}{4kT}\right)^{1/3}\right] m^{-3}\ s^{-1}$$

$$= 6.48 \times 10^{-24} \frac{(1+15) \times (1.48 \times 10^5\ kg\ m^{-3})^2 \times 0.5}{(1 \times 15 \times 1.661 \times 10^{-27}\ kg)^2 \times 1 \times 7} \times \frac{78\ keV\ barns}{[keV\ barns]}$$

$$\times (8370)^{2/3} \exp\left[-3(8370)^{1/3}\right] m^{-3}\ s^{-1}$$

$$= 3.0 \times 10^{16}\ m^{-3}\ s^{-1}$$

Question 19

(a) In equilibrium $R_{p12C} = R_{p14N}$, so $3.5 \times 10^{17} X_{12C} = 0.015 \times 10^{17} X_{14N}$

$$X_{14N}/X_{12C} = 3.5/0.015 = 2.3 \times 10^2 \approx 230$$

$$^{14}N/^{12}C = 12/14 \times 2.3 \times 10^2 = 2.0 \times 10^2 \approx 200$$

(b) In equilibrium $R_{p14N} = R_{p15N}$, so $0.015 \times 10^{17} X_{14N} = 0.30 \times 10^{17} X_{15N}$

$$X_{14N}/X_{15N} = 0.30/0.015 = 20$$

$$^{14}N/^{15}N = 15/14 \times 20 = 21$$

Question 20

Your edited figure should resemble Figure 59:

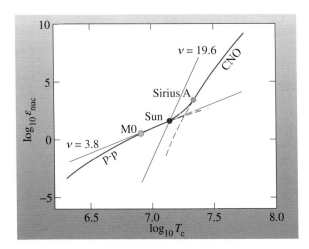

Figure 59 Copy of Figure 30, but with lines for $\varepsilon \propto T^v$ added, for $v = 3.8$ (p-p chain) and $v = 19.6$ (CNO cycle).

Question 21

(a) $2E_{KE} + E_{GR} = 0$ (e.g. Phillips 1.11)

(b) If there are N_p protons and N_e electrons, the equipartition theorem gives

$$E_{KE} = N_p \tfrac{3}{2} kT_I + N_e \tfrac{3}{2} kT_I$$

Since the matter is neutral overall, there must be the same number of electrons as protons, i.e. $N_e = N_p$, and the total kinetic energy is $E_{KE} = 3N_p kT_I$.

(c) $M = N_p m_p + N_e m_e \approx N_p m_p$, so $N_p = M/m_p$, and hence $E_{KE} = 3(M/m_p)kT_I$.

(d) $E_{GR} = -\tfrac{3}{5} GM^2/R$.

(e) (a) gives $2E_{KE} + E_{GR} = 0$, and inserting the results from (c) and (d) gives

$$2 \times 3 \frac{M}{m_p} kT_I - \frac{3}{5} \frac{GM^2}{R} = 0$$

Rearranging this to isolate the term kT_I gives

$$kT_I = \frac{1}{10} \frac{GMm_p}{R}$$

Using $\langle \rho \rangle = M / \tfrac{4}{3} \pi R^3$ which gives $1/R = \left(\tfrac{4}{3} \pi \langle \rho \rangle / M \right)^{1/3}$

$$kT_I = \tfrac{1}{10} GMm_p \left(\tfrac{4}{3} \pi \langle \rho \rangle / M \right)^{1/3} = \tfrac{1}{10} \left(\tfrac{4}{3} \pi \right)^{1/3} GM^{2/3} m_p \langle \rho \rangle^{1/3}$$

(f) $E_{KE,e} = \tfrac{3}{2} kT_c = \tfrac{1}{2} m_e v^2$, so multiplying the last two terms by $2m_e$ gives $3kT_c m_e = m_e^2 v^2$. Hence the momentum $p_e = m_e v = (3kT_c m_e)^{1/2}$.

Therefore the de Broglie wavelength of an electron in the core is $\lambda_e \equiv h/p_e = h/(3kT_c m_e)^{1/2}$.

(g) Note that $\rho = m_p/l^3$, so $l = (m_p/\rho)^{1/3}$. To avoid degeneracy in the core, we require $l > \lambda_e$, i.e. $(m_p/\rho_c)^{1/3} > \lambda_e$, so

$$\rho_c < \frac{m_p}{\lambda_e^3} = m_p \Big/ \left(\frac{h}{(3kT_cm_e)^{1/2}}\right)^3$$

i.e. $$\rho_c < \frac{m_p(3kT_cm_e)^{3/2}}{h^3}$$

(h) From (e),

$$kT_I = \tfrac{1}{10}\left(\tfrac{4}{3}\pi\right)^{1/3}GM^{2/3}m_p\langle\rho\rangle^{1/3}$$

$$\tfrac{1}{7}kT_c = \tfrac{1}{10}\left(\tfrac{4}{3}\pi\right)^{1/3}GM^{2/3}m_p(\rho_c/100)^{1/3}$$

and the density to avoid degeneracy in the core gives

$$\tfrac{1}{7}kT_c < \tfrac{1}{10}\left(\tfrac{4}{300}\pi\right)^{1/3}GM^{2/3}m_p\left(\frac{m_p(3kT_cm_e)^{3/2}}{h^3}\right)^{1/3}$$

$$< \tfrac{1}{10}\left(\tfrac{4}{300}\pi\right)^{1/3}GM^{2/3}m_p\frac{m_p^{1/3}(3kT_cm_e)^{1/2}}{h}$$

Dividing by $(kT_c)^{1/2}$ and multiplying by 7 gives

$$(kT_c)^{1/2} < \tfrac{7}{10}\left(\tfrac{4}{300}\pi\right)^{1/3}GM^{2/3}\frac{m_p^{4/3}(3m_e)^{1/2}}{h}$$

and squaring this gives

$$kT_c < \tfrac{147}{100}\left(\tfrac{4}{300}\pi\right)^{2/3}G^2\frac{m_p^{8/3}m_e}{h^2}M^{4/3} \text{ to avoid degeneracy}$$

(i) $kT_c < \tfrac{147}{100}\left(\tfrac{4}{300}\pi\right)^{2/3}G^2\frac{m_p^{8/3}m_e}{h^2}M^{4/3}$ to avoid degeneracy, so if $T_c = T_{ign}$, we require

$$M^{4/3} > kT_{ign}\Big/ \tfrac{147}{100}\left(\tfrac{4}{300}\pi\right)^{2/3}G^2\frac{m_p^{8/3}m_e}{h^2}$$

$$= \frac{1.381\times10^{-23}\,\text{J K}^{-1}\times1.5\times10^6\,\text{K}}{\tfrac{147}{100}\left(\tfrac{4}{300}\pi\right)^{2/3}(6.673\times10^{-11}\,\text{N m}^2\,\text{kg}^{-2})^2\dfrac{(1.673\times10^{-27}\,\text{kg})^{8/3}\times9.109\times10^{-31}\,\text{kg}}{(6.626\times10^{-34}\,\text{J s})^2}}$$

$$= \frac{2.072\times10^{-17}\,\text{J}}{7.895\times10^{-22}\,\text{N}^2\,\text{m}^4\,\text{kg}^{-4}\times8.184\times10^{-36}\,\text{kg}^{1/3}\,\text{J}^{-2}\,\text{s}^{-2}}$$

$$= 3.207\times10^{39}\,\text{J}^3\,\text{N}^{-2}\,\text{m}^{-4}\,\text{kg}^{1/3}\,\text{s}^2$$

Taking the (3/4)-power of both sides gives

$$M > (3.207\times10^{39})^{3/4}[(\text{N m})^3\,\text{N}^{-2}\,\text{m}^{-4}\,\text{kg}^{1/3}\,\text{s}^2]^{3/4}$$

$$= (4.3\times10^{29})(\text{N m}^{-1}\,\text{kg}^{1/3}\,\text{s}^2)^{3/4}$$

$$= (4.3\times10^{29})(\text{kg m s}^{-2}\,\text{m}^{-1}\,\text{kg}^{1/3}\,\text{s}^2)^{3/4}$$

$$= (4.3\times10^{29})(\text{kg}^{4/3})^{3/4}$$

$$= 4.3\times10^{29}\,\text{kg}$$

Since $1M_\odot = 1.99 \times 10^{30}$ kg, we can also express the limiting mass as
$M > 4.3 \times 10^{29}$ kg$/1.99 \times 10^{30}$ kg $M_\odot^{-1} = 0.22M_\odot$.

Question 22

The initial hydrogen content of the Sun is $0.70M_\odot$.

If it converted all of this into helium via the proton-proton chain, 0.0066
(i.e. $\approx 0.7\%$) of the hydrogen mass would be converted into energy. The total mass
consumed would be

$$(M_\odot \times 0.70 \times 0.0066) = 1.99 \times 10^{30} \text{ kg} \times 0.70 \times 0.0066, \text{ or } 9.2 \times 10^{27} \text{ kg}$$

This corresponds to an energy

$E_{\text{fusion}} = mc^2 = 9.2 \times 10^{27}$ kg $\times (2.998 \times 10^8 \text{ m s}^{-1})^2 = 8.3 \times 10^{44}$ J over its lifetime.

Its current luminosity is $L_\odot = 3.83 \times 10^{26}$ J s^{-1}, so it could radiate at the same rate for
a lifetime

$\tau_{\text{nuc}} = E_{\text{fusion}}/L_\odot = 8.3 \times 10^{44}$ J$/3.83 \times 10^{26}$ J s$^{-1} = 2.2 \times 10^{18}$ s $\approx 70 \times 10^9$ yr

if it could indeed burn all of its hydrogen to helium.

Question 23

Lifetime $\propto M/L \propto M/M^{3.5} = 1/M^{2.5}$. If the solar lifetime is 10×10^9 yr, then the
lifetime of a $0.5M_\odot$ star will be $1/0.5^{2.5} = 5.7$ times longer, i.e. 57×10^9 yr, and the
lifetime of a $10M_\odot$ star will be $1/10^{2.5} = 0.0032$ times as long, i.e. 32×10^6 yr.

Question 24

(a) $\mu = \dfrac{\sum\limits_i n_i \frac{m_i}{u}}{\sum\limits_i n_i} = (N_H m_p + N_{He} m_{He} + N_e m_e)/u(N_H + N_{He} + N_e)$

Let N_{nuc} be the (unknown) total number of nuclei, so
$N_H = 0.93N_{\text{nuc}}$, $N_{He} = 0.07N_{\text{nuc}}$, $N_e = N_H + 2N_{He} = 0.93N_{\text{nuc}} + 2 \times 0.07N_{\text{nuc}}$,
$m_{He} \approx 4m_p$, and $m_e/m_p = 9.109 \times 10^{-31}$ kg$/1.673 \times 10^{-27}$ kg $= 1/1837$,
so $m_e = m_p/1837$.

Note also that $m_p/u = 1.673 \times 10^{-27}$ kg$/1.661 \times 10^{-27}$ kg $= 1.007$.

Substituting these into the expression for μ gives:

$$\mu = \frac{0.93N_{\text{nuc}}m_p + 0.07N_{\text{nuc}}4m_p + (0.93N_{\text{nuc}} + 2 \times 0.07N_{\text{nuc}})\dfrac{m_p}{1837}}{u(0.93N_{\text{nuc}} + 0.07N_{\text{nuc}} + 0.93N_{\text{nuc}} + 2 \times 0.07N_{\text{nuc}})}$$

but the N_{nuc} terms cancel, and m_p is a common factor on the top line, so

$$\mu = \frac{(0.93 + 0.28 + 0.00058)}{(0.93 + 0.07 + 1.07)}\frac{m_p}{u}$$

$$= 0.58 \times 1.007 = 0.58$$

Note that the electrons make a negligible contribution to the mass of the material
(the numerator of the equation), but account for more than half of the *number* of
particles, and hence greatly affect the denominator.

(b) $\mu = \dfrac{\sum_i n_i \frac{m_i}{u}}{\sum_i n_i} = (N_H m_p + N_{He} m_{He} + N_e m_e)/u(N_H + N_{He} + N_e)$

Let N_{nuc} be the (unknown) *initial* number of nuclei. After 10% of the hydrogen has been burnt to helium, the number of hydrogen nuclei has decreased by 10% (i.e. by $0.093N_{nuc}$) and the number of helium nuclei has increased by one-quarter of that number ($0.093N_{nuc}/4$). At the *end* of the burning,

$$N_H = (0.93 - 0.093)N_{nuc} = 0.837N_{nuc}$$

$$N_{He} = (0.07 + 0.093/4)N_{nuc} = 0.093N_{nuc}$$

$$N_e = N_H + 2N_{He} = 0.837N_{nuc} + 2 \times 0.093N_{nuc}$$

$m_{He} = 4m_p$, $m_e = m_p/1837$ and $m_p/u = 1.007$, so

$$\mu = \frac{0.837N_{nuc}m_p + 0.093N_{nuc}4m_p + (0.837 + 0.186)N_{nuc}(m_p/1837)}{u(0.837N_{nuc} + 0.093N_{nuc} + (0.837 + 0.186)N_{nuc})}$$

$$= \frac{(0.837 + 0.372 + 0.000557)}{0.837 + 0.093 + 1.023} \frac{m_p}{u} = 0.619 \times 1.007$$

$$= 0.624$$

(c) $\mu = \dfrac{\sum_i n_i \frac{m_i}{u}}{\sum_i n_i} = (N_{He} m_{He} + N_e m_e)/u(N_{He} + N_e)$

$N_e = 2N_{He}$, $m_{He} = 4m_p$ and $m_e = m_p/1837$, so

$$\mu = \frac{N_{He}4m_p + 2N_{He}(m_p/1837)}{u(N_{He} + 2N_{He})} = \frac{(4 + 0.00109)}{1 + 2} \frac{m_p}{u}$$

$$= 1.33 \times 1.007 = 1.34$$

(d) The ratio of (b) over (a) is $0.624/0.58 = 1.1$.

The ratio of (c) over (a) is $1.34/0.58 = 2.3$.

Question 25

For high-mass stars, the CNO cycle dominates energy production and the opacity is electron scattering. For this case, $v \approx 17$. For stars of uniform chemical composition, μ is constant, so the μ-term can be absorbed into the unknown constant of proportionality.

(a) Equation 30 becomes $L \propto M^3 \mu^4$, i.e. $L \propto M^3$.

(b) Equation 33 becomes

$$T_c \propto M^{\frac{4}{v+3}} \mu^{\frac{7}{v+3}} \propto M^{\frac{4}{17+3}} \propto M^{\frac{4}{20}}$$

i.e. $T_c \propto M^{0.2}$.

(c) Equation 32 becomes

$$R \propto M^{\frac{\nu-1}{\nu+3}} \mu^{\frac{\nu-4}{\nu+3}} \propto M^{\frac{17-1}{17+3}} \propto M^{\frac{16}{20}}$$

i.e. $R \propto M^{0.8}$.

That is, the luminosity increases with mass, the central temperatures increases weakly with mass, and the radius increases almost linearly with mass.

Question 26

For a high-mass star, the CNO cycle dominates energy production and the opacity is electron scattering. For this case, $\nu \approx 17$. For a star of constant mass, the M-term can be absorbed into the unknown constant of proportionality.

(a) Equation 30 becomes $L \propto M^3 \mu^4$, i.e. $L \propto \mu^4$.

(b) Equation 33 becomes

$$T_c \propto M^{\frac{4}{\nu+3}} \mu^{\frac{7}{\nu+3}} \propto \mu^{\frac{7}{17+3}} \propto \mu^{\frac{7}{20}}$$

i.e. $T_c \propto \mu^{0.4}$.

(c) Equation 32 becomes

$$R \propto M^{\frac{\nu-1}{\nu+3}} \mu^{\frac{\nu-4}{\nu+3}} \propto \mu^{\frac{17-4}{17+3}} \propto \mu^{\frac{13}{20}}$$

i.e. $R \propto \mu^{0.7}$.

Question 27

(a) $R \propto \mu^0$, so $R_{final}/R_{initial} \propto (\mu_{final}/\mu_{initial})^0 \propto 2.3^0 \approx 1$; the object would be the same size.

$L \propto \mu^4$, so $L_{final}/L_{initial} \propto (\mu_{final}/\mu_{initial})^4 \propto 2.3^4 \approx 28$; a lot brighter!

$T_c \propto \mu^1$, so $T_{c,final}/T_{c,initial} \propto (\mu_{final}/\mu_{initial})^1 \propto 2.3^1 \approx 2.3$; hotter.

(b) $R \propto \mu^{+0.7}$, so $R_{final}/R_{initial} \propto (\mu_{final}/\mu_{initial})^{+0.7} \propto 2.3^{+0.7} \approx 1.8$; i.e. the object would expand.

$L \propto \mu^4$, so $L_{final}/L_{initial} \propto (\mu_{final}/\mu_{initial})^4 \propto 2.3^4 \approx 28$; a lot brighter!

$T \propto \mu^{0.4}$, so $T_{c,final}/T_{c,initial} \propto (\mu_{final}/\mu_{initial})^{0.4} \propto 2.3^{0.4} \approx 1.4$; hotter.

Question 28

The ideal gas law gives

$$\rho = \frac{\overline{m}}{k}\frac{P}{T} \quad \text{so} \quad \ln\rho = \ln\frac{\overline{m}}{k} + \ln P - \ln T$$

Differentiating gives

$$\frac{d\ln\rho}{dP} = \frac{d\ln(\overline{m}/k)}{dP} + \frac{d\ln P}{dP} - \frac{d\ln T}{dP}$$

Using the chain rule and setting the first right-hand term to zero gives

$$\frac{d\ln\rho}{d\rho}\frac{d\rho}{dP} = \frac{d\ln P}{dP} - \frac{d\ln T}{dT}\frac{dT}{dP}$$

using Hint 2 and multiplying through by dP gives

$$\frac{1}{\rho}\frac{d\rho}{1} = \frac{dP}{P} - \frac{1}{T}\frac{dT}{dP}dP$$

$$\frac{d\rho}{\rho} = \frac{dP}{P} - \frac{dT}{T}$$

considering a *small* finite displacement (rather than an infinitesimal one) gives

$$\frac{\Delta\rho}{\rho} = \frac{\Delta P}{P} - \frac{\Delta T}{T}$$

Question 29

Let the constant of proportionality in $P \propto \rho^\gamma$ be C, so $P = C\rho^\gamma$.

Differentiating with respect to density gives $dP/d\rho = C\gamma\rho^{\gamma-1}$, i.e. $(1/\gamma)dP = C\rho^{\gamma-1}d\rho$.

Dividing through by P gives $(1/\gamma)dP/P = C\rho^{\gamma-1}d\rho/P$.

On the right-hand side, use the fact that $P = C\rho^\gamma$ to obtain $C\rho^{\gamma-1}d\rho/C\rho^\gamma = \rho^{-1}d\rho = d\rho/\rho$.

Substituting this into the previous expression therefore gives $(1/\gamma)dP/P = d\rho/\rho$.

Provided you consider very small but finite increments $\delta P \ll P$ and $\delta\rho \ll \rho$, it is permissable to replace the infinitesimal increments dP by δP and dρ by $\delta\rho$. Doing so gives: $(1/\gamma)\delta P/P = \delta\rho/\rho$, as required.

Question 30

(a) For $s = 3$, $\gamma = \dfrac{1+\frac{s}{2}}{\frac{s}{2}} = \dfrac{1+\frac{3}{2}}{\frac{3}{2}} = \dfrac{\frac{5}{2}}{\frac{3}{2}} = \dfrac{5}{3}$, so the coefficient $\dfrac{\gamma-1}{\gamma} = \dfrac{\frac{5}{3}-1}{\frac{5}{3}} = \dfrac{2}{5}$.

(b) For $s = \infty$, $\gamma = \dfrac{1+\frac{s}{2}}{\frac{s}{2}} = \dfrac{1+\infty}{\infty} = 1$, so the coefficient $\dfrac{\gamma-1}{\gamma} = \dfrac{1-1}{1} = 0$.

The critical temperature gradient for convection is $\dfrac{dT}{dx} < \dfrac{\gamma-1}{\gamma}\dfrac{T}{P}\dfrac{dP}{dx}$ (Phillips 3.23).

Since in question (b) $dT/dx < 0$ and $\dfrac{\gamma-1}{\gamma} = 0$, this material is *always* unstable to convection.

Question 31

The paper describes new models for the mixing of material in red giant branch stars, over and above that due to (standard) convection of the type described in this course. Standard mixing predicts for low-mass stars (here $0.8M_\odot$) that, due to the first dredge-up of CN-cycled material, the ^{12}C/^{13}C isotope ratio decreases from ≈ 94 in main sequence stars (having $L \sim L_\odot$) to ≈ 40 once the star evolves on to the red giant branch and increases in luminosity between $\log L/L_\odot = 1.0$ and 1.5 (see Figure 1, top left panel). However, observations (xs and os in the figure) show that the isotope ratio decreases further as the star continues to ascend the red giant branch (i.e. as its luminosity increases), reaching ^{12}C/^{13}C ~ 5 (i.e. close to the CN cycle equilibrium isotope ratio) in stars with log $L/L_\odot > 2$. This points to the need for extra mixing (beyond that expected with convection alone) in the red giant branch stars. Stellar models with extra mixing have been computed for stars of 0.8 and 1.0 $M_\odot$, and for a range of heavy element abundances Z (where the solar abundance is $Z_\odot = 2 \times 10^{-2}$). The standard convection models also predict the dilution of Li as the star evolves across the subgiant branch from the main-sequence turnoff at $T_{eff} = 6300$ K towards the base of the red giant branch (see Figure 2). Dilution as the star cools through the effective temperature interval 5800 K to 5300 K matches observations (os in the figure), and first dredge-up is expected to be completed by the time the star reaches 5000 K. When the stars cool to 4800 K they continue to destroy Li whereas the standard (convective) models do not. However, models with extra mixing can simultaneously fit both the lithium and carbon isotope ratio observations in these cooler, more luminous giants.

Question 32

(a) $\mu'(^8Be) = \mu'(^4He) + \mu'(^4He) = 2\mu'(^4He)$

(b) $\mu' = mc^2 - kT \ln[g_s n_{QNR}/n]$ (Phillips 2.21) so substituting this into the equilibrium expression gives

$$m_8 c^2 - kT \ln\left(\frac{g_8 n_{Q8}}{n_8}\right) = 2\left[m_4 c^2 - kT \ln\left(\frac{g_4 n_{Q4}}{n_4}\right)\right]$$

We need to find an expression for n_8/n_4, so rearrange the equation to work towards that goal. As a first step, collect the logarithms on one side and the mc^2 terms on the other:

$$m_8 c^2 - 2m_4 c^2 = kT \ln\left(\frac{g_8 n_{Q8}}{n_8}\right) - 2kT \ln\left(\frac{g_4 n_{Q4}}{n_4}\right)$$

$$(m_8 - 2m_4)c^2/kT = \ln\left[\left(\frac{g_8 n_{Q8}}{n_8}\right) \Big/ \left(\frac{g_4 n_{Q4}}{n_4}\right)^2\right]$$

$$\exp[(m_8 - 2m_4)c^2/kT] = \left(\frac{g_8 n_{Q8}}{n_8}\right) \Big/ \left(\frac{g_4 n_{Q4}}{n_4}\right)^2$$

$$\frac{n_8}{n_4^2} = \exp[-(m_8 - 2m_4)c^2/kT]\frac{g_8 n_{Q8}}{(g_4 n_{Q4})^2} \quad \text{(expression A)}$$

Since $n_{Q,A} = (2\pi m_A kT/h^2)^{3/2}$, the n_Q-term at the end of expression A is

$$\frac{n_{Q8}}{(n_{Q4})^2} = \left(\frac{2\pi m_8 kT}{h^2}\right)^{3/2} \Big/ \left[\left(\frac{2\pi m_4 kT}{h^2}\right)^{3/2}\right]^2$$

$$= \left(\frac{2\pi m_8 kT}{h^2}\right)^{3/2} \Big/ \left(\frac{2\pi m_4 kT}{h^2}\right)^3 = \left(\frac{2\pi kT}{h^2}\right)^{-3/2}\left(\frac{m_8}{m_4^2}\right)^{3/2}$$

Substituting this into expression A gives

$$\frac{n_8}{n_4^2} = \exp[-(m_8 - 2m_4)c^2/kT]\frac{g_8}{g_4^2}\left(\frac{m_8}{m_4^2}\right)^{3/2}\left(\frac{h^2}{2\pi kT}\right)^{3/2}$$

As we want to find the relative abundances of the nuclei, n_8/n_4, we must multiply both sides by n_4. Doing this, and using $n_4 = \rho X_4/m_4$, we obtain the final expression

$$\frac{n_8}{n_4} = \exp\left[-(m_8 - 2m_4)c^2/kT\right]\frac{g_8}{g_4^2}\rho X_4 \frac{m_8^{3/2}}{m_4^4}\left(\frac{h^2}{2\pi kT}\right)^{3/2} \quad \text{(expression B)}$$

We assume that the material is primarily ^{4}He, so $X_4 = 1$. In evaluating the ratio $m_8^{3/2}/m_4^4$ we can use the approximation $m_4 = 4u$ and $m_8 = 8u$, but the term $m_8 - 2m_4$ involves the subtraction of nearly equal numbers, and for that we cannot use this approximation. However, we are informed that $Q = (m_8 - 2m_4)c^2 = 91.8\,\text{keV}$.

So, evaluating expression B at $T = 2 \times 10^8\,\text{K}$ and $\rho = 10^8\,\text{kg m}^{-3}$ gives:

$$\frac{n_8}{n_4} = \exp\left[-\frac{91.8 \times 10^3\,\text{eV} \times 1.602 \times 10^{-19}\,\text{J eV}^{-1}}{1.381 \times 10^{-23}\,\text{J K}^{-1} \times 2 \times 10^8\,\text{K}}\right]\frac{1}{1^2}10^8\,\text{kg m}^{-3}$$

$$\times \frac{(8u)^{3/2}}{(4u)^4}\left(\frac{(6.626 \times 10^{-34}\,\text{J s})^2}{2\pi \times 1.381 \times 10^{-23}\,\text{J K}^{-1} \times 2 \times 10^8\,\text{K}}\right)^{3/2}$$

$$= 4.87 \times 10^{-3} \times 10^8\,\text{kg m}^{-3} \times 0.0884u^{-2.5} \times 1.27 \times 10^{-79}\,\text{J}^{3/2}\,\text{s}^3$$

$$= 5.47 \times 10^{-75} \times (1.661 \times 10^{-27}\,\text{kg})^{-2.5}\,\text{kg m}^{-3}\,\text{J}^{3/2}\,\text{s}^3$$

$$= 4.86 \times 10^{-8}\,\text{kg}^{-1.5}\,\text{m}^{-3}\,(\text{kg m}^2\,\text{s}^{-2})^{3/2}\,\text{s}^3$$

$$= 4.86 \times 10^{-8}$$

That is, there is one ^{8}Be nucleus for every 20 million ^{4}He nuclei!

Question 33

(a) The Gamow energy is $E_G = 2m_r c^2(\pi\alpha Z_A Z_B)^2$, where m_r is the reduced mass of the two-body system, given by $m_r = m_A m_B/(m_A + m_B)$.

Begin by calculating the reduced mass:

$$m_r = \frac{m_4 m_4}{m_4 + m_4} = \frac{m_4^2}{2m_4} = \frac{m_4}{2} = \frac{4u}{2}$$

$$= 2 \times 1.661 \times 10^{-27}\,\text{kg} = 3.322 \times 10^{-27}\,\text{kg}$$

Then $\quad E_G = 2m_r c^2(\pi\alpha Z_4 Z_4)^2$

$$= 2 \times 3.322 \times 10^{-27}\,\text{kg} \times (2.998 \times 10^8\,\text{m s}^{-1})^2(\pi \times \tfrac{1}{137.0} \times 2 \times 2)^2$$

$$= 5.024 \times 10^{-12}\,\text{kg m}^2\,\text{s}^{-2} = 5.024 \times 10^{-12}\,\text{J}$$

Since $1\,\text{J} = 1.602 \times 10^{-19}\,\text{eV}$, $E_G = 5.024 \times 10^{-12}\,\text{J}/1.602 \times 10^{-19}\,\text{J eV}^{-1} = 31.4\,\text{MeV}$

(b) $E_0 = \left[\dfrac{E_G(kT)^2}{4}\right]^{1/3}$ (Phillips 4.23)

Cubing both sides and multiplying by $4/E_G$ gives $(kT)^2 = 4E_0^3/E_G$;

taking the square-root and diving by k gives

$$T = \frac{2}{k}\sqrt{E_0^3/E_G}$$

The energy of the Gamow peak E_0 coincides with the Q-value, 91.8 keV, which can be written in SI units as $Q = 91.8 \times 10^3 \, \text{eV} \times 1.602 \times 10^{-19} \, \text{J eV}^{-1} = 1.47 \times 10^{-14} \, \text{J}$.

Then $\quad T = \frac{2}{k}\sqrt{E_0^3/E_G} = \dfrac{2}{1.381 \times 10^{-23} \, \text{J K}^{-1}} \sqrt{\dfrac{(1.47 \times 10^{-14} \, \text{J})^3}{5.024 \times 10^{-12} \, \text{J}}}$

$\qquad = 1.448 \times 10^{23} \, \text{J}^{-1} \, \text{K} \times 7.95 \times 10^{-16} \, \text{J}$

$\qquad = 1.15 \times 10^8 \, \text{K}$

(c) $\sim 1 \times 10^8 \, \text{K}$ (i.e. the value from part (b)).

Question 34

(a) The Gamow energy is $E_G = 2m_r c^2 (\pi \alpha Z_A Z_B)^2$ (Phillips 4.10), where m_r is the reduced mass of the two-body system, given by $m_r = m_A m_B/(m_A + m_B)$.

Begin by calculating the reduced mass:

$\quad m_r = \dfrac{m_4 m_8}{m_4 + m_8} \approx \dfrac{4u \times 8u}{4u + 8u} = \dfrac{32u^2}{12u} = \dfrac{8u}{3} = \dfrac{8}{3} \times 1.661 \times 10^{-27} \, \text{kg}$

$\qquad = 4.429 \times 10^{-27} \, \text{kg}$

Then $\quad E_G = 2m_r c^2 (\pi \alpha Z_4 Z_8)^2$

$\qquad = 2 \times 4.429 \times 10^{-27} \, \text{kg} \times (2.998 \times 10^8 \, \text{m s}^{-1})^2 (\pi \times \frac{1}{137.0} \times 2 \times 4)^2$

$\qquad = 2.679 \times 10^{-11} \, \text{kg m}^2 \, \text{s}^{-2} = 2.679 \times 10^{-11} \, \text{J}$

Since $1 \, \text{J} = 1.602 \times 10^{-19} \, \text{eV}$, $E_G = 2.679 \times 10^{-11} \, \text{J}/1.602 \times 10^{-19} \, \text{J eV}^{-1} = 167.2 \, \text{MeV}$

(b) $E_0 = \left[\dfrac{E_G(kT)^2}{4}\right]^{1/3}$

Cubing both sides and multiplying by $4/E_G$ gives $(kT)^2 = 4E_0^3/E_G$

taking the square-root and diving by k gives

Then $\quad T = \dfrac{2}{k}\sqrt{E_0^3/E_G}$

The energy of the Gamow peak E_0 coincides with the energy excess, 287.7 keV, which can be written in SI units as $Q = 287.8 \times 10^3 \, \text{eV} \times 1.602 \times 10^{-19} \, \text{J eV}^{-1} = 4.611 \times 10^{-14} \, \text{J}$.

Then $T = \dfrac{2}{k}\sqrt{E_0^3/E_G}$

$\quad = \dfrac{2}{1.381 \times 10^{-23} \, \text{J K}^{-1}} \sqrt{\dfrac{(4.611 \times 10^{-14} \, \text{J})^3}{2.679 \times 10^{-11} \, \text{J}}}$

$\quad = 1.448 \times 10^{23} \, \text{J}^{-1} \, \text{K} \times 1.913 \times 10^{-15} \, \text{J}$

$\quad = 2.770 \times 10^8 \, \text{K}$

(c) $\sim 3 \times 10^8 \, \text{K}$ (i.e. the value from part (b)).

Question 35

(a) $m_e = 9.109 \times 10^{-31}$ kg/1.661×10^{-27} kg amu^{-1} = 0.000 5484 amu. Subtracting the *electronic* parts from the *atomic* masses to get *nuclear* masses, we find the mass defect is

$$m_{\text{initial}} - m_{\text{final}} = 3 \times (4.002\,60 - 2 \times 0.000\,5484) \text{ amu}$$
$$- (12 - 6 \times 0.000\,5484) \text{ amu} = 0.007\,800 \text{ amu}$$

(b) Ignoring the *electronic* parts, we find the mass defect is

$$m_{\text{initial}} - m_{\text{final}} = 3 \times 4.002\,60 \text{ amu} - 12 \text{ amu} = 0.007\,800 \text{ amu}$$

(c) As a fraction of the initial mass this is 0.007 800 amu/$(3 \times 4.002\,60$ amu$)$ = 0.000 65. Recall that for hydrogen burning, the mass defect corresponds to 0.0066 of the initial mass, a factor of ten larger.

Question 36

(a)(i) $\lambda_{\text{dB}}(\text{p}) = h/(m_p kT)^{1/2}$

$$= \frac{6.626 \times 10^{-34} \text{ J s}}{\sqrt{1.673 \times 10^{-27} \text{ kg} \times 1.381 \times 10^{-23} \text{ J K}^{-1} \times 15.6 \times 10^6 \text{ K}}}$$

$$= 1.104 \times 10^{-12} \text{ m}$$

(ii) $\lambda_{\text{dB}}(\text{e}) = h/(m_e kT)^{1/2}$

$$= \frac{6.626 \times 10^{-34} \text{ J s}}{\sqrt{9.109 \times 10^{-31} \text{ kg} \times 1.381 \times 10^{-23} \text{ J K}^{-1} \times 15.6 \times 10^6 \text{ K}}}$$

$$= 4.730 \times 10^{-11} \text{ m}$$

(b) $\dfrac{\lambda_{\text{dB}}(\text{e})}{\lambda_{\text{dB}}(\text{p})} = \dfrac{h}{(m_e kT)^{1/2}} \bigg/ \dfrac{h}{(m_p kT)^{1/2}}$

$$= (m_p/m_e)^{1/2} = (1.673 \times 10^{-27} \text{ kg}/9.109 \times 10^{-31} \text{ kg})^{1/2} = 42.85$$

The de Broglie wavelength of the electron is greater than that of a proton, by a factor of ≈ 43.

(c) From part (b), this ratio depends only on the mass of the particles, and hence is independent of the environment and hence of the temperature. The electron's wavelength is ≈ 43 times longer than the proton's in all stars.

Question 37

The second condition is $n \gg n_Q$, i.e. $n \gg (2\pi m kT/h^2)^{3/2}$.

Since $n = 1/l^3$, substituting for n gives $1/l^3 \gg (2\pi m kT/h^2)^{3/2}$.

Taking the (1/3)-power gives $1/l \gg (2\pi m kT/h^2)^{1/2}$, and multiplying through by $l/(2\pi m kT/h^2)^{1/2}$ gives

$$l \ll h/(2\pi m kT)^{1/2} = 1/(2\pi)^{1/2} \times h/(m kT)^{1/2} = 1/(2\pi)^{1/2} \times \lambda_{\text{dB}} \approx 0.4\lambda_{\text{dB}} < \lambda_{\text{dB}}$$

That is, from the second degeneracy condition $n \gg n_Q$ we obtain the first degeneracy condition $l \ll \lambda_{\text{dB}}$.

Question 38

(a) $n_Q = (2\pi m kT/h^2)^{3/2}$, so the degeneracy condition $n \gg n_Q$ implies that $n \gg (2\pi m kT/h^2)^{3/2}$.

Taking the (2/3)-power and multiplying both sides by $h^2/2\pi m$ gives

$$n^{2/3}h^2/(2\pi m) \gg kT, \text{ i.e. } kT \ll n^{2/3}h^2/(2\pi m)$$

The third equivalent condition for degeneracy is: the gas is degenerate if $T \ll n^{2/3}h^2/(2\pi mk)$.

(b) (i) $n_p = \rho_{\odot c}X_H/m_p = 1.48 \times 10^5 \text{ kg m}^{-3} \times 0.5/1.673 \times 10^{-27} \text{ kg} = 4.42 \times 10^{31} \text{ m}^{-3}$ (i.e. hydrogen nuclei per m³).

Therefore $h^2n_p^{2/3}/(2\pi m_p k) = (6.626 \times 10^{-34} \text{ J s})^2 \times (4.42 \times 10^{31} \text{ m}^{-3})^{2/3}$

$$/(2 \times \pi \times 1.673 \times 10^{-27} \text{ kg} \times 1.381 \times 10^{-23} \text{ J K}^{-1})$$

$$= 3.78 \times 10^3 \text{ J s}^2 \text{ m}^{-2} \text{ kg}^{-1} \text{ K}$$

$$= 3.78 \times 10^3 (\text{kg m}^2\text{s}^{-2}) \text{ s}^2 \text{ m}^{-2} \text{ kg}^{-1} \text{ K} \approx 3780 \text{ K}$$

(ii) In the solar centre, all atoms are ionized. The electrons are provided by the hydrogen and helium which each account for 0.5 of the composition by mass.

$$n_e = n_p + 2n_{He} = \rho_c X_H/m_p + 2\rho_c X_{He}/m_{He} = \rho_c\left(\frac{X_H}{m_p} + \frac{2X_{He}}{4u}\right)$$

$$= 1.48 \times 10^5 \text{ kg m}^{-3}\left(\frac{0.5}{1.673 \times 10^{-27} \text{ kg}} + \frac{2 \times 0.5}{4 \times 1.661 \times 10^{-27} \text{ kg}}\right)$$

$$= 6.65 \times 10^{31} \text{ m}^{-3}$$

Therefore $h^2n_e^{2/3}/(2\pi m_e k) = (6.626 \times 10^{-34} \text{ J s})^2 \times (6.65 \times 10^{31} \text{ m}^{-3})^{2/3}$

$$/(2 \times \pi \times 9.109 \times 10^{-31} \text{ kg} \times 1.381 \times 10^{-23} \text{ J K}^{-1})$$

$$= 9.12 \times 10^6 \text{ J s}^2 \text{ m}^{-2} \text{ kg}^{-1}\text{K}$$

$$= 9.12 \times 10^6 \text{ K}$$

(c) The temperature condition for degeneracy is $T \ll n^{2/3}h^2/(2\pi mk)$. $T_{\odot,c} = 15.6 \times 10^6 \text{ K}$, so the temperature in the centre of the Sun is (i) much too high for proton degeneracy to have set in, and (ii) marginally too high for electron degeneracy to have set in.

Question 39

(a) Equating the central pressure $P_c = (\pi/36)^{1/3}GM^{2/3}\rho_c^{4/3}$ to the pressure of non-relativistic degenerate electrons

$$P_{NR} = K_{NR}(\rho_c Y_e/m_H)^{5/3}, \quad \text{where} \quad K_{NR} = \frac{h^2}{5m_e}\left(\frac{3}{8\pi}\right)^{2/3}$$

we have $K_{NR}(\rho_c Y_e/m_H)^{5/3} = (\pi/36)^{1/3}GM^{2/3}\rho_c^{4/3}$

Collecting terms in ρ on the left-hand side, and all others on the right, we get

$$\rho_c^{1/3} = \left(\frac{\pi}{36}\right)^{1/3}\frac{G}{K_{NR}}\frac{1}{Y_e^{5/3}}m_H^{5/3}M^{2/3}$$

cubing this gives

$$\rho_c = \left(\frac{\pi}{36}\right)\left(\frac{G}{K_{NR}}\right)^3\frac{1}{Y_e^5}m_H^5 M^2$$

and substituting for K_{NR} gives

$$\rho_c = \left(\frac{\pi}{36}\right)\left(\frac{5m_e}{h^2}\right)^3\left(\frac{8\pi}{3}\right)^2 G^3 \frac{1}{Y_e^5} m_H^5 M^2$$

(b) Since $M_* = \left(\frac{Gm_H^2}{\hbar c}\right)^{-3/2} m_H$, multiply by $\left(\left(\frac{Gm_H^2}{\hbar c}\right)^{-3/2} m_H / M_*\right)^2$, i.e. multiply by 1. This leads to

$$\rho_c = \left(\frac{\pi}{36}\right)\left(\frac{5m_e}{h^2}\right)^3\left(\frac{8\pi}{3}\right)^2 G^3 \frac{1}{Y_e^5} m_H^5 M^2 \times \left(\left(\frac{Gm_H^2}{\hbar c}\right)^{-3/2} \frac{m_H}{M_*}\right)^2$$

$$= \left(\frac{\pi}{36}\right)\left(\frac{5m_e}{h^2}\right)^3\left(\frac{8\pi}{3}\right)^2 G^3 \frac{1}{Y_e^5} m_H^5 M^2 \left(\frac{hc}{2\pi Gm_H^2}\right)^3 \left(\frac{m_H}{M_*}\right)^2$$

There are a lot of terms to cancel, but doing so leads to

$$\rho_c = \frac{250}{81}\left(\frac{m_e c}{h}\right)^3 \frac{1}{Y_e^5} m_H \left(\frac{M}{M_*}\right)^2$$

(c) The electron number density in the centre of the star is $n_e = \rho_c Y_e/m_H$, so substituting the central density from (b) gives

$$n_e = \left(\frac{250}{81}\right)\left(\frac{m_e c}{h}\right)^3 \frac{1}{Y_e^4}\left(\frac{M}{M_*}\right)^2$$

(d) $M_* = \left(\frac{Gm_H^2}{\hbar c}\right)^{-3/2} m_H$

$$= \left(\frac{6.673 \times 10^{-11}\,\text{m}^3\,\text{kg}^{-1}\,\text{s}^{-2} \times (1.673 \times 10^{-27}\,\text{kg})^2}{1.055 \times 10^{-34}\,\text{J s} \times 2.998 \times 10^8\,\text{m s}^{-1}}\right)^{-3/2}$$

$$\times 1.673 \times 10^{-27}\,\text{kg}$$

$$= 3.687 \times 10^{30}\left(\frac{\text{m}^3\,\text{kg s}^{-2}}{\text{J m}}\right)^{-3/2} \text{kg}$$

$$= 3.687 \times 10^{30}\left(\frac{\text{m}^3\,\text{kg s}^{-2}}{\text{kg m}^2\,\text{s}^{-2}\,\text{m}}\right)^{-3/2} \text{kg}$$

$$= 3.687 \times 10^{30}\,\text{kg}$$

(since all of the units cancel in the term to the power of $-3/2$).

Since $M_\odot = 1.99 \times 10^{30}\,\text{kg}$, $M_* = 3.687 \times 10^{30}\,\text{kg}/1.99 \times 10^{30}\,\text{kg}\,M_\odot^{-1} = 1.85 M_\odot$.

(e) $n_e \approx 3.1\left(\frac{m_e c}{h}\right)^3 \frac{1}{Y_e^4}\left(\frac{M/M_\odot}{1.85}\right)^2$

Question 40

(a) For the ultra-relativistic case, equating P_{UR} to P_c gives

$$P_{UR} = K_{UR}(\rho_c Y_e/m_H)^{4/3} = (\pi/36)^{1/3} G M^{2/3} \rho_c^{4/3} \quad \text{where} \quad K_{UR} = \frac{hc}{4}\left(\frac{3}{8\pi}\right)^{1/3}$$

Note that in contrast to the non-relativistic case, the density term is the same on both sides ($\rho^{4/3}$), so cancels, leaving

$$K_{UR}\left(\frac{Y_e}{m_H}\right)^{4/3} = \left(\frac{\pi}{36}\right)^{1/3} G M^{2/3}$$

Collecting M on one side and swapping left and right sides, gives

$$M^{2/3} = \left(\frac{36}{\pi}\right)^{1/3}\left(\frac{K_{UR}}{G}\right)\left(\frac{Y_e}{m_H}\right)^{4/3}$$

taking the (3/2)-power gives

$$M = \left(\frac{36}{\pi}\right)^{1/2}\left(\frac{(hc/4)(3/8\pi)^{1/3}}{G}\right)^{3/2}\left(\frac{Y_e}{m_H}\right)^2$$

$$= \left(\frac{3 \times 36}{4^3 \times 8\pi^2}\right)^{1/2}\left(\frac{hc}{G}\right)^{3/2}\left(\frac{Y_e}{m_H}\right)^2$$

$$= \frac{1}{\pi}\left(\frac{27}{128}\right)^{1/2}\left(\frac{hc}{G}\right)^{3/2}\left(\frac{Y_e}{m_H}\right)^2$$

(b) $M = \dfrac{1}{\pi}\left(\dfrac{27}{128}\right)^{1/2}\left(\dfrac{hc}{G}\right)^{3/2}\left(\dfrac{Y_e}{m_H}\right)^2$

$$= \frac{1}{\pi}\left(\frac{27}{128}\right)^{1/2}\left(\frac{6.626 \times 10^{-34}\,\text{J s} \ \times \ 2.998 \times 10^8\,\text{m s}^{-1}}{6.673 \times 10^{-11}\,\text{m}^3\,\text{kg}^{-1}\,\text{s}^{-2}}\right)^{3/2}\left(\frac{0.5}{1.673 \times 10^{-27}\,\text{kg}}\right)^2$$

$$= 2.121 \times 10^{30}\left(\frac{\text{J}}{\text{m}^2\,\text{kg}^{-1}\,\text{s}^{-2}}\right)^{3/2}\,\text{kg}^{-2}$$

$$= 2.121 \times 10^{30}\left(\frac{\text{kg}\,\text{m}^2\,\text{s}^{-2}}{\text{m}^2\,\text{kg}^{-1}\,\text{s}^{-2}}\right)^{3/2}\,\text{kg}^{-2}$$

$$= 2.121 \times 10^{30}\,\text{kg}$$

Since $M_\odot = 1.99 \times 10^{30}\,\text{kg}$, $M = 2.121 \times 10^{30}\,\text{kg}/1.99 \times 10^{30}\,\text{kg}\,M_\odot^{-1} = 1.07 M_\odot$.

Question 41

(a) We have $P_{UR} = K_{UR}(\rho_c Y_e/m_H)^{4/3} = 0.87 \times (\pi/36)^{1/3}GM^{2/3}\rho_c^{4/3}$, so following the solution for Question 40 we have:

$$M^{2/3} = \frac{1}{0.87}\left(\frac{36}{\pi}\right)^{1/3}\left(\frac{K_{UR}}{G}\right)\left(\frac{Y_e}{m_H}\right)^{4/3}$$

$$M = \left(\frac{1}{0.87}\right)^{3/2}\left(\frac{36}{\pi}\right)^{1/2}\left(\frac{K_{UR}}{G}\right)^{3/2}\left(\frac{Y_e}{m_H}\right)^{2}$$

$$= \left(\frac{1}{0.87}\right)^{3/2}\frac{1}{\pi}\left(\frac{27}{128}\right)^{1/2}\left(\frac{hc}{G}\right)^{3/2}\left(\frac{Y_e}{m_H}\right)^{2}$$

Most of the right-hand side was already evaluated in the previous question, so we can write

$$M = \left(\frac{1}{0.87}\right)^{3/2} \times 2.121 \times 10^{30} \text{ kg}$$

(b) Hence $M = 1.15 \times 2.121 \times 10^{30}\text{ kg} = 1.15 \times 1.066 M_\odot \approx 1.3 M_\odot$.

Question 42

(a) $R = \left(\dfrac{3M}{4\pi\langle\rho\rangle}\right)^{1/3}$

(b) $R = \left(\dfrac{9M}{2\pi\rho_c}\right)^{1/3}$

(c) Substituting in the central density from Phillips Equation 6.4 gives:

$$R = \left(\frac{9M}{2\pi}\right)^{1/3}\left(\frac{3.1}{Y_e^5}\left(\frac{M/M_\odot}{1.85}\right)^2\frac{m_H}{(h/m_e c)^3}\right)^{-1/3}$$

Rewriting the terms with negative powers gives

$$R = \left(\frac{9M}{2\pi}\right)^{1/3}\left(\frac{Y_e^5}{3.1}\left(\frac{1.85}{M/M_\odot}\right)^2\frac{(h/m_e c)^3}{m_H}\right)^{1/3}$$

These terms can now be combined under a single power

$$R = \left(\frac{9}{2\pi}\frac{Y_e^5}{3.1}(1.85)^2\frac{(h/m_e c)^3}{m_H}\right)^{1/3}M^{1/3}\left(\frac{M}{M_\odot}\right)^{-2/3}$$

Expand the final bracket and consolidate terms in M

$$R = \frac{h}{m_e c}\left(\frac{9}{2\pi}\frac{Y_e^5}{3.1}\frac{(1.85)^2}{m_H}\right)^{1/3}M_\odot^{2/3}M^{-1/3}$$

and for convenience, write the remaining M term in terms of $M_\odot$

$$R = \frac{h}{m_e c}\left(\frac{9}{2\pi}\frac{Y_e^5}{3.1}\frac{(1.85)^2}{m_H}\right)^{1/3} M_\odot^{1/3}\left(\frac{M}{M_\odot}\right)^{-1/3}$$

$$= \frac{6.626\times10^{-34}\,\text{J\,s}}{9.109\times10^{-31}\,\text{kg}\ \times2.998\times10^8\,\text{m\,s}^{-1}}\left(\frac{9}{2\pi}\frac{0.5^5}{3.1}\frac{(1.85)^2}{1.673\times10^{-27}\,\text{kg}}\right)^{1/3}$$

$$\times(1.99\times10^{30}\,\text{kg})^{1/3}\left(\frac{M}{M_\odot}\right)^{-1/3}$$

$$= 9.43\times10^6\,\frac{\text{kg\,m}^2\,\text{s}^{-2}\,\text{s}}{\text{kg\,m\,s}^{-1}}\left(\frac{\text{kg}}{\text{kg}}\right)^{1/3}\left(\frac{M}{M_\odot}\right)^{-1/3}$$

$$= 9.43\times10^6\left(\frac{M}{M_\odot}\right)^{-1/3}\text{m}$$

Since $R_\odot = 6.96\times10^8$ m,

$R_{WD} = (9.43\times10^6\,\text{m}/6.96\times10^8\,\text{m}\,R_\odot^{-1})\times(M/M_\odot)^{-1/3} = (R_\odot/74)(M/M_\odot)^{-1/3}$

(d) Since $R_{Earth} = 6.4\times10^6$ m,

$R_{WD} = (9.43\times10^6\,\text{m}/6.4\times10^6\,\text{m}\,R_{Earth}^{-1})\times(M/M_\odot)^{-1/3} = 1.5R_{Earth}(M/M_\odot)^{-1/3}$

Question 43

Process	Major reactions	Major products	Mass range of stars	Ignition temp/K	Timescale
Big Bang	(not studied)	^{1}H, ^{2}H, ^{3}He, ^{4}He, ^{7}Li	(not applicable)	(not studied)	~1–15 minutes
H-burning	p-p chain (3 branches) CNO cycle^{4}He, ^{13}C, ^{14}N	^{4}He	$M \gtrsim 0.08M_\odot$	2–10×10^6	~10^7–10^{10} yr
He-burning	triple-alpha process	^{12}C, ^{16}O	$M_{ms} \gtrsim 0.5M_\odot$	1–2×10^8	~10^6 yr
C-burning	^{12}C$(^{12}$C, $\alpha)^{20}$Ne ^{12}C$(^{12}$C, p$)^{23}$Na ^{12}C$(^{12}$C, n$)^{23}$Mg	^{20}Ne ^{23}Na ^{23}Mg	$M_{ms} \gtrsim 8M_\odot$	5–9×10^8	~10^3 yr
Ne-burning	^{20}Ne$(\gamma, \alpha)^{16}$O ^{20}Ne$(\alpha, \gamma)^{24}$Mg	^{16}O ^{24}Mg	$M_{ms} \gtrsim 10M_\odot$	1–2×10^9	~1 yr
O-burning	^{16}O$(^{16}$O, $\alpha)^{28}$Si	^{28}Si	$M_{ms} \gtrsim 10M_\odot$	2×10^9	~6 months
Si-burning	^{28}Si$(\gamma, \alpha)^{24}$Mg ^{28}Si$(\alpha, \gamma)^{32}$S$(\alpha, \gamma)^{36}$Ar... ...$(\alpha, \gamma)^{40}$Ca$(\alpha, \gamma)^{44}Ti$... ...$(\alpha, \gamma)^{48}Cr(\alpha, \gamma)^{52}Fe$... ...$(\alpha, \gamma)^{56}Ni$ (*italics* = unstable)	^{24}Mg ^{32}S , ^{36}Ar ^{40}Ca, ^{44}Ca ^{48}Ti, ^{52}Cr ^{56}Fe	$M_{ms} \gtrsim 10M_\odot$	3–4×10^9	~1 day
neutron-capture	^{A}X(n, $\gamma)^{A+1}$X$(\beta^-\ \bar{\nu}_e)^{A+1}$X+1	$Z > 30$			
	s-process	Sr, Ba, Pb	$1 \lesssim M_{ms}/M_\odot \lesssim 8$		~10^4 yr
	r-process	Sr, Ba, Pb, Th, U	$M_{ms} \gtrsim 10M_\odot$		~1second

Question 44

The mass M of a sample of material is given by the total number of particles N multiplied by their individual masses m, $M = Nm$,

so $\quad N = M/m = 1\,\text{kg}/56u = 1\,\text{kg}/56 \times 1.661 \times 10^{-27}\,\text{kg} = 1.075 \times 10^{25}$ nuclei

Each nucleus absorbs

$$124.4\,\text{MeV} = 124.4 \times 10^{6}\text{eV} \times 1.602 \times 10^{-19}\,\text{JeV}^{-1} = 1.993 \times 10^{-11}\,\text{J}$$

so 1 kg absorbs $1.075 \times 10^{25} \times 1.993 \times 10^{-11}\,\text{J} = 2.142 \times 10^{14}\,\text{J}$

Question 45

(a) $E_{\text{G}}(\text{released}) = GM^2/R_2 - GM^2/R_1 = GM^2(1/R_2 - 1/R_1)$,

but since $R_1 \gg R_2$, $1/R_1 \ll 1/R_2$, and so $E_{\text{G}}(\text{released}) \approx GM^2/R_2$.

$$E_{\text{G}}(\text{released}) = \frac{GM^2}{R_2} = GM_{\odot}^2\left(\frac{M^2}{M_{\odot}}\right)^2\left(\frac{10\,\text{km}}{10\,\text{km}}\right)\left(\frac{1}{R_2}\right)$$

$$= \left(\frac{GM_{\odot}^2}{10\,\text{km}}\right)\left(\frac{M^2}{M_{\odot}}\right)^2\left(\frac{10\,\text{km}}{R_2}\right) = 2.640 \times 10^{46}\,\text{J}\left(\frac{M^2}{M_{\odot}}\right)^2\left(\frac{10\,\text{km}}{R_2}\right)$$

(c) Least = (ii) radiation (light curve) $\sim 10^{42}\,\text{J}$, typically 0.004% of the gravitational energy released.

Middle rank = (i) kinetic energy of the ejecta $\sim 10^{44}\,\text{J}$, typically 0.4% of the gravitational energy released.

Most = (iii) neutrino flux believed to account for the remainder, $\sim 2.6 \times 10^{46}\,\text{J}$, essentially 99.5% of the released energy.

Question 46

	White dwarf	Neutron star
(a) Pressure of non-relativistic degenerate matter (Phillips 5.10)	$P_{NR} = \dfrac{h^2}{5m_e}\left(\dfrac{3}{8\pi}\right)^{2/3} n_e^{5/3}$	$P_{NR} = \dfrac{h^2}{5m_n}\left(\dfrac{3}{8\pi}\right)^{2/3} n_n^{5/3}$
(b)	$n_e = Y_e\rho_c/m_H,$ so $P_{NR} = \dfrac{h^2}{5m_e}\left(\dfrac{3}{8\pi}\right)^{2/3}\left(\dfrac{Y_e\rho_c}{m_H}\right)^{5/3}$	$n_n = \rho_c/m_n,$ so $P_{NR} = \dfrac{h^2}{5m_n}\left(\dfrac{3}{8\pi}\right)^{2/3}\left(\dfrac{\rho_c}{m_n}\right)^{5/3}$
(c) Clayton model	$P_c = (\pi/36)^{1/3}GM^{2/3}\rho_c^{4/3},$ so $\rho_c = (36/\pi)^{1/4}G^{-3/4}M^{-1/2}P_c^{3/4}$	$P_c = (\pi/36)^{1/3}GM^{2/3}\rho_c^{4/3},$ so $\rho_c = (36/\pi)^{1/4}G^{-3/4}M^{-1/2}P_c^{3/4}$
(d) Put (b) into (c)	$\rho_c = \left(\dfrac{36}{\pi}\right)^{1/4} G^{-3/4}M^{-1/2}$ $\times\left[\dfrac{h^2}{5m_e}\left(\dfrac{3}{8\pi}\right)^{2/3}\left(\dfrac{Y_e\rho_c}{m_H}\right)^{5/3}\right]^{3/4}$ $= \left(\dfrac{36}{\pi}\right)^{1/4} G^{-3/4}M^{-1/2}$ $\times\left(\dfrac{h^2}{5m_e}\right)^{3/4}\left(\dfrac{3}{8\pi}\right)^{1/2}\left(\dfrac{Y_e\rho_c}{m_H}\right)^{5/4}$	$\rho_c = \left(\dfrac{36}{\pi}\right)^{1/4} G^{-3/4}M^{-1/2}$ $\times\left[\dfrac{h^2}{5m_n}\left(\dfrac{3}{8\pi}\right)^{2/3}\left(\dfrac{\rho_c}{m_n}\right)^{5/3}\right]^{3/4}$ $= \left(\dfrac{36}{\pi}\right)^{1/4} G^{-3/4}M^{-1/2}$ $\times\left(\dfrac{h^2}{5m_n}\right)^{3/4}\left(\dfrac{3}{8\pi}\right)^{1/2}\left(\dfrac{\rho_c}{m_n}\right)^{5/4}$
Collect powers of ρ:	$\rho_c^{-1/4} = \left(\dfrac{36}{\pi}\right)^{1/4} G^{-3/4}M^{-1/2}$ $\times\left(\dfrac{h^2}{5m_e}\right)^{3/4}\left(\dfrac{3}{8\pi}\right)^{1/2}\left(\dfrac{Y_e}{m_H}\right)^{5/4}$	$\rho_c^{-1/4} = \left(\dfrac{36}{\pi}\right)^{1/4} G^{-3/4}M^{-1/2}$ $\times\left(\dfrac{h^2}{5m_n}\right)^{3/4}\left(\dfrac{3}{8\pi}\right)^{1/2}\left(\dfrac{1}{m_n}\right)^{5/4}$
Raise both sides to power 4/3:	$\rho_c^{-1/3} = \left(\dfrac{36}{\pi}\right)^{1/3} G^{-1}M^{-2/3}$ $\times\left(\dfrac{h^2}{5m_e}\right)\left(\dfrac{3}{8\pi}\right)^{2/3}\left(\dfrac{Y_e}{m_H}\right)^{5/3}$ $= \dfrac{324^{1/3}}{4\pi G}\left(\dfrac{h^2}{5m_e}\right)\left(\dfrac{Y_e}{m_H}\right)^{5/3} M^{-2/3}$	$\rho_c^{-1/3} = \left(\dfrac{36}{\pi}\right)^{1/3} G^{-1}M^{-2/3}$ $\times\left(\dfrac{h^2}{5m_n}\right)\left(\dfrac{3}{8\pi}\right)^{2/3}\left(\dfrac{1}{m_n}\right)^{5/3}$ $= \dfrac{324^{1/3}}{4\pi G}\left(\dfrac{h^2}{5m_n}\right)\left(\dfrac{1}{m_n}\right)^{5/3} M^{-2/3}$
(e) Adopt $\langle\rho\rangle = \rho_c/6$	$R = (3M/4\pi\langle\rho\rangle)^{1/3} = (9M/2\pi\rho_c)^{1/3}$ i.e. $R = (9/2\pi)^{1/3}\rho_c^{-1/3}M^{1/3}$	$R = (3M/4\pi\langle\rho\rangle)^{1/3} = (9M/2\pi\rho_c)^{1/3}$ i.e. $R = (9/2\pi)^{1/3}\rho_c^{-1/3}M^{1/3}$
(f) substitute for ρ_c using (d)	$R_{WD} = \left(\dfrac{9}{2\pi}\right)^{1/3}\dfrac{324^{1/3}}{4\pi G}$ $\times\left(\dfrac{h^2}{5m_e}\right)\left(\dfrac{Y_e}{m_H}\right)^{5/3} M^{-1/3}$	$R_{NS} = \left(\dfrac{9}{2\pi}\right)^{1/3}\dfrac{324^{1/3}}{4\pi G}$ $\times\left(\dfrac{h^2}{5m_n}\right)\left(\dfrac{1}{m_n}\right)^{5/3} M^{-1/3}$

COMMENTS ON ACTIVITIES

Completed spreadsheets for all the activities have been installed on your hard disk along with the S381 MM guide. The relevant spreadsheet can be found as *BX_AcY.sdc* where *X* is the block number and *Y* is the activity number, via a link from the multimedia guide.

Activity 3

You are required to compute the luminosity *L* for six different temperatures T_{eff} and three radii *R*. The equation which relates stellar radii to luminosities is $L = 4\pi R^2 \sigma T_{eff}^4$. You will not need to rearrange the equation to do this exercise. Within the spreadsheet page, probably you will want to compute a table with six columns, one for each temperature, and three rows, one for each radius. Begin by typing in some column headings, but don't start in the top-left cell, as you will probably want to enter some numerical constants in the first few rows and columns. Click in cell C11, say, and type the first radius, 0.1. Put a heading above it in cell C10, R/Rsun, so you remember that this number is in units of solar radii. Then in C12 and C13 give the two other radii, 1 and 10. As headings to the adjacent columns, enter the temperatures: in D10 put 2000, in E10 put 4000, etc., up to 40000 in I10. Record a heading in cell D9, **Effective temperature/K**.

You could enter the luminosity equation into cell D11, but it will be better to define the constants elsewhere on the page, and then refer to them rather than bury everything inside the final equation. Somewhere near the top, say cell C3, enter Stefan's constant 5.671e–08. You, as a physicist, know that this number alone is meaningless, and you need to specify its units. Spreadsheets know nothing about units, but you would be wise to note them in the adjacent cell, D3, for your own benefit. You would also be wise to record the name of the constant so you know what it is next time you come back to it; do this in cell A3 or B3. (If you develop the habit of setting out your work neatly and logically, it will be easier to debug it for mistakes and to extend it later to do more than you originally intended.) Think of the other constants you will need. You will have to convert the stellar radii into metres from solar units ($R/R_\odot$), and you will have to express the final result in terms of the solar luminosity ($L/L_\odot$), so give the solar luminosity in C4 and the radius in C5, below Stefan's constant.

You are now ready to compute the luminosities of the 18 stars. In cell D11, type in the luminosity formula

    =4*PI()*($C11*$C$5)^2*$C$3*D$10^4/$C$4

The term ($C11*$C$5)^2 multiplies $R/R_\odot$ by $R_\odot$ to get *R*, and then squares it to get R^2. You could also have entered the equation by a combination of typing and clicking on cells, but you should note that doing so will not include the dollar signs in the equations; these are essential and you will have to add them by editing the equation in the small equation-editing window. If you had typed the equation as stated, you could 'copy' it, highlight all of the cells from D11 to I13, and 'paste' the correct formula into the whole table. The '$' signs in the equation freeze certain cell references. The term $C$5 freezes both the column and row, so that the correct constant is picked off every time. The term $C11 freezes the column but not the row, so that when the formula is copied and pasted, the same value of R/Rsun will be applied to all columns in that row, but in subsequent rows (12 and 13) the row references will increment and the appropriate value of R/Rsun will be used. Likewise, the term D$10 ensures that row 10 is always used for the temperature, but when the formula is copied and pasted, the column references will increment.

By now you should have values of the luminosity $L/L_\odot$ which range from 0.000 14 to 230 743. If you see a value 0 in cell D11, you may not be displaying enough decimal places. You can adjust the number of decimal places displayed by highlighting the table (click and drag with the cursor), selecting the Format/Cells.../Numbers/ Category/Number option and increasing the decimal digit counter. Once you have done that, you may find that the cell I13 shows an entry like '######', which means that there isn't enough width in the columns to display the numbers. The easiest way to overcome this is to highlight the table again and then select the pull-down menu Format/Column/Optimal width.../OK, which will adjust the cell boundaries. You can play with these options to make the table appear as you like.

As the vertical axis of the H–R diagram is log luminosity, you should either create a second table which takes logarithms of the one you have already computed, or else edit the table you have already produced. To do the former, enter the formula =LOG10(D11) in cell D16 and then copy and paste this over the range D16 to I18. The latter is accomplished by editing the equation in D11 to read

$$\text{=LOG10(4*PI()*(\$C11*\$C\$5)\textasciicircum 2*\$C\$3*D\$10\textasciicircum 4/\$C\$4)}$$

and then copying and pasting this again over the range D11 to I13.

When you come to draw these values on the H–R diagram in Figure 1 (Phillips Fig. 1.6), you may find it helpful to write values of $\log L/L_\odot$ on the vertical axis, since the values of $L/L_\odot$ are given as powers of ten instead.

Activity 11

Take $\overline{m} = m_p + m_e = 1.673 \times 10^{-27}\,\text{kg} + 9.109 \times 10^{-31}\,\text{kg} = 1.674 \times 10^{-27}\,\text{kg}$. You will need to produce a small table of temperatures for each density and protostellar mass. To plot three data sets, you need to highlight four columns (or four rows, depending on how you have set out your table), one series for the x-axis values and three series for the y-axis values.

There is the option of tabulating either (a) temperature and density or (b) log temperature and log density values. If you do the latter, you can plot the graphs as usual, but if you do the former you then have to set a special option within the plotting process to get a log graph. You might like to experiment with both approaches to see which you prefer.

If these data series are all adjacent in the table, you can highlight all of them for plotting in one go, by clicking on the top-left cell and dragging the pointer to the lower-right cell. If the four data series are not all side by side, then you have to use a different technique. First highlight the x-axis data series. Move the pointer to the beginning of the second data series, press and hold down the control key, and while you are holding it down, click and drag to highlight the second data series. Release the mouse button at the end of the second series, move it to the beginning of the third series, and while still holding down the control key, click and drag to highlight the third series. Do likewise for the fourth. Then select the menu items Insert/Chart etc. to produce the plot.

Activity 15

A sample output of the graphs is shown in Figure 60. Note that while wave functions take on both positive and negative values, the position probability density, being the square of the wave function, is always zero or positive. Recall that the position probability density tells you the probability of finding the particle at some particular position. Note from your graphs that while a particle described by the lowest energy wave function, ψ_1, is most likely to be found near the centre of the potential well, particles described by wave functions ψ_2 and ψ_4 are actually more likely to be found *away* from the centre.

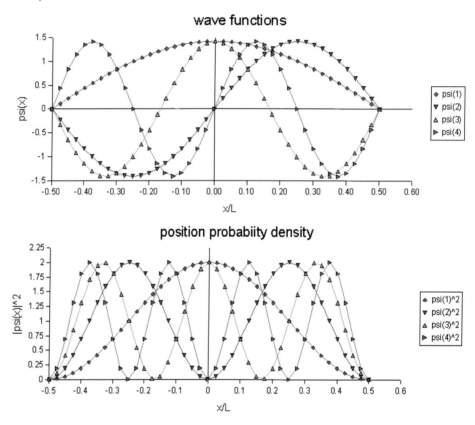

Figure 60 Example of graphs of wave functions and position probability densities for Activity 15.

APPENDIX

A1 SI units and cgs units

The main units used in science are SI (standing for Système International [d'Unités]).

SI base units

Physical quantity	Name of unit	Symbol of unit
length	metre	m
mass	kilogram	kg
time	second	s
electric current	ampere	A
temperature	kelvin	K
luminous intensity	candela	cd
amount of substance	mole	mol

Standard SI multiples and submultiples

Multiple	Prefix	Symbol for prefix	Sub-multiple	Prefix	Symbol for prefix
10^{12}	tera	T	10^{-3}	milli	m
10^{9}	giga	G	10^{-6}	micro	μ
10^{6}	mega	M	10^{-9}	nano	n
10^{3}	kilo	k	10^{-12}	pico	p
10^{0}	–	–	10^{-15}	femto	f

Common SI unit conversions and derived units

Quantity	Unit	Conversion		
speed	$m\,s^{-1}$			
acceleration	$m\,s^{-2}$			
angular speed	$rad\,s^{-1}$			
angular acceleration	$rad\,s^{-2}$			
linear momentum	$kg\,m\,s^{-1}$			
angular momentum	$kg\,m^2\,s^{-1}$			
force	newton (N)	$1\,N$	$=$	$1\,kg\,m\,s^{-2}$
energy	joule (J)	$1\,J$	$=$	$1\,N\,m = 1\,kg\,m^2\,s^{-2}$
power	watt (W)	$1\,W$	$=$	$1\,J\,s^{-1} = 1\,kg\,m^2\,s^{-3}$
pressure	pascal (Pa)	$1\,Pa$	$=$	$1\,N\,m^{-2} = 1\,kg\,m^{-1}\,s^{-2}$
frequency	hertz (Hz)	$1\,Hz$	$=$	$1\,s^{-1}$
charge	coulomb (C)	$1\,C$	$=$	$1\,A\,s$
potential difference	volt (V)	$1\,V$	$=$	$1\,J\,C^{-1} = 1\,kg\,m^2\,s^{-3}\,A^{-1}$
electric field	$N\,C^{-1}$	$1\,N\,C^{-1}$	$=$	$1\,V\,m^{-1} = 1\,kg\,m\,s^{-3}\,A^{-1}$
magnetic field	tesla (T)	$1\,T$	$=$	$1\,N\,s\,m^{-1}\,C^{-1} = 1\,kg\,s^{-2}\,A^{-1}$

In astrophysics, you will frequently see some quantities expressed in the cgs system (standing for centimetre, gram, second). The difference here is that the base units for length and mass are the centimetre and gram, rather than the metre and kilogram, where $1\,\mathrm{cm} = 10^{-2}\,\mathrm{m}$ and $1\,\mathrm{g} = 10^{-3}\,\mathrm{kg}$.

Use of the cgs system in turn gives rise to different derived units, so you will often see speeds quoted in $\mathrm{cm\,s^{-1}}$ for instance. Three particular derived units that you should be aware of are the cgs units for energy, force and magnetic field, namely the erg, the dyne and the gauss respectively.

The conversions are

energy	$1\ \mathrm{joule} = 10^7\,\mathrm{erg}$	or	$1\ \mathrm{erg} = 10^{-7}\,\mathrm{joule} = 1\,\mathrm{g\,cm^2\,s^{-2}}$
force	$1\ \mathrm{newton} = 10^5\,\mathrm{dyne}$	or	$1\ \mathrm{dyne} = 10^{-5}\,\mathrm{newton} = 1\,\mathrm{g\,cm\,s^{-2}}$
magnetic field	$1\ \mathrm{tesla} = 10^4\,\mathrm{gauss}$	or	$1\ \mathrm{gauss} = 10^{-4}\,\mathrm{tesla}$

The basic unit of electric charge is also defined somewhat differently in the cgs system. In fact, *two* different definitions are sometimes seen, the simplest of which is the 'emu' system where

$1\ \mathrm{coulomb} = 0.1\,\mathrm{emu}$ or $1\ \mathrm{emu} = 10\ \mathrm{coulomb}$

A2 Useful constants and conversions

Name of constant	Symbol	cgs/emu value	SI value
Fundamental constants			
gravitational constant	G	$6.673 \times 10^{-8}\,\mathrm{dyne\,cm^2\,g^{-2}}$	$6.673 \times 10^{-11}\,\mathrm{N\,m^2\,kg^{-2}}$
Boltzmann constant	k	$1.381 \times 10^{-16}\,\mathrm{erg\,K^{-1}}$	$1.381 \times 10^{-23}\,\mathrm{J\,K^{-1}}$
speed of light in vacuum	c	$2.998 \times 10^{10}\,\mathrm{cm\,s^{-1}}$	$2.998 \times 10^{8}\,\mathrm{m\,s^{-1}}$
Planck constant	h	$6.626 \times 10^{-27}\,\mathrm{erg\,s}$	$6.626 \times 10^{-34}\,\mathrm{J\,s}$
	$\hbar = h/2\pi$	$1.055 \times 10^{-27}\,\mathrm{erg\,s}$	$1.055 \times 10^{-34}\,\mathrm{J\,s}$
fine structure constant	$\alpha = e^2/4\pi\varepsilon_0\hbar c$	$1/137.0$	$1/137.0$
Stefan–Boltzman constant	σ	$5.671 \times 10^{-5}\,\mathrm{erg\,cm^{-2}\,K^{-4}\,s^{-1}}$	$5.671 \times 10^{-8}\,\mathrm{J\,m^{-2}\,K^{-4}\,s^{-1}}$
Thomson cross-section	σ_e	$6.652 \times 10^{-25}\,\mathrm{cm^2}$	$6.652 \times 10^{-29}\,\mathrm{m^2}$
permittivity of free space	ε_0	$8.854 \times 10^{-23}\,\mathrm{cm^{-2}\,s^2}$	$8.854 \times 10^{-12}\,\mathrm{C^2\,N^{-1}\,m^{-2}}$
permeability of free space	μ_0	$4\pi\,\mathrm{dyne\,emu^{-2}\,s^2}$	$4\pi \times 10^{-7}\,\mathrm{T\,m\,A^{-1}}$
Particle constants			
charge of proton	e	$1.602 \times 10^{-20}\,\mathrm{emu}$	$1.602 \times 10^{-19}\,\mathrm{C}$
charge of electron	$-e$	$-1.602 \times 10^{-20}\,\mathrm{emu}$	$-1.602 \times 10^{-19}\,\mathrm{C}$
electron rest mass	m_e	$9.109 \times 10^{-28}\,\mathrm{g}$	$9.109 \times 10^{-31}\,\mathrm{kg}$
		$0.511\,\mathrm{MeV}/c^2$	$0.511\,\mathrm{MeV}/c^2$
proton rest mass	m_p	$1.673 \times 10^{-24}\,\mathrm{g}$	$1.673 \times 10^{-27}\,\mathrm{kg}$
		$938.3\,\mathrm{MeV}/c^2$	$938.3\,\mathrm{MeV}/c^2$
neutron rest mass	m_n	$1.675 \times 10^{-24}\,\mathrm{kg}$	$1.675 \times 10^{-27}\,\mathrm{kg}$
		$939.6\,\mathrm{MeV}/c^2$	$939.6\,\mathrm{MeV}/c^2$
atomic mass unit	u or amu	$1.661 \times 10^{-24}\,\mathrm{g}$	$1.661 \times 10^{-27}\,\mathrm{kg}$
Astronomical constants			
mass of the Sun	$M_\odot$	$1.99 \times 10^{33}\,\mathrm{g}$	$1.99 \times 10^{30}\,\mathrm{kg}$
radius of the Sun	$R_\odot$	$6.96 \times 10^{10}\,\mathrm{cm}$	$6.96 \times 10^{8}\,\mathrm{m}$
luminosity of the Sun	$L_\odot$	$3.83 \times 10^{33}\,\mathrm{erg\,s^{-1}}$	$3.83 \times 10^{26}\,\mathrm{J\,s^{-1}}$

angular measure

$1° = 60 \, \text{arcmin} = 3600 \, \text{arcsec}$

$1° = 0.01745 \, \text{radian}$

$1 \, \text{radian} = 57.30°$

temperature

absolute zero: $0 \, \text{K} = -273.15 \, °\text{C}$

$0 \, °\text{C} = 273.15 \, \text{K}$

energy

$1 \, \text{eV} = 1.602 \times 10^{-19} \, \text{J} = 1.602 \times 10^{-12} \, \text{erg}$

$1 \, \text{erg} = 10^{-7} \, \text{J} = 6.242 \times 10^{11} \, \text{eV}$

$1 \, \text{J} = 10^7 \, \text{erg} = 6.242 \times 10^{18} \, \text{eV}$

spectral flux density

$1 \, \text{jansky (Jy)} = 10^{-26} \, \text{W m}^{-2} \, \text{Hz}^{-1} = 10^{-23} \, \text{erg s}^{-1} \, \text{cm}^{-2} \, \text{Hz}^{-1}$

$1 \, \text{W m}^{-2} \, \text{Hz}^{-1} = 10^{26} \, \text{Jy} = 10^3 \, \text{erg s}^{-1} \, \text{cm}^{-2} \, \text{Hz}^{-1}$

$1 \, \text{erg s}^{-1} \, \text{cm}^{-2} \, \text{Hz}^{-1} = 10^{-3} \, \text{W m}^{-2} \, \text{Hz}^{-1} = 10^{23} \, \text{Jy}$

mass-energy equivalence

$1 \, \text{kg} = 8.99 \times 10^{16} \, \text{J}/c^2$ (c in m s^{-1})

$1 \, \text{kg} = 5.61 \times 10^{35} \, \text{eV}/c^2$ (c in m s^{-1})

$1 \, \text{g} = 8.99 \times 10^{16} \, \text{erg}/c^2$ (c in cm s^{-1})

$1 \, \text{g} = 5.61 \times 10^{28} \, \text{eV}/c^2$ (c in cm s^{-1})

wavelength

$1 \, \text{nanometre (nm)} = 10 \, \text{Å} = 10^{-9} \, \text{m} = 10^{-7} \, \text{cm}$

$1 \, \text{ångstrom (Å)} = 0.1 \, \text{nm} = 10^{-10} \, \text{m} = 10^{-8} \, \text{cm}$

distance

$1 \, \text{astronomical unit (AU)} = 1.496 \times 10^{11} \, \text{m} = 1.496 \times 10^{13} \, \text{cm}$

$1 \, \text{light-year (ly)} = 9.461 \times 10^{15} \, \text{m} = 9.461 \times 10^{17} \, \text{cm} = 0.307 \, \text{pc}$

$1 \, \text{parsec (pc)} = 3.086 \times 10^{16} \, \text{m} = 3.086 \times 10^{18} \, \text{cm} = 3.26 \, \text{ly}$

A3 Mathematical signs and symbols

$\equiv$	identical to
$=$	equals
$\approx$	approximately equals
$\sim$	is of order of (i.e. is less than 10 times bigger or smaller than)
$\neq$	is not equal to
$>$	is greater than
$\gg$	is much greater than
$\geq$	is greater than or equal to (i.e. is no less than)
$\gtrsim$	is greater than or of order of
$<$	is less than
$\ll$	is much less than
$\leq$	is less than or equal to (i.e. is no more than)
$\lesssim$	is less than or of order of
$\propto$	is proportional to
∞	infinity
$\sqrt{x}$	the positive square root of x
$\sqrt[n]{x}$	the nth root of x which is equal to $x^{1/n}$
$\pm$	plus and minus the following number
$\mp$	minus and plus, taken in the same order as a preceding $\pm$
Δx	the change in x
$f(x)$	a function f depending on the variable x
$|x|$	the absolute value of a number (i.e. ignoring any $-$ sign)
$|\boldsymbol{a}|$	the magnitude or length of a vector
$\sum_{i=1}^{N} m_i$	the sum of $m_1 + m_2 + m_3 + \cdots + m_N$
$\langle x \rangle$	the average value of x
$dy/dt, y', \dot{y}$	the derivative of y with respect to t; or the gradient of y versus t
$d^2y/dt^2, y'', \ddot{y}$	the second derivative of y with respect to t
$\int_{t_A}^{t_B} x(t)\,dt$	the definite integral of the t-dependent function $x(t)$ with respect to t, evaluated over the interval from $t = t_A$ to $t = t_B$

A4 The Greek alphabet

name	upper case	lower case	name	upper case	lower case
alpha	A	α	nu	N	ν
beta	B	β	xi	Ξ	ξ
gamma	Γ	γ	omicron	O	o
delta	Δ	δ	pi	Π	π
epsilon	E	ε	rho	P	ρ
zeta	Z	ζ	sigma	Σ	σ
eta	H	η	tau	T	τ
theta	Θ	θ, ϑ	upsilon	Y	υ
iota	I	ι	phi	Φ	ϕ, φ
kappa	K	κ	chi	X	χ
lambda	Λ	λ	psi	Ψ	ψ
mu	M	μ	omega	Ω	ω

ACKNOWLEDGEMENTS

Grateful acknowledgement is made to the following sources for permission to reproduce material within this block:

Cover: © 2000 Mark A. Garlick

Figure 3 Jeff Hester and Paul Scowen (AZ State University), NASA; *Figure 19* N. Walborn (ST ScI), R. Barbá (La Plata Observatory) and NASA; *Figure 20* Yohko Tsuboi, Pennsylvania State University; *Figure 21* C. Burrows (ST ScI), J. Hester (AZ State University), J. Morse (ST ScI), NASA; *Figure 22* Stahler, S. W., *Astrophysics Journal*, **274**, 822, 1983; *Figure 23* A. Schultz (Computer Sciences Corp.), S. Heap (NASA Goddard Space Flight Center), NASA; *Figure 24* M. J. McCaughrean (MPIA), C. R. O'Dell, Vanderbilt University and NASA; *Figures 30 and 59* Schwarzschild, M., (1958), *Structure and Evolution of the Stars*, Dover Publications, Inc.; *Figure 31* *Handbook of Physics*, Arp, H. C., Vol. 51, p. 75, 1958, © Springer-Verlag; *Figure 32* *Astronomy and Astrophysics*, Vol. 329, 87–100, 1998, p. 96, 'Hipparcos subdwarfs and globular cluster ages: M 92', Pont, F. *et al.*, Fig. 7, with kind permission from Kluwer Academic Publishers; *Figure 33(a)* Royal Observatory Edinburgh/Anglo Australian Telescope Board/David Malin; *Figure 33(b)* Nigel Sharp, Mark Hanna/AURA/NOAO/NSF; *Figure 33(c)* Hubble Heritage Team (AURA/ST ScI/NASA); *Figure 36* Böhm-Vitense, E., *Introduction to Stellar Astrophysics*, 1992, Cambridge University Press; *Figure 38* Mateo, M., (1987) *PhD Thesis*, University of Washington; *Figure 39(a) and (b)* Stetson, P. B. *et al.*, 'Ages for globular clusters in the Outer Galactic Halo', *The Astronomical Journal*, Vol. 117, January, 1999, University of Chicago Press. © Stetson *et al.*; *Figure 40* Strohmeier, W., *Variable Stars*, Pergamon Press. © 1972 W. Strohmeier; *Figure 42* With permission from *Annual Review of Astronomy and Astrophysics*, Volume 37 © 1999 by Annual Reviews http://www.AnnualReviews.org; *Figure 43* This article originally appeared in the *Publications of the Astronomical Society of the Pacific*, Volume 99, 1987, Hesser, Harris and Vandenberg. © 1987 the Astronomical Society of the Pacific; reproduced with permission of the Editors; *Figure 44* S. Kwok (University of Calgary), R. Rubin (NASA Ames Research Center), H. Bond (ST ScI) and NASA; *Figure 45* H. Bond (ST ScI) and NASA; *Figure 46* NASA, A. Fruchter and the ERO team (ST ScI); *Figure 48* Kitt Peak National Observatory 0.9-meter telescope, National Optical Astronomy Observatories; courtesy of M. Bolte (University of California, Santa Cruz); *Figure 55(a) and (b)* Anglo Australian Observatory; *Figure 55(c)* Hubble Heritage Team (AURA/ST ScI/NASA); *Figure 56(a)* MDM Observatory http://chandra.harvard.edu/photo; *Figure 56(b)* ISO http://chandra.harvard.edu/photo; *Figure 56(c)* VLA http://chandra.harvard.edu/photo; *Figure 56(d)* NASA/CXC/SAO/Rutgers/J. Hughes; *Figure 58* Palomar Observatory http://chandra.harvard.edu/photo.

INDEX

Glossary terms and their page references are printed in **bold**.